Proceedings of a Symposium held at the AIBS meetings at Bloomington, Indiana in September, 1958, under the joint auspices of the AMERICAN INSTITUTE OF BIOLOGICAL SCIENCES, the ECOLOGICAL SOCIETY OF AMERICA and the AMERICAN SOCIETY OF ZOOLOGISTS, with support from the OFFICE OF NAVAL RESEARCH.

A standard 12 inch LP Record, prepared from tape recordings that accompanied the papers at the Indiana meeting, is included with the volume to illustrate the principles discussed in each chapter.

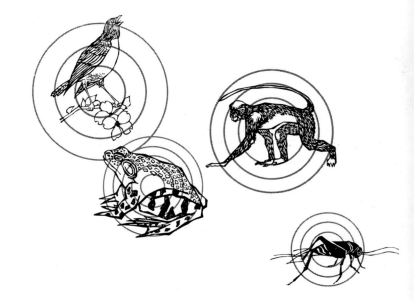

ANIMAL SOUNDS AND COMMUNICATION

Edited by W. E. LANYON and W. N. TAVOLGA

PUBLICATION NO. 7 • AMERICAN INSTITUTE OF BIOLOGICAL SCIENCES,
WASHINGTON 6, D. C., U.S.A.

Preface

Two diverse fields of biological research are currently enjoying rapid development and broadening coverage. These are: studies in general animal behavior and investigations into biological acoustics. A distinct need has appeared for improved communication between the workers in these two fields. Communication by sound, through the medium of a symposium, is recognized as one of the best ways in which people in separate disciplines and specialties can resolve common problems and achieve mutual intellectual stimulation. Dr. John T. Emlen, of the University of Wisconsin, translated this need into a symposium on "Animal Sounds and Communication," which he organized under the auspices of the *Section of Animal Behavior and Sociobiology* of the *Ecological Society of America*. A series of invited papers was presented on August 27, 1958, at the annual meeting of the *American Institute of Biological Sciences* on the campus of Indiana University at Bloomington, Indiana.

As a result of the large attendance and general interest expressed in the symposium, the question of publication of the proceedings naturally arose. This idea was greatly encouraged by Dr. Lester R. Aronson, chairman of the publications committee of the above *Section*. Dr. Aronson, of the Department of Animal Behavior at the American Museum of Natural History, offered the additional suggestion of including with the published symposium a phonograph record to illustrate the several papers. Since most of the papers given at the symposium were accompanied by tape recordings, the advantages of this method were immediately obvious. At this point we should like to acknowledge the invaluable assistance of Dr. Peter Paul Kellogg, of Cornell University, for applying his experience to the task of editing the tape recordings submitted by the authors and preparing them for transfer to standard 33 1/3 rpm discs.

During the actual symposium, the time allotted to each speaker was necessarily short, and, because of other commitments, several important aspects of animal acoustics could not be included. In the present volume, the coverage was expanded in two ways. First, the contributing authors were asked to submit papers of a length which they deemed adequate to develop their data and conclusions. Second, two additional chapters were solicited on material not represented at the original symposium. Dr. Peter Paul Kellogg contributed a paper on recording techniques, and Mr. Charles M. Bogert, of the American Museum of Natural History, added a chapter on the vocalizations of reptiles and amphibians.

To achieve a measure of integration of these various fields, Dr. Charles F. Hockett was given an opportunity to read the other papers to aid him in the preparation of his concluding chapter.

We wish to acknowledge the interest and encouragement of Dr. Sidney R. Galler, of the Biology Branch, Office of Naval Research, and the financial assistance for the publication through a contract between the Office of Naval Research and the American Institute of Biological Sciences. Dr. Hiden T. Cox, Executive Director, and Mr. Francis C. Harwood, Director of Publications of the AIBS, were instrumental in the publication of these papers as part of the AIBS Symposium Series.

W. E. LANYON
W. N. TAVOLGA

Table of Contents

Introduction [1]

JOHN T. EMLEN, JR.

Department of Zoology, University of Wisconsin, Madison

A CRICKET CHIRPS, a dog barks, a thrush sings; sounds older than man, sounds pleasing to the ear, often complex in structure, each distinctive, each stereotyped. All of us have known these and many other sounds of nature since childhood. Nearly all of us must have stopped at one time or another to ask ourselves: what do they mean? what do they express? what do they accomplish? why do they exist? and why have they evolved to their present complex and improbable forms?

ANIMAL SOUNDS AS COMMUNICATION

Man has attributed communication functions to animal sounds since the time of Hiawatha and King Solomon, and probably since he first developed an imagination and a language with which to construct analogies. Modern science has confirmed the essential elements of these primitive ideas and provided a conceptual basis for the objective study of information transfer which can be applied to all forms of animal life including man himself. Communication in animals by auditory, visual, olfactory or other signals is no longer just an interesting topic for discussion. It is now recognized as the mechanism by which all the essential interactions between organisms are accomplished; a system of transmitters and receivers which integrates organisms and coordinates their activities into functioning social groups or communities much as the nervous system coordinates the activities of the tissues in a smoothly functioning organism.

But what is the nature of the information transmitted in the communication of animals, and how does it accomplish this social coordination? In theory it may seem easy enough to obtain an answer to at least the first question by examining some simple animal sound such as the cluck of a mother hen and noting the sequence of events which follows. In practice, however, the problem becomes complicated as we observe a wide variety of responses or more often, no response at all.

---

[1] Manuscript received November 1959.

We are, in fact, soon forced to admit that despite the ingenious and persistent efforts of many brilliant investigators we still know very little about the nature of the information transmitted in such simple sounds as the grunt of a grouper or the trill of a tree frog.

The reason for these difficulties is probably related in large part to the dependence of animals on contextual data accompanying a sound signal. The information carried in most animal signals is comparable to that carried in the exclamations and interjections of our own speech rather than the nouns, adjectives, verbs and adverbs. In such words, the information is contained not so much in the word itself as in the context in which it is given. Thus, to a pheasant hunter stalking cautiously along the edge of a weed field a soft "stop" from a companion is loaded with information beyond the intrinsic meaning of the word itself. He is alerted, he readies his gun, he plans a complicated course of hunting strategy according to the exact environmental situation in which he finds himself. Later in the day as he is driving home, the same signal, "stop" at a Game Department checking station has a totally different significance to him, the exact form of which will again depend on the circumstances of the moment. Relaxed and proud of his success, he may show his trophies to the warden; on the other hand, if he has more than the legal limit in his possession, he may recoil and organize a strategy of deceit. We might say that the exclamation "stop" has as many meanings as there are contexts in which it is used. A dictionary can go no farther than to give its meaning as a verb or noun and then note that the word may also be used alone as an exclamation.

Perhaps the basic effect of most animal sounds on other individuals within hearing range is to alert them to the conditions of the immediate environment and thus prepare them to respond to more specific stimuli which may accompany or follow. The sound may be general in both time and space as the droning hum of a swarm of midges. It may have incorporated within it certain directional cues enabling the receiver to orient its distance receptors for further information toward a particular spot or situation. Or it may carry special motivational significance as an "alarm call" or a "distress call" in which the sound contains particular associational cues meaningful to the hearer.

ORIGIN AND EVOLUTION OF SONANT COMMUNICATION

The evolutionary origin of auditory communication, though beyond demonstration, is not difficult to imagine. The appearance of audio-receptors in Arthropods and Vertebrates provided a basis for the utilization of vibrational energy in the transmission of information and may be regarded as the essential first step in the evolution of all sonant communication systems. Special mechanisms for sound production though commonly used in higher forms are not necessary for basic communication and probably evolved later as a phase of the control and refinement of sound signals.

Sounds arising in the inanimate environment such as a babbling stream or a falling rock are potential carriers of useful information. The crashing of branches and twigs incidental to the escape flight of a wild hog in brushy vegetation may transmit to its herdmates vitally useful information concerning the presence of an enemy, its position and the imminence of danger. In a similar way the sloshing noise of mastication by a sow in soft mud may signal the presence of food to her litter of hungry piglets. Snorts and grunts produced in the upper respiratory tract, and scarcely less extraneous than the sloshing sounds, may supplement and augment this simple communication system and provide a basis for elaborating and refining the information content. And finally, variations of the grunts in relation to good fortune, danger or tragedy may furnish nearby animals with clues for appropriate action.

True communication systems utilizing specialized signals probably evolved in incidental or accidental sound producing situations like those envisioned above in which the information transmitted held survival value for the receiver. Under this theory the modification of structures used in such movements as thumping the substrate, rubbing parts of the body or forcing air over folds of membrane would be favored in selection insofar as they enhanced the loudness or specificity of the sound produced. Sound signals which served to coordinate or facilitate the vital activities of the members of a population would be selected and developed; signals which drew the attention of predators would be selected against, and signals which attracted symbionts would be fostered. Thus a number of independent selective forces may operate in the evolution of sound signals, and the ultimate course of development is probably determined by a balance of these forces.

To the naturalist perhaps the most striking feature of animal signals is specificity on a background of tremendous sonant diversity. Every species has its own distinctive signals and some have a considerable repertoire of calls, each corresponding to a particular environmental situation or context. The evolution of specificity and distinctiveness is readily visualized in the light of natural selection when we consider the theoretical value of correct identification of pertinent sounds in a complex sonant environment. This survival value of distinctiveness is thought to be responsible for the marvelous variety of sounds we encounter in nature today, a variety based on an almost infinite number of permutations and combinations of pitch, tonality, rhythm and pattern.

THE STUDY OF ANIMAL COMMUNICATION

The study of communication in animals has made great strides in recent years. Still evident, however, is a serious lack of basic organization. Theories we have, some of them brilliantly conceived, excitingly challenging and reasonably satisfactory for interpreting and coordinating our observations. But where is our foundation of empirical data on which to build inductively? Much exists, to be sure, but this is often so inadequately recorded and so loosely organized that a good share must be counted as valueless.

One basic problem has been the absence of any uniform system for describing and classifying animal sounds. One ornithologist recently noted that at least 375 different descriptive terms have been used in characterizing bird calls in America. Animal sounds are commonly labelled and classified according to 1) their physical features (low hum, harsh scream, rapid trill, etc), 2) their effect on companions or supposed function (warning or rally calls), 3) the circumstances of the moment (danger or food calls), 4) the general context (mating or territorial calls), 5) the social context (challenge or submission calls), 6) the presumed physiological or emotional state of the animal (alarm, pleasure or contentment calls), or 7) the supposed intention of the caller (self-advertisement, appeasement, etc.). It would be nice to resolve this confusing situation now with a simple concrete proposal, that all teleological (7), causational (6), and contextual terms (3, 4, and 5) be dropped but I'm afraid there would be many indignant dissenters.

In theory, effect (2) might be the ideal basis for a standard system of categorizing and classifying animal sounds. As we have already noted, however, the effect of a particular sound signal is often highly complex and diffuse and may be widely different in different individuals. Furthermore, the distinction between immediate effect, long range effect and ultimate function presents basic difficulties which cannot easily be resolved.

Many workers have emphasized the value of descriptive characterization in terms of pitch, timbre, duration, inflexion and the repetitive or rhythmic patterns of multi-unit phrases and songs. This system has the great advantage of relative objectivity and recently has achieved exciting new potentialities with the development of sensitive recording and analyzing instruments. The sound spectrograms obtained from these instruments constitute an accurate and objective representation of most of the pertinent physical characteristics of sound patterns in a form that can be stored as a permanent record. The significance of this development for the future of communication research is hard to overestimate; like photography and printing, it offers a means of capturing and preserving data which previously remained elusive and ephemeral.

But it must not be forgotten that a sound spectogram is only a symbol of a sound which, in turn, is only a symbol of the information transmitted in animal communication. To become meaningful as a part of communication a sound signal must be correlated with all internal and external conditions up to the moment it is given and to all changes which follow its reception, a fantastically difficult assignment. The real challenge ahead is to devise means for objectively describing these conditions and accurately correlating them. As we improve our skills in this direction we shall gradually accumulate a solid body of data on which we can build and move forward with confidence to a new understanding of the mechanisms of social integration of animals from Amoeba to Man. The contributions of this symposium suggest that we are moving ahead rapidly in this important and challenging young science. Certainly the road ahead is open and inviting.

Considerations and Techniques in Recording Sound for Bio-Acoustics Studies [1]

PETER PAUL KELLOGG

Professor of Ornithology and Biological Acoustics, Laboratory of Ornithology, Cornell University, Ithaca, New York.

Accuracy in the aural perception of sound depends a great deal on our familiarity with the sound in question. This is most easily illustrated by experience with a foreign language. At first only a jumble of sounds is perceived. A simple but convincing experiment is to record your own voice, speaking your own name or some simple phrase or sentence. Reproduce these sounds in reverse. Then diligently try to reproduce with your voice what you hear. Record this jumble of sounds, and in turn, reproduce them in reverse. Normally what you hear will be astonishing, and an indication of how superficially you comprehend the intricacies of unfamiliar sounds. Usually great improvements are achieved with practice.

It is much the same with the vocalizations of birds and other animals. With experience we become sensitive to smaller and smaller variations. This normal change or improvement in our perception of given sound has a direct bearing on our recording techniques and even in the choice of a recorder.

There seems to be little doubt that birds are much more sensitive to the extreme complexity of their songs than are human beings. This is especially true when the human being is unfamiliar with the bird's song. Perhaps much of the gap is closed by study, but the fact remains that the average human being is in a very poor position to judge the adequacy of a recorded sound unless he is very familiar with the sound. Also there is a large personal equation in what different people hear from the same sound source. For example, an individual whose hearing is deficient in the low frequencies may not notice hums, buzzes, wind and traffic noises which would utterly ruin a recording for purposes of study, while a person deficient in hearing high frequencies may never even suspect the presence of frequencies of great importance to the species being recorded or to other listeners. To be satisfied with what seems

[1] Manuscript received November 1959.

1

to be acceptable to one's ear alone is a very dangerous and unscientific practice. For these reasons serious workers, using sound recordings, should at least consider the accuracy of their recordings compared to the original sound. This consideration must be objective and, normally, it is based on laboratory tests. Many field workers and biologists must, because of lack of engineering training, be dependent on others for the actual testing and evaluation of their equipment, but they should understand the significance of the reports they receive and be able to use the information intelligently in solving their own problems, and especially in choosing and using their equipment.

THE PROBLEM

1. Available Equipment

Almost all equipment for recording sound is designed around the requirements imposed by human speech and music, just as most cameras are designed for recording what the human eye normally sees. Equipment for recording other phases of nature, either in sound or picture, is definitely special and often not readily available. The problem is to select from what is available, that which may most readily be modified to meet our individual field requirements.

2. Environmental and Species Consideration

Where we find our subjects, and how the sound spectrum they produce differs from that encountered in human speech and music, presents other problems. With insects and frogs we can normally place our microphone as close to the subject as we wish. With birds, because of distance, we may often receive only 1/1000 as much sound energy at our listening point as a studio control man expects his microphones to pick up. This is very important and indicates that the amount of gain available in field recorders should normally be greater than that which would be satisfactory for home or studio recording.

3. Frequency Ranges and Energy Distribution

A frequency range of 20 cps to 20,000 cps is usually considered sufficient to cover all sounds important to human beings. This is a range of ten octaves which presents a staggering engineering problem when compared to the frequencies encountered in visible light, where we have slightly less than one octave to worry about.

With some animals the frequency range may be greatly extended at the high end with the bats hearing out to about 100 kc, or two octaves beyond that of man. Dogs probably hear at least an octave beyond the highest frequencies perceived by man.

Readily available recording equipment seldom goes beyond the speech and music frequencies important to man's communications needs. Equipment for sound studies beyond this range is very special and usually very expensive.

It has, for a long time, been considered that so far as fidelity is concerned in man's world of sound, high frequencies, though important, are usually of low amplitude. Recent acoustical studies indicate that this assumption may not be warranted, but engineers have taken advantage of the belief to improve the signal-to-noise ratio. American standards uniformly have called for great pre-emphasis of high frequencies during the recording process, and a de-emphasis during playback. Unfortunately this practice produces a serious defect in natural history recording, especially in bird song recording, since birds are quite likely to put most of the energy of their songs in the upper part of the sound spectrum, often just where the equipment has been designed to expect low levels of energy. The importance of this fault will be discussed further when we consider appropriate tape speeds.

RECORDING EQUIPMENT

1. General

The quality and fidelity of recording equipment may well be considered in the light of the study for which it is being used. For example, if only the number of times an animal vocalizes per unit of time is important, then any recorder which has a fairly uniform rate of speed, and gives some indication each time a sound is made, will suffice. Many studies of this type have been made with dictating or similar machines which make no pretense of high quality. The more that is demanded from the equipment in the way of uniform frequency response, low noise, broad dynamic range and low distortion, the higher its quality must be.

2. Microphones

Since the microphone is the transducer responsible for changing acoustical energy into electrical energy, it is the first step in the chain of successful recording. Nothing beyond it will adequately correct for a poor job done by the microphone.

Selection of Microphones:

Crystal microphones are usually found on home-type recorders because they are cheap, and because they have a high electrical output especially in the human voice range. Their drawbacks are that they do not generally have a uniform frequency response, and they will not transmit signals over more than a few feet of line. Their use is therefore not recommended.

Dynamic microphones are much used in professional recording. Their frequency response can be very good. Their electrical output is reasonably high, and may be sent over very long lines without substantial loss. With the addition of an impedance matching transformer, the home-type recorder may often be used with this type of microphone with greatly improved results.

Velocity or ribbon type microphones have excellent frequency response but they are delicate and very sensitive to wind disturbances.

Capacitor microphones are probably best of all, but they have drawbacks which generally prevent them from being used in the field. Their output is relatively low, and they require a high voltage supply and usually an amplifier or impedance matching tube with its associated power supply close to the microphone. With small light weight transistor power supplies and amplifiers, this type of microphone may be expected to become more popular.

Directional microphones are often very useful in picking up more signal energy from a given direction, and may be used to advantage without or with a parabolic reflector. One type, often called the "Machine Gun Microphone" has the microphone located in a chamber from which originate a bundle of metal tubes each of a different length, the longest being 4 to 6 feet long. Effectively this microphone samples the spectrum of the source at which it is pointed. It is very efficient in greatly reducing the sound energy picked up from all other directions. It is claimed that such a device has the directivity of a six foot parabolic reflector. However, the output of the device is so low that it has never been used for natural history recording.

Hydrophones for converting sound energy in water to electrical energy are relatively special devices and usually quite expensive (see Tavolga's chapter in this volume). Because of the broad band of frequencies usually covered by these instruments, sometimes from 50 cps to 100,000 cps, their electrical output is very low, and the problems of noise and hum pick-up become very serious. For listening or recording sounds under water up to about 8,000 cps, contact microphones designed for attaching to musical instruments may be waterproofed with a thin coating of plastic. These microphones are quite cheap and have relatively high output.

3. Parabolic Reflectors

These serve to collect hundreds of times as much sound energy as would be collected by the microphone alone. Frequency distortion and their unavoidable size are the most severe drawbacks to using reflectors, but for many types of recording, especially birds, they are almost indispensable.

Effectively, the value of a reflector in collecting sound energy stems from the relative area of the microphone diaphram and the reflector disc. When the reflector, at a distance, collects as much sound energy from a given source as the microphone alone would collect if it were close to the source, the effect is to reduce the apparent distance. The fact that this apparent reduction of distance, or increase of signal, occurs only in a relatively narrow beam along the axis of the reflector is very desirable, and has the effect of enhancing the signals from objects in the beam relative to those coming from other directions. The width of the beam is a function of the size of the parabola and the wave length of the signal being picked up. As the wave length approaches the diameter of the reflector, the beam width becomes very broad and the effectiveness of the reflector is greatly reduced. Conversely, to effectively collect sound energy and concentrate it on the microphone, the size of the reflector must be large compared to the wave length of the sound concerned. With a reflector 40 inches in diameter, this drop off in effectiveness is very noticeable below the frequencies of 2,000 cps.

Frequency distortion, mentioned earlier as a fault of parabolic reflectors, is directly the result of their inability to concentrate low frequencies. However, the fact that most bird song is above 2,000 cps and the fact that the human ear will, to some extent, subjectively recreate low frequencies from the harmonics of a fundamental tone, combine to make the parabola a very acceptable and often a most necessary tool for most bird song recording.

The choice of a reflector is always a compromise between effectiveness and convenience. Parabolas six feet in diameter have been used. They are effective but unwieldly. Parabolas 20 inches in diameter give good results with insect sounds and with the higher pitched bird songs and they are convenient to transport. A compromise of 36 inches for diameter and a focal length of 12 or 15 inches is perhaps most acceptable but it introduces distortion on many low frequency bird songs, such as the notes of the prairie chicken (*Tympanuchus*).

The focal length of a reflector is not critical, but if it is very short, the microphone will be enclosed on all sides by the reflector walls and cavity resonance will occur. If the focal length is very long, the microphone must be far out in front of the reflector and this is inconvenient. The best focal length, considering both effectiveness and convenience, is probably one which places the microphone a few inches further out than the front edge of the reflector.

Metal reflectors tend to be noisy, and unless the microphone is supported elastically the noise is transmitted directly into the system. Coating the back of the reflector with auto body deadener to a thickness of ⅛ or ¼ inch helps reduce noise. Camouflaging the bright front surface of the reflector makes it less conspicuous to animals and to human beings at least.

4. Recorders

General. Since modern recorders vary in price from less than thirty dollars to more than five thousand dollars, it is reasonable to expect some differences in them which will be important when considering an instrument for bio-acoustics studies. A very rough division may be made into home-type and professional type recorders, but there is no sharp line of demarkation. Professional studio recorders invariably have a separate playback head and amplifier in addition to the recording head and amplifiers. The additional head and amplifier permit hearing the recorded signal a small fraction of a second after it has been recorded. This is especially important in bird song recording since it enables the operator to detect distortions in the recordings immediately, and to make, on the spot, appropriate adjustments. Meters and other indicators are, at best, poor substitutes for monitoring the recorded program on a good pair of earphones.

Portable recorders apparently include all those "having handles." Some classed as portable models weigh as much as 100 pounds and require commercial power for operation. There are perhaps a dozen truly portable recorders on the market, if we limit the total weight, with batteries, to 25 pounds or less and if we require in our definition that the recorder will function properly without external sources of power for reasonable periods of time. Most portable recorders are designed for recording speech, and while they are very useful for recording field notes, they often fail miserably in recording natural animal sounds. A very few portable recorders are designed for, and will do a good job of, recording the high frequencies so often encountered in music or bird songs. At least three units are advertised as comparing favorably with studio recorders, those including separate monitoring of the recorded signal, high quality, and high speed rewind and advance. However, none of these recorders is readily available in America at the present writing.

FIG. 1. Transflyweight. 8.5 lb. Transistorized, battery operated MAGNEMITE. Courtesy of Amplifier Corporation of America, New York City.

Small recorders weighing as little as eight pounds, but without the instantaneous monitoring feature, are available either in spring driven or electrically driven models (Fig. I).

What to look for in a recorder:

Frequency response is not the most important characteristic to look for, but it is a good indicator. Many of us can no longer hear 15,000 cps but your recorder should be able to handle this frequency. Very few birds, if any, have fundamental frequencies as high as this but harmonics, which may be of importance in study, do go even higher than 15,000 cps.

Distortion may be broadly defined as any energy in the recording which was not present in the original. It is usually measured by recording a constant frequency and playing it back while measuring all energy in the recording other than the recorded frequency. The best recorders today claim distortion as low as a small fraction of 1 per cent when recording at full volume. At times distortion below 1 per cent is objectionable but most sound systems such as radios and recorders may run as high as 2 per cent to 4 per cent and still be acceptable for music and speech.

Noise, or signal-to-noise ratio is usually an important consideration. In professional recorders, the noise is often more than 60 db below the loudest recording level. This is a power ratio of a million to one and the noise is practically absent. With some home type machines the noise may be only 30 db below the loudest signal, a power ratio of one thousand to one, and you will always be conscious of hiss, hum or other noise in the background. With much field recording, the recorded signal is likely to be weak, and so the level must be increased on playback. This accentuates the noise, and for this reason, all recordings should be made at the highest possible level which will not introduce objectionable distortion.

"Wow" and "Flutter" are probably more serious defects in natural history recording than is generally realized. "Wow" is usually considered to be low frequency changes in tape speed up to about 5 or 10 cps, while "flutter" is any variation above this. "Wow" is the onomatopoetic word which most closely describes the effect of these slow speed changes. Many birds and frogs have trills and tremolos and it is very easy to introduce these into a steady tone by recorder or reproducer with high flutter or wow. For most purposes a recorder with not more than $\frac{1}{4}\%$ of flutter and wow combined is satisfactory. A fairly satisfactory test is to record the steady note of a pitch pipe, or a piano note, and listen to the reproduction, comparing it with the original.

Power for field recorders is a problem more closely associated with natural history recording than is usually appreciated. This type of recording usually requires more amplification between the microphone and recording medium than is usually allowed for in studio or home recording. With studio type equipment in the field, power supplies which operate from storage batteries and produce 60 cycle, 115 volt power are readily available, but special care is often necessary to eliminate hum and other noises when low level signals are being recorded. With light-weight portable equipment, small batteries are always used for the electronics and either a spring motor or an electric motor is used to drive the tape. Spring motors are sometimes mechanically noisy and with electron tubes, this mechanical noise may be picked up by the tubes which are always in close proximity to the motor and quite sensitive to vibration. Modern transistors are probably the best answer to this problem since transistors are notoriously insensitive to physical vibration. Spring motors have reached a high degree of development for constant speed and reliability but they have the great disadvantage of requiring frequent winding. Battery operated electric motors seem to have a great advantage except that they are notorious for their production of electrical noise and the fact that it is difficult to maintain a constant speed with diminishing battery voltage. The problem of electrical noise is most serious and this is especially true in natural history recording where more than usual amplification is almost always required. A recorder of this type should always be tested with weak signals and full amplification to check on this kind of noise. Some workers have modified their equipment to overcome this difficulty by using a tiny transistorized, battery operated preamplifier close to the microphone so that the signal sent to the recorder is more powerful and will then not require so much amplification in the amplifiers close to the motor. Better batteries which maintain nearly constant voltage almost to the end of their useful life, and better governors on the motors have done much to make the electric motor drive acceptable in portable recorders. In one modern recorder (Fig. 2) a tone is generated by a toothed wheel on the motor shaft. This tone is amplified and compared to the natural frequency of a resonant circuit of high stability. If the frequencies are the same, nothing happens, but if there is a difference, a voltage is generated and applied to the motor in such a direction as to correct the speed. Such sophisticated systems of speed control probably point the way to field recorders of the future.

Better motors, better methods of speed control and better batteries will probably replace the spring motors in the near future.

Ultrasonic bias considerations for tape recorders. The use of a very high inaudible frequency, usually many times the amplitude of the signal being recorded, is the advance which has enabled magnetic recording to supplant every other recording technique for original recording. The high frequency which accompanies the signal is referred to as *bias.* Its action is not completely understood, but there are general rules which govern its use and it is desirable to be able to apply these rules. In the first place, the bias frequency should be high, preferably at least five times as high as the highest frequency you are interested in recording. If it is not sufficiently high, you will be plagued by chirps, "birdies" and squeals whenever you try to record very high frequencies. These are apparently caused by interaction between the harmonics of your high frequencies and bias frequencies (inter-modulation distortion). Most professional recorders use a bias frequency in the neighborhood of 100,000 cps.

Fig. 2. Nagra—III. An 18 lb. battery operated, 3 speed recorder with erase, record and playback heads. Courtesy of Electronic Applications, Inc., Stamford, Connecticut.

The amplitude of the bias used is most important.   Bias enables you to record much higher signals on tape than would otherwise be possible and it greatly reduces distortion at low and medium frequencies, but it tends to erase and greatly reduce high frequencies in recording, therefore some sort of a compromise is usually in order.   A pretty standard procedure is to feed a signal of 1,000 cps into the recorder and slowly adjust the bias.   Choose the bias setting which results in the maximum signal on the tape at this frequency.   On a professional machine, this adjustment is simple and routine.   Most modern recorders have a means of adjusting the bias, and most older recorders should certainly be checked for bias adjustment because some modern tapes require less than one-half the bias, on the same recorder, than was needed ten years ago.   It is not usually difficult to install a bias control and the recorder manufacturer will often have good suggestions or be willing to do it.

The bias wave form is important.   Any asymmetry of the wave form or deviation from a pure sine wave, is likely to result in a direct current component which produces noise. It is very difficult to achieve and maintain good symmetry and most professional recorders have adjustments for balancing out any direct current which appears as the result of asymmetry. This control is usually labeled "Noise Balance".

Equalization of tape recorders as it affects natural history recording. Burstein and Pollak (1957) give the modern thinking on this subject, but their problem is the recording of human speech and music. It was stated earlier in this paper that it is assumed that high frequencies, while important, are always low in amplitude. By following this reasoning it has been possible to achieve a considerable improvement in signal-to-noise ratio. Unfortunately birds seem to be unaware that they should soft pedal the high frequencies, and they certainly don't do it. The result is that bird songs often overload the amplifier or the tape or both, long before a conventional meter shows that the song is loud enough to be worth recording. With some admitted increase in noise, it should be possible to do better and more faithful recording of high frequency animal sounds if we placed less emphasis on them during the recording process and more emphasis on them during reproduction. The only drawbacks to such a change in equalization would be that our recordings would be different from the accepted standards and would reproduce correctly only on our own altered reproducers. If played on "standard" reproducers our recordings would be deficient in high frequencies but there would be much less distortion on the high notes. Most workers would probably hesitate to be so different, but it is something to think about if you begin to notice distortion when you try to record loud high notes. One small ray of hope is that the industry is examining the basic premise of very high frequencies in music being of low intensity. They are beginning to suspect that the premise is not always right and this may result in recording standards much more favorable to the recording of many natural history sounds.

5. *Manufacturers' Recording Specifications.*

Before we complete our discussion of equipment characteristics as a guide to choosing the tools we work with, we should recognize the great variability which exists in descriptions of equipment. It should be noted that dependable manufacturers are usually the most conservative. For example, two meters carried almost identical specifications as to accuracy. One instrument cost $30.00, the other $200.00. Both were purchased. Both met specifications, but the more expensive meter was five times as accurate, on every scale as the description called for, and after six years of service, it is still within specifications. The cheaper meter just made the grade when new. It has needed constant attention and after a year it was far below specifications. As another example, two recorders were purchased. Specifications were almost identical, and in fact favored the cheaper one. One cost $2,000.00, and one $400.00. Both met specifications, but the cheaper one was so difficult to work on when minor adjustments were needed, that it became a major problem of maintenance and was soon discarded. With microphones it's a different story since there is no simple way of making adequate tests. Apparently the only reason that any microphone is ever advertised as having a flat frequency response of less than 10 or 15 thousand cps is to justify the manufacturer's need for a microphone to be sold at a lower price. For most of us, the only rule is to try to pick the most reputable manufacturers, and from a number of instruments, select the microphone that sounds most faithful and which seems to have a reasonably high output, remembering that wide band frequency response and high output are not often found together.

6. *Factors Governing Choice of Tape Speed*

Recording equipment is available which uses tape speeds as high as 30″ per second and as low as 1″ per second or even less. Advantages of low tape speed are several, such as low cost, longer playing time on a reel, less storage space and less weight and packing space when traveling. High tape speed gives better frequency response, lower distortion and greater ease of editing.

Tape cost is actually small when compared with the time required to make a recording or the cost of the equipment. Also, when it is considered that only a small portion of original tape is saved, and the rest may be reused, the cost at any speed is small unless the worker insists on saving everything which has run through the recorder. The lower the tape speed used, the higher must be the preemphasis on the high frequencies during the recording process, and therefore the greater will be the tendency for distortion to creep in. Most professional studios today record at a speed of 30″/sec. At this speed hardly any preemphasis of the high frequencies is required. Better broadcast networks and stations have standardized on 15″/sec. 7.5″/sec. is the lowest speed normally used by smaller radio stations. Slower speeds are used only for poor quality home entertainment, dictating machines and other similar services.

Much satisfactory recording, even of bird voices, can be done at 7.5″/sec. Some species are difficult to record even at 15″/sec. It is almost axiomatic that anything which can be recorded at a low speed can be recorded with less distortion and with greater ease at the next higher speed.

For most natural history recording a tape speed of 15″/sec. is satisfactory. A speed of 30″/sec. would sometimes be very useful, but there is no portable equipment on the market today which will record at this speed.

7. Choice of Magnetic Tape

In the United States today there are about five major producers of magnetic recording tapes. While tapes are manufactured in a variety of widths for various special purposes, all natural history recording today is done on ¼″ tape. The major producers of tape each offer about eight varieties to choose from. These differ, first in base or backing material of two kinds: either an acetate or a polyester film is available. The base material is offered in three thicknesses, and finally there is a slight variation in the magnetic coating for special purposes. In addition to this, most companies offer under their own name, or dump on the market, quantities of tape which has failed to meet their highest standards.

The first problem is to decide between the cheaper acetate tapes and the slightly more expensive polyester tapes, such as Mylar—a registered trade name of the Dupont Company.

There is no good information available as to how long either type of base material will last but some feel that while Mylar may last longer, either type may be expected to last for fifty years.

Much more important is *how long the magnetic coating may be expected to adhere to the backing.* Here again there is no reliable information, but all tape should be inspected occasionally for this defect.

Assuming that the two types are about equal on the above two points, the next question is *pliability* which is important because it controls the ability of the tape to move close to the recording or playback heads and conform to their irregularities. Very pliable tapes have a better high frequency response, especially when used with very light tension, as is usually the case with portable recorders.

Mylar tapes, when subjected to a sudden strain, are likely to stretch or elongate. It is practically impossible to recover a tape damaged in this manner. Acetate tape, when subjected to a similar strain, breaks cleanly and may usually be repaired with no observable loss. Mylar tape's weakness in this respect, is its most serious defect. Many people refuse to use it because of this. As the backing material becomes thinner, the fault is more obvious and more potentially dangerous. However, great improvements have recently been made in the strength of Mylar tapes, and those of us who use it because of its other good qualities are learning that, with a little more care, most accidents even with the thinnest Mylar can be avoided.

Tapes with a base thickness of about 1.5 mils have become quite standard in the last ten years. With this thickness, it is possible to wind about 1,200 feet of tape on a reel seven inches in diameter. This gives a recording time of 16 minutes at 15″/sec.

Now, tapes with a ½ mil Mylar base are available, and it is possible to wind 2,400 feet on a seven inch reel, giving a recording time of 32 minutes. This long recording time combined with the extreme pliability of this very thin tape, is a very real advantage in field recording but there is one very real drawback in addition to the tendency of the tape to stretch. This is *"print-through"* or *"print"*.

Print-through is the tendency shared by all magnetic tapes to transfer the magnetic image recorded on one layer to adjacent layers; sometimes the transfer takes place through several layers of tape. The result is that a signal may sometimes be heard from its transferred image several seconds before the main signal arrives, becoming louder and louder and then fading away as a series of echoes after the signal has passed. Actually all of these transferred signals are quite weak compared to the real signal but the logarithmic response of the ear accentuates their true value and they can be very annoying and objectionable. Print-through is more evident when the recording level is very high. It is also easier for the transfer to be made through thin layers of base material than through thick layers. Therefore, thin tapes always suffer more from print-through than do thicker tapes with the same magnetic coating. Fortunately great strides have been made in understanding the reason for print-through, and it is now believed that it is caused by a small percentage of supersensitive magnetic domains in the magnetic coating. Manufacturers seem to be learning to make the magnetic coatings more homogeneous and with fewer of the supersensitive particles which cause the trouble. Low-print tapes are now available and most tapes are now much better in this respect than they were five years ago. It is even estimated that the thinnest tapes today suffer less from print-through than did standard thickness tapes a few years ago. However, it is still true that the thicker tapes today have less trouble from print-through than do the thin tapes. Another consideration is that print-through is often less objectionable in most natural history recording than it is in, say, human speech. For example, print-through of a bird song would often be difficult to distinguish from a song of the same species in the distance. Because of the convenience and the better performance of the very thin Mylar tape we are using it almost entirely for field work in spite of its two drawbacks. For laboratory work, and the preparation of master tapes from which discs or films are to be prepared, it is probably best to use the standard thickness low print tapes.

8. *Accessories for Field Recording.*

Earphones. Good earphones are a necessity for field recording since loud speakers such as are used in studio monitoring booths would interfere with the signal coming to the microphone. Most ear phones leave much to be desired with respect to a broad frequency band. Low frequency reproduction is almost entirely dependent on having a tight seal between earphone and the ear. While low frequencies are not usually of great importance with most animals, they are important as objectionable noises or hums coming from wind, traffic or generated in the equipment. It is therefore important to achieve an airtight seal, if possible, between the earphone and the ear. Most earphones have very poor response above six or eight thousand cycles per second. However, the best earphones do have some useful response even out to 15,000 cps.

Windscreens for microphones are very desirable and some microphones may be purchased with removable wind screens. Strangely enough, windscreens do not, or should not, remove the sound of the wind, for if they did they would remove many of the desirable high frequencies. What they do do, is to prevent the wind from striking the microphone directly, and thereby causing a very powerful low frequency fluttering sound. Sometimes it is helpful to cover the entire front of the parabolic reflector, including the microphone, with a screen made of a tightly woven, thin cloth which excludes direct blasts of the wind. Wind is always objectionable but windscreens often permit recordings to be made which would otherwise be impossible.

Microphone cables and connectors. Cannon X-L-3 series connectors are becoming quite standard on field recorders although it is probable that in the near future some smaller and lighter connector will be adopted. In this country it is general to have the prong part of the connector on the microphone and the socket or receptacle part on the recorder. The three terminals of these connectors are numbered and it is customary to use # 1 terminal for the shield and # 2 and # 3 terminals for the two microphone wires. If one of these wires is to be grounded, it should be # 2. If this system is followed, as it is on most professional recorders, it makes for ready interchangeability. Outputs from a recorder to a line or speaker are usually prongs. There is nothing sacred about this system and there are exceptions. European equipment is likely to be just opposite.

Cables for the microphones should be the best quality obtainable and should contain two wires surrounded by a woven wire shield. The shield should be covered with rubber or plastic. Good shielding practice dictates that the shield should be grounded at only one point, usually the common ground point in the recorder. It is often very important that the cable shield carry no current of any kind lest its effectiveness as a shield be reduced. Some microphone cables, designed for use in or near very strong electric fields, have two separate shields completely insulated from each other. Each shield should be grounded, as before, at only one point. The best non-technical discussion of shielding, and elimination or reduction of noise and hum, is a chapter in Burstein and Pollak (1957). While it is seldom necessary, with modern portable recorders, to have a microphone cable more than ten feet long, it is sometimes useful to have a length or two 100 feet long.

Protection from dust and water. Plastic bags are ideal for protecting recording equipment, supplies and clothing. If bags are secured with some air in them they will even serve to float the equipment in case of an upset.

Reproduction facilities. These may, at first, seem out of place in recording equipment, but more and more it is becoming standard practice in the field, to attract birds and amphibians by reproducing to them their own vocal efforts. Sometimes this results in better recordings, and often it gives useful behavioral information. Sometimes the recorder is used to double as a reproducer, but more often a separate reproducer is used so that the recorder may be kept ready for any recording opportunity that may come while the animal is very close. Small power amplifiers and speakers are available which may be used with any reproducer to play back the sounds to the animal being studied.

Sling shots for shooting cords over high limbs of trees are useful in placing microphones close to a song perch. In this manner it is sometimes possible to approximate studio conditions in the open with the microphone only a foot or so from the songster.

Microphone preamplifiers. Because it is frequently impossible to place a microphone near a performer in the field, the signal to the recorder is likely to be very weak, even when a reflector is used with the microphone and full gain is used on the recorder. Preamplifiers will sometimes help in this situation but it should be pointed out that unless the preamplifier has a very excellent signal-to-noise ratio it will do but little good. To really improve matters, the signal reaching the tape, in addition to being louder, should contain less hiss and other noise than it would without the preamplifier. Unless this is so, it is probably as satisfactory to record the signal and supply the needed amplification on playback.

FIELD TECHNIQUES IN RECORDING

1. *General*

In general field recording techniques tend to simulate studio techniques but almost always there is more noise and interference to contend with and the performers are likely to be less cooperative. The use of parabolic reflectors and playback techniques, both referred to earlier, are examples of problems encountered in the field. Sometimes when recording a group of animals, such as a chorus of frogs, microphone placement is quite critical if one is to get the best and most pleasing balance between the nearby soloists and the remainder of the group.

2. *Voice Identification and Notes on Tape*

This practice is becoming very standard. Certainly the date and locality of the recording should be dictated on every tape, and additional notes are often very useful. Whether or not any of the voiced material is to be saved will depend on the policy of the worker. Certainly the notations should be listened to before they are discarded and the more important information entered onto the editing sheets. A musical note such as middle "A" (440 cps) is also very useful if recorded on each tape as a quick check on the speed of the field recorder at that instant, and also as a quick check on distortion, wow and flutter. A simple musical pitch pipe is the simplest way of producing such a note.

EDITING TAPE

1. *Types of Editing*

The purpose of editing tape is primarily to determine what parts of a recording are to be saved and put away in some orderly fashion, and to separate this material from the material which is to be discarded, or erased and put back into stock. More and more this *preliminary type of editing* is being done in the field after hours or on bad or inclement recording days. This practice has the advantage that an inadequate or unsatisfactory recording may be discovered while an expedition is still in the field where it may secure additional material. At the time of this preliminary editing, it is usual to prepare a recorded leader tape giving the scientific and common name of the species, and the "cut" or take number of the recording. At the same time an editing sheet is made out for the recording, using the same cut number as recorded on the leader. The editing sheet contains all pertinent data about the recording including such biological information as was observed, and the identification of background sounds (Fig. 3).

A "cut" is defined as a recording of an individual or group of a species or congregation, or of an inanimate sound or sounds, such as wind, thunder, water, steamboat whistle or other industrial or man-made sound, made at a given time and place. If two recordings of different individuals were made at the same place, they would constitute two different cuts. If the same individual was recorded in the same place but with several hours separating the two recordings, these would constitute separate cuts. If more than one species is recorded on a cut, and the sounds of each are equally good, the recording is filed under one species and cross indexed to the other species. In the editing process,

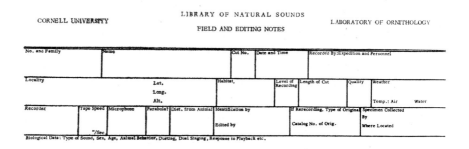

Editing Sheet used by Laboratory of Ornithology, Cornell University

Fig. 3. Editing Sheet used by Laboratory of Ornithology, Cornell University.

background species which are well recorded may be underlined on the editing sheets to indicate that they should be cross indexed. *If editing is done in the field,* the edited tapes are spliced together on a storage reel, "tail out," in the order in which the editing is done. Later, in the laboratory, each cut is added to a species reel which contains other earlier cuts of that species. For convenience, cuts are separated by a short piece of white leader tape. *If the editing is done in the laboratory,* instead of in the field, the cuts are added directly to the species reels. All species reels are stored "tail out" so that new cuts may be added without the necessity of rewinding. *Another type of editing,* beyond the scope of this paper, well covered by Haynes (1957), or Tall (1958), concerns itself with the preparation and use of recorded material as in preparing programs for radio, motion pictures or disc production, and involves re-recording, elimination of noises, correcting off-speed recording, correcting frequency response, and mixing with other sounds including voice or music.

2. *Tools for Editing*

These may be very simple. Any kind of a reproducer can be used if it gives a true concept of what is on the tape, but the large studio consoles such as the Ampex 350, are more convenient. In the field a convenient arrangement is to use a small home-type recorder, such as a Revere T-1100, modified to operate at 15"/sec. The Revere is driven by a storage battery and a converter which furnishes the 60 cycle power. The storage battery may be charged by connecting it in parallel with the car battery while driving.

Perhaps the most important requisite for editing is the proper *splicing tape.* There's no substitute for this! It's special, but easily obtainable. If only a few splices are to be made, scissors may be the only tools necessary (Haynes, 1957; p. 158). However, if many splices are to be made, the "Edi-Tall" splicing block is probably fastest, simplest and most nearly perfect. It is true that this block does require a somewhat special splicing tape 7/32" wide, but this is usually available in larger cities and it is well worth going after if much splicing is to be done.

3. *Scientific Names in Editing*

These have been restricted to genus and species as used by an authority selected for the region. The question of subspecies is left for the user of the recordings to decide upon, based on data, such as locality, date, elevation, etc. Specimens of the individuals recorded are almost never secured except in special studies, or with lower groups such as amphibians or insects.

CATALOGUING RECORDED MATERIALS

The purpose of cataloguing is to give an idea of what is available, quickly and with a reasonable amount of data regarding locality, date, quality of recording, etc., which will enable a worker to choose from the collection intelligently without the necessity for listening to everything recorded on a given species or subject. To this end, pertinent data from each editing sheet is transferred to 3x5 catalogue cards and these cards are later used in compiling a bound catalogue of the collection. From time to time, supplements are prepared to bring the bound catalogue up to date. The catalogue is arranged phylogenetically, with the phyla kept separate. Birds are arranged according to Wetmore (1951), with the orders being assigned Roman numerals for convenience while the families within an order are assigned Arabic numbers. Within the family the forms are entered alphabetically, by genus and species according to the scientific name used by the chosen authority for each region. Many non-biological subjects find their way into the collection and these are classified under such headings as Environmental Sounds and Incidental Sounds. There is also a growing collection of human voice recordings, consisting of voice descriptions of a locality or incident made on the spot, comments of local authorities familiar with problems of the people or the fauna, reminiscences of outstanding people, and sometimes complete papers, with illustrative sound, which have been delivered at scientific meetings. All these recordings of people are catalogued under the name of the person, the name of the species described, the name of the locality or under all pertinent categories.

STORAGE OF RECORDINGS

For the past ten years, practically all original recordings have been made on $\frac{1}{4}''$ magnetic tape. This is conveniently stored on plastic or metal reels and the reels are kept in individual cardboard or metal boxes. Recommended storage conditions call for a controlled temperature of between 50° F and 70° F with a humidity of 50%.

Little is really known about the expected life of magnetic tape, and even less about the length of time the magnetic material may be expected to cling to the tape backing. Some authorities estimate 50 years as the useful life of a stored tape, but this is little more than an intelligent guess based on experience with motion picture films. It is known, however, that the magnetic qualities of a recording deteriorate little, if any, with age. This knowledge is based on experience with magnetic recordings made before 1900.

Seven inch reel boxes may be conveniently stored on edge on book shelves, much as books in a library. Suitable labels are available for marking the front edge of the boxes. It is usual to arrange the collection phylogenetically according to order and family, and then alphabetically according to scientific name; the same arrangement as is used in the card catalogue.

MAINTENANCE OF EQUIPMENT

1. *General*

It is unfortunate that in recording, such a large proportion of a field worker's time must go into maintenance of equipment. It is possible that sometime in the future recording equipment will be simplified and become as dependable as photographic equipment, but that day is not yet here. Certainly the problems of sound recording do not appear more complex than the photographic problems and perhaps in time sound recording techniques will improve.

2. *Servicing*

Maintenance naturally divides into two parts: that which must be done *in the field* in order to continue operations; and the more fundamental maintenance usually done *in the laboratory,* which includes checking and testing to see that the equipment is actually performing according to specifications.

Unfortunately, dependable service for high quality recorders is not common. Most radio or TV repairmen can find a definite fault and repair it so that the instrument works. How well it works is something which they seem to have no time to worry about. Chief engineers of radio or TV stations are a much better bet. They usually have the ability, and they are forced by the government, to have most of the tools for testing. If they can be interested in the problem, they can often do a very good job. The same is true of other specialists in the field, but field recording equipment, especially high quality equipment, is still uncommon outside of large centers, and it does require uncommon interest and attention to keep it working at its best.

To get the kind of service needed, if he hasn't the time to become a specialist himself, the field worker must learn sufficient about his equipment so that he has some idea of when it is working correctly. When the recorder is new, he should study it and even make notes on its performance. If it has a meter or meters, he should make notes about meter readings under various conditions. Perhaps most important of all, he should procure a *schematic diagram* of the circuit of his machine and, if possible, a maintenance and repair manual. With these two items, almost any one trained in electronics, and having proper tools, can service a recorder, although lack of special spare parts may be a problem. Without schematics, finding trouble can be a very long hit-or-miss procedure. Even with information, the serious recordist will probably have to supply some special tools or test equipment normally found only in the factory or in the hands of specialized repair men.

3. *Electronic Tests*

One of these items is a *standard test tape* such as that produced by N.C.B. Laboratories, Ithaca, New York. These tapes should be handled with great care to avoid stretching or change in magnetic qualities. Always, before using a standard tape, the heads of the recorder, and any other magnetic metal parts likely to come in contact with the tape, should be demagnetized—this suggests that a *head demagnetizer* may well become part of the recording tool kit. Many recorders require a special tool for aligning the azimuth of the record and playback heads. *Audio oscillators,* also called *audio signal generators,* are usually available in radio stations and some service stations. Such instruments are absolute necessities for properly checking and adjusting recorders. Prices range all the way from about $35.00 for a very satisfactory kit of parts which you can put together, to several thousand dollars for high precision laboratory instruments. Another very desirable tool not usually found in service shops is a *stroboscope* (Fig. 4), for checking exact speed of the tape. This is a carefully made wheel with spokes or radial lines on one side or edge, which appear to stand still, when viewed with 60 cycle light, if the tape is running at proper speed. Since this adjustment requires 60 cycle illumination, it is best made in the laboratory, but frequent field checks by sounding a pitch pipe are well worth while since they will not only show up off speed operation when the tape is later reproduced on a machine operating at standard speed, but they will permit accurate speed correction in the laboratory.

Distortion measurements and wow and flutter determinations usually require equipment which is expensive and not readily available. Careful listening tests will usually be sufficient to show up serious defects in these areas.

Noise generated in equipment is also important, but it requires high quality equipment to evaluate it unless it is very bad.

Most maintenance manuals give specific information and directions,

Fig. 4. Tape stroboscope for precisely measuring tape speeds.   Courtesy of Scott Instrument Labs., Inc., New York City.

including necessary special equipment for all test procedures.   From these one can determine which maintenance problems must be taken to specialists and which can be cared for with the equipment at hand.

4. Mechanical Care

While emphasis has been placed on electronic maintenance, the *mechanical features* of a recorder should not be overlooked.   Cleanliness of heads and guides over which the tape moves is very important in maintaining high quality and constant speed.   Motor and idler bearings may need lubrication, while brakes or belts which control tape tension need cleaning and adjustment.

5. Field Maintenance

This should be kept to a minimum but breakdowns do occasionally occur and may waste much valuable time unless they are corrected quickly.

Some modern field recorders are equipped with plug-in amplifiers and bias oscillators which may be readily changed if they go bad in the field. This is a great convenience and often saves much valuable time.

Every field worker going far from his home base should carry at least the following tools and spare parts:

1. Instructions and maintenance manual
2. Long-nosed pliers (small)
3. Diagonal cutters (small)
4. Pliers
5. Soldering iron (6, 12 or 115 volts)
6. Solder
7. Small volt-ohm meter
8. Special spare tubes or transistors which may not be readily available
9. Spare plug-in amplifier and oscillator if available
10. Spare batteries

If preparations are being made for a long expedition where more major troubles may be expected, the list should be augmented by the following:

1. Spare recorder
2. Audio signal generator
3. Standard alignment tape
4. Portable vacuum-tube voltmeter
5. Spare oscillator coil and other parts not expected to be available in area
6. Spare microphone
7. Spare earphones
8. Head demagnetizer

THE CORNELL LIBRARY OF NATURAL SOUNDS

This facility is set up with over 10,000 recordings edited, catalogued and stored as previously described. The Library's primary purpose is to make recorded material available for scientific study, and to store and make available complete or partial studies in biological acoustics already finished (in cooperation with the International Committee on Biological Acoustics). The recordings have been gathered from every continent and more than 50 cooperators have made their recordings available for inclusion in the Library. Normally recordings are accepted only with the understanding that they will be made available to scholars anywhere in the world for research purposes. It is planned to print the catalogues of recorded sounds and make them widely available to institutions of learning throughout the world, but more assistance will be needed before this plan becomes a reality.

LITERATURE CITED

Burstein, H. and H. C. Pollak. 1957. Elements of tape recorder circuits. Gernsback Publications. New York. 223 pp.

Haynes, N. M. 1957. Elements of magnetic tape recording. Prentice-Hall. New Jersey. 392 pp.

Tall, J. 1958. Techniques of magnetic recording. Macmillan. New York. 472 pp.

Wetmore, A. 1951. A revised classification for birds of the world. Smithsonian Misc. Coll. *117:* 1–22.

The Analysis Of Animal Sounds [1,2]

DONALD J. BORROR

Department of Zoology and Entomology, Ohio State University, Columbus

THE SOUNDS PRODUCED by animals are of two general types; those produced incidentally as the animal moves about, feeds or engages in other activities, and those produced by special sound-producing organs or structures. Sounds of the latter type are of particular interest to the biologist because they are generally different in different species and hence may have taxonomic significance, and because of the role they play in the animal's behavior.

CHARACTERISTICS OF SOUND

Sound waves are initiated by the vibration of strings, air columns, drum-like structures, or various three-dimensional bodies. When a violin string vibrates, the entire string vibrates with a certain frequency, and portions of the string vibrate with frequencies that are integral multiples of the vibration frequency of the whole string. The lowest frequency in the sound produced by this vibrating string is the fundamental; the higher frequencies are called harmonics. The vibration of strings and air columns generally produces harmonics; the vibration of plates and three-dimensional structures produces a large number of sound waves, the frequencies of which often do not bear a simple relationship to one another.

Pitch is determined by the frequency of the sound waves, particularly of the fundamental; quality is determined by the number and relative intensity of the harmonics. A musical tone is a sound with a single frequency, or, more often, a sound with a fundamental and one or more harmonics; a noise is a sound without a definite pitch and containing many frequencies.

Tones of different pitch are arranged in a musical scale; the interval between two notes on this scale is the ratio of their frequencies. The interval between two notes an octave apart is expressed by the ratio 2:1;

---

[1] Manuscript received May 1959.
[2] Recordings illustrating this chapter are on Side II, Band 1 of the Demonstration Record.

in other words, frequencies are doubled each octave. In our equally tempered musical scale the A above middle C has a frequency of 440 cps; the top note of the piano, four octaves above middle C, has a frequency of 4,186 cps.

Sound waves are detected by the ear only when their frequencies are within certain limits, and these limits vary in different people and in different animals. For most people the limits are between about 25 and 15,000 cps, but some people can hear up to 21,000, and many animals can detect frequencies even higher.

Sound waves of sufficiently different intensities are heard as differing in loudness; loudness is usually measured on a logarithmic scale in terms of decibels (db). The range of the decibel scale, from the threshold of hearing to an intensity that is painful, is about 130 db.

The rhythm or pattern of an animal sound involves the length and number of the individual notes, or pulses of sound—how rapidly they are uttered, how they are grouped, and the interval of time between successive notes, phrases, or songs. Notes or phrases uttered faster than about six or eight a second cannot be counted by most people, and up to a rate of about thirty a second produce what might be called a trill. If notes are uttered faster than about thirty a second, or if a continuous note is modulated (fluctuated up and down in pitch) more than about thirty times a second, we hear it as a buzz.

THE INSTRUMENTAL ANALYSIS OF ANIMAL SOUNDS

To analyze an animal sound we need to determine the frequencies of the various notes, their relative loudness, and their rhythm. Most of these features can only be estimated by ear; for accurate analysis something better is needed. This "something better" is now available in some recent developments in the field of electronic instruments.

The instrumental analysis of sounds produced by animals involves the use of equipment to record the sounds and equipment to analyze the sounds.

Prior to about twelve years ago, recordings were made principally on discs or on sound film; now they are generally made on magnetic tape. The progress in the development of tape recorders has now reached the point where the biologist no longer needs a truckload of equipment to make a field recording; he can carry all he needs in his hands or over his shoulder. Such portable equipment is adequate for recording many animal sounds, but might not be adequate for other sounds. A person making recordings should use the type of equipment—recorder, microphone, and tape speed—which will yield the maximum fidelity in the recordings obtained. The first prerequisite for getting accurate analyses of animal sounds is recordings of high fidelity.

Most analyses of animal sounds are made with one or the other of two general types of instruments, an oscillograph or a sound spectrograph. Other instruments are often of value in determining certain characteristics of the sound. Where minute details of rhythm and loudness are more important than details of frequency composition, as in most insect sounds, the oscillograph may be the preferred instrument. Where details of frequency as well as rhythm are important, as in most bird songs, the sound spectrograph is probably better. The writer's interest in the analysis of animal sounds has been principally in bird songs, and he has used the sound spectrograph; for this reason, the following discussion will be concerned with the sound spectrograph.

The particular sound spectrograph used by the writer in the analysis of animal sounds is the Vibralyzer (Borror and Reese, 1953), manufactured by the Kay Electric Co., Pine Brook, New Jersey. This instrument makes graphs of sounds, and the graphs can portray a great deal of detail. In the operation of the Vibralyzer a tape-recorded sound is fed into the instrument, where it is recorded on a magnetic disc. To graph this sound, a piece of special paper is placed on a drum that is mounted synchronously with the magnetic disc, the drum is rotated, and the graph is made electrically as a marking stylus moves up the drum. In effect, the recorded sound is scanned for a particular band of frequencies at any position of the marking stylus. As the drum rotates the stylus moves upward, and at each revolution there is a slight shift upward in the scanning frequencies. Where the frequencies scanned for occur, a current is set up to the stylus, and a mark is made on the paper. Variations in the intensity of the sound appear on the paper as variations in the darkness of the mark. The graph shows time on the horizontal axis and frequency on the vertical axis. It is also possible with this instrument to make a section graph, one which for any selected point in time shows frequencies on the vertical axis and relative intensity on the horizontal axis.

With the recorded signal fed to the Vibralyzer at normal tape speed, the range of frequency and time in any particular graph can be varied; eight different ranges are possible. The lowest frequency range has about 250 cps as the top frequency on the graph, and portrays about twenty seconds of the sound; the highest frequency range has about 13,000 cps as the top frequency, and portrays about three-fourths of a second of the sound. By reducing the tape speed as the recorded sound is fed to the instrument, the frequency range can be extended and the time reduced. Graphs can be made of sounds within and beyond the human hearing range, and time elements can be measured down to a thousandth of a second or less.

Time calibrations for the graphs are determined by clocking the revolutions of the drum and measuring the drum's circumference. Frequency calibrations are made in either of two ways: the Vibralyzer has a built-in calibrator which will produce lines on the graph either 30 or 240 cycles apart, or oscillator notes can be fed into the instrument and graphed.

The graphs of any given sound will vary in appearance, depending on the settings on the control panel of the instrument; the controls can be set to bring out specific characteristics of the sound.

The feature of an animal sound about which the Vibralyzer gives the least information is loudness. As has been mentioned, the darkness of the mark gives an indication of the relative intensity of various parts of the recorded sound; the range in intensity that can be satisfactorily portrayed in any one graph is about twenty db. The relative intensity of different moments of the sound can be read from the VU meter of the Vibralyzer. It is possible to get definite db figures on the relative loudness of different frequencies at any given moment of the sound by means of section graphs, but it takes quite a bit of careful calibrating. To get definite db figures on actual loudness requires the use of a sound level meter under standard conditions with the animal itself. Accurate information on loudness is highly desirable in any work on animal behavior in relation to sounds; such information can probably be obtained more easily with a sound level meter than with the Vibralyzer.

ANALYTICAL STUDIES OF BIRD SONGS

A number of analytical studies of animal sounds have been made in recent years—the sounds of birds (Borror, 1956 and 1959; Borror and Reese, 1953, 1954, 1956a, and 1956b; Collias and Joos, 1953; Fish, 1953; Thorpe, 1954, 1958a, and 1958b; et al.), amphibians (Blair, 1955, 1956a, 1956b, 1957a, 1957b, 1958a, 1958b; et al.), fish (Moulton, 1958; Tavolga, 1958a, 1958b, and 1958c; et al.), and insects (Alexander, 1957a and 1957b; Alexander and Moore, 1958; Borror, 1954; Broughton, 1954; Busnel, Busnel, and Dumortier, 1956; Busnel and Gramet, 1956; Loher, 1957; Walker, 1957; et al.). These studies have shown many interesting things—details of frequency and rhythm not apparent to the ear, variations within species and individuals, and differences between species. A few examples from bird songs may serve to illustrate the sort of information revealed by the sound spectrograph.

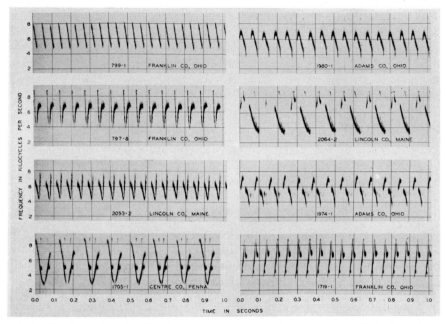

FIG. 1. Portions of eight chipping sparrow songs. The songs from which these spectrograms were made are reproduced in Selection 1 and were recorded as follows: 799–1, April 30, 1954; 797–8, April 30, 1954; 2053–2, June 20, 1956; 1705–1, April 18, 1956; 1980–1, June 2, 1956; 2064–2, June 20, 1956; 1974–1, June 2, 1956; 1719–1, April 27, 1956.

Figure 1[3] (Selection 1) contains sound spectrograms of one second from each of eight songs of the chipping sparrow *(Spizella passerina)*. Most bird books (e.g., Peterson, 1947; Saunders, 1935) describe the song of this bird as a series of rapid notes "all on one pitch." The graphs show that none of the notes in these songs is uniform in pitch; all are slurred, and they are slurred in different ways in the different songs. Most of this slurring is extremely rapid; in 797-8 the pitch is slurred downward for more than an octave in about a hundredth of a second.

Different chipping sparrow songs sound very much alike to our ears; about all the difference we can detect is a difference in the rate with which the notes are uttered, and in most cases we can only guess what this rate actually is. The phrase rate in the songs shown in Figure 1

---

[3] All graphs shown in this paper were made with a Vibralyzer from songs in the collection of recorded sounds of the Department of Zoology and Entomology, Ohio State University. The recordings were made with a Magnemite recorder, Model 610–E. The numbers on each graph represent the number of the recording, and the song in the recording, from which that graph was made.

varies from 7.4 phrases per second in 2064-2 to 22.5 per second in 799-1; the phrases contain from 1 to 3 notes each. The graphs show that there is actually a great deal of variation in the songs of different birds; the figure shows eight of the more than two dozen patterns of chipping sparrow songs represented in the collection of bird recordings at Ohio State University.

Studies of bird songs with the sound spectrograph (Borror, 1959; Borror and Reese, 1953 and 1956a) have shown that some birds are able to utter more than one note at a time; the graphs in Figure 2 (Selection 2) show some additional examples of this. In each of the introductory phrases of the song sparrow song (2159-1) the bird is uttering a note that is relatively steady in pitch (about 5,500 cps), and at the same time a rapid series (about 150 per second) of short notes at a lower pitch. In the last part of the wood thrush song (1175-19) the bird utters four high-pitched notes which, after an abrupt initial down-slur, are relatively steady in pitch at about 7,000 cps; at the same time it is uttering a rapid series (105 per second) of abruptly down-slurred notes at a lower pitch. In each phrase of the trill in the towhee's song (2715-2) the bird utters an up-slurred note, and at the same time a note that slurs upward and then downward. All by itself each of these birds is singing what amounts to a duet.

The songs of a given hermit thrush (*Hylocichla guttata*) are of several different patterns; these patterns are apparently not sung in any definite sequence, but successive songs are nearly always different. Some songs are much higher in pitch than others. Each song consists of a relatively long note that is steady in pitch, followed by one or two complex and musical phrases in which the notes are uttered quite rapidly. Hermit thrush songs are considered by many people to be among the most musical of bird songs.

Among the recordings of bird songs at Ohio State University there are four, containing a total of 126 songs, of a hermit thrush in Lincoln Co., Maine. These songs are of 13 different patterns, which are shown in Figures 3 and 4. Most of the notes in these songs are steady in pitch, and their pitch follows our musical scale. At normal speed these songs are too fast for our ears to appreciate fully, but slowed down they are found to contain some very pleasing melodies (Selections 3 and 4).

The spectrogram shows that songs which appear non-musical to our ears are characterized by wide bands of frequencies occurring either simultaneously or within a very short time interval, with the result that it is difficult or impossible to assign any particular pitch to the notes by ear. The chipping sparrow has such songs. Songs that appear musical are characterized by notes that are musical tones rather than

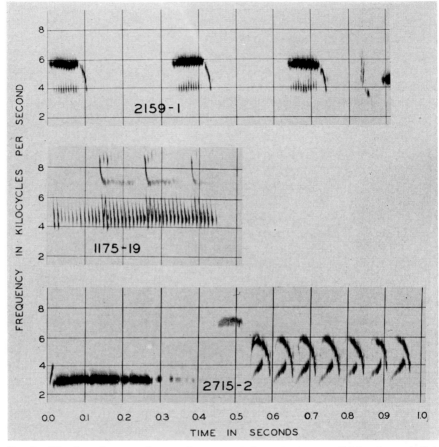

FIG. 2. The introductory phrases of a song of the song sparrow (*Melospiza melodia*),
Lincoln Co., Maine, July 11, 1956 (2159–1); the last part of a song of the wood
thrush (*Hylocichla mustelina*), Franklin Co., Ohio, July 2, 1954 (1175–19); a song of
the rufous-sided towhee (*Pipilo erythrophthalmus*), Kanawha City, West Virginia,
May 25, 1957 (2715–2). The songs from which these spectrograms were made are
reproduced in Selection 2.

noises, that is, the notes contain a fundamental and possibly harmonics,
they are either steady in pitch or are slurred relatively slowly, and their
pitch follows our musical scale. The hermit thrush has such songs.

The sound spectrograph is often an aid in identification, not only of
the species but of the individual. In many species of birds, including
the hermit thrush, wood thrush, and song sparrow, each individual has
songs that are different from the songs of most other individuals; these
differences are not always apparent to the ear, but they are shown by the

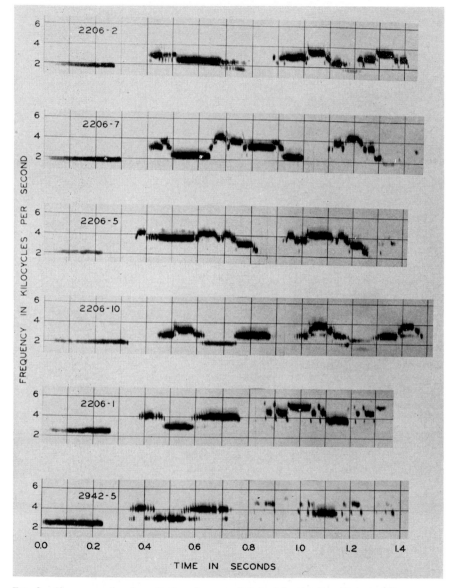

FIG. 3. Six songs of a hermit thrush, recorded in Lincoln Co., Maine. These songs are reproduced in Selection 3 and were recorded as follows: 2206, July 19, 1956; 2942, July 3, 1957.

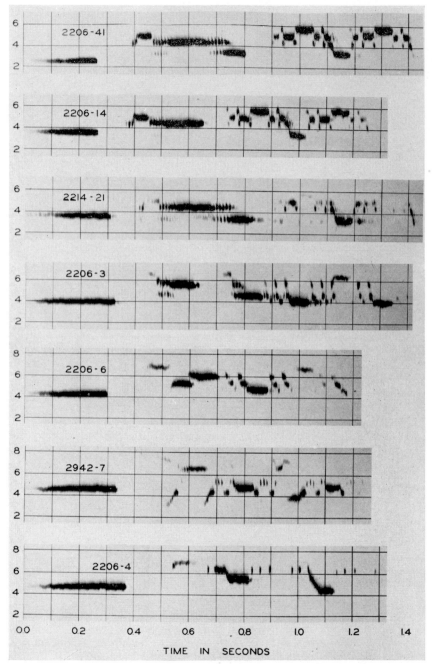

FIG. 4. Seven songs of the same hermit thrush represented in Fig. 3. These songs are reproduced in Selection 4 and were recorded as follows: 2206, July 19, 1956; 2214, July 25, 1956; 2942, July 3, 1957.

graphs. The graphs are like a signature; they are characteristic for the individual bird. It is thus often possible to recognize individuals by their song—if not by ear, then by means of sound spectrographs of the songs. The 126 hermit thrush songs mentioned above were obtained in two seasons, but since the recordings each season contained the same unique song patterns, and were obtained in the same area, there is no doubt that they were of the same bird. Our recordings contain many examples, based on song graphs, of individual birds returning to the same area in successive years; the graphs provide an identification that is just as positive as a numbered leg band.

The sound spectrograph is an ideal instrument for studying the variations in the complex songs of birds. The graphs reveal many details not apparent to the ear, and enable us to describe a song in objective terms. They place the study of animal acoustics on a new level, and provide techniques applicable to many biological studies.

LITERATURE CITED

Alexander, R. D. 1957a. The taxonomy of the field crickets of the eastern United States (Orthoptera: Gryllidae: *Acheta*). Ann. Ent. Soc. Amer. *50:* 584–602.

————. 1957b. Sound production and associated behaviour in insects. Ohio Jour. Sci. *57:* 101–113.

————, and T. E. Moore. 1958. Studies on the acoustical behaviour of the seventeen-year cicadas (Homoptera: Cicadidae: *Magicicada*). Ohio Jour. Sci. *58:* 107–127.

Blair, W. F. 1955. Differentiation of mating call in spadefoots, genus *Scaphiopus*. Tex. Jour. Sci. *7:* 183–188.

————. 1956a. Call difference as an isolating mechanism in southwestern toads (genus *Bufo*). Tex. Jour. Sci. *8:* 87–106.

————. 1956b. The mating calls of hybrid toads. Tex. Jour. Sci. *8:* 350–355.

————. 1957a. Mating call and relationship of *Bufo hemiophrys* Cope. Tex. Jour. Sci. *9:* 99–108.

————. 1957b. Structure of the call and relationships of *Bufo microscaphus* Cope. Copeia 1957: 208–212.

————. 1958a. Mating call in the speciation of anuran amphibians. Amer. Naturalist *92:* 27–51.

————. 1958b. Call difference as an isolation mechanism in Florida species of hylid frogs. Quart. Jour. Fla. Acad. Sci. *21:* 32–48.

Borror, D. J. 1954. Audio-spectrographic analysis of the song of the cone-headed grasshopper, *Neoconocephalus* ensiger (Harris) (Orthoptera: Tettigoniidae). Ohio Jour. Sci. *54:* 297–303.

————. 1956. Variation in Carolina wren songs. Auk 73: 211–229.

————. 1959. Variation in the songs of the rufous-sided towhee. Wilson Bull. *71:* 54–72.

————, and C. R. Reese. 1953. The analysis of bird songs by means of a Vibralyzer. Wilson Bull. *65:* 271–303.

————, and ————. 1954. Analytical studies of Henslow's sparrow songs. Wilson Bull. *66:* 243–252.

————, and ————. 1956a. Vocal gymnastics in wood thrush songs. Ohio Jour. Sci. *56:* 177–182.

————, and ————. 1956b. Mockingbird imitations of Carolina wren. Bull. Mass. Audubon Soc. *40:* 245-250.

Broughton, W. D. 1954. L'analysis de l'émission acoustique des Orthoptères à partir d'un enregistrement sur disque reproduit à des vitesses ralenties. Ann. Epiphyties 1954: 81–88.

Busnel, R. G., M. C. Busnel, and B. Dumortier. 1956. Relations acoustiques interspecifiques chez les ephippigères (Orthoptères, Tettigoniidae). Ann. Epiphyties 1956: 451–469.

Collias, N. and M. Joos. 1953. The spectrographic analysis of sound signals of the domestic fowl. Behaviour *5:* 175–188.

Fish, W. R. 1953. A method for the objective study of bird song and its application to the analysis of Bewick wren songs. Condor *55:* 250–257.

Loher, W. 1957. Untersuchungen über den aufbau und die Entstehung der Gesänge einiger Feldheuschreckenarten und den Einfluss von Lautzeichen auf das aküstiche Verhalten. Ztschr. Vergleich. Physiol. *39:* 313–356.

Moulton, J. M. 1958. The acoustical behaviour of some fishes in the Bimini area. Biol. Bull. *114:* 357–374.

Peterson, R. T. 1947. A field guide to the birds. Boston: Houghton Mifflin Co. 290 pp.

Saunders, A. A. 1935. A guide to bird songs. New York: D. Appleton-Century Co. 285 pp.

Tavolga, W. N. 1958a. Underwater sounds produced by two species of toadfish, *Opsanus tau* and *Opsanus beta*. Bull. Mar. Sci. Gulf and Caribbean. *8:* 278–284.

————. 1958b. The significance of underwater sounds produced by males of the gobiid fish, *Bathygobius soporator*. Physiol. Zool. *31:* 259–271.

————. 1958c. Underwater sounds produced by males of the blenniid fish, *Chasmodes bosquianus*. Ecology *39:* 759–760.

Thorpe, W. H. 1954. The process of song-learning in the chaffinch as studied by means of spectrograph. Nature *173:* 465–469.

————. 1958a. The learning of song-patterns by birds, with especial reference to the song of the chaffinch *Fringilla coelebs*. Ibis. *100:* 535–570.

————. 1958b. Further studies on the process of song learning in the chaffinch *(Fringilla coeleba gengleri)*. Nature *182:* 554–557.

Walker, T. J., Jr. 1957. Specificity in the response of female tree crickets (Orthoptera, Gryllidae, Oecanthinae) to calling songs of the males. Ann. Ent. Soc. Amer. *50:* 626–636.

CAPTIONS TO SELECTIONS ON DEMONSTRATION RECORD

Selection 1. Eight chipping sparrow songs shown in Fig. 1. Each song is reproduced first at normal speed, then a portion of the song is reproduced at one-fourth speed. (See Fig. 1 for localities and dates of recordings)

Selection 2. Three songs shown in Fig. 2. Song sparrow song, first at normal speed, then at one-fourth speed. Wood thrush song, first at normal speed, then at one-eighth speed. Rufous-sided towhee song, first at normal speed, then at one-fourth speed. (See Fig. 2 for localities and dates of recordings)

Selection 3. Six hermit thrush songs shown in Fig. 3. Each song is reproduced first at normal speed, then at one-fourth speed. (See Fig. 3 for locality and dates of recordings)

Selection 4. Seven hermit thrush songs shown in Fig. 4. Each song is reproduced first at normal speed, then at one-fourth speed. (See Fig. 4 for lᴵ ᵗlity and dates of recordings)

Sound Communication In Orthoptera And Cicadidae [1,2]

Richard D. Alexander

Museum of Zoology and Department of Zoology, University of Michigan, Ann Arbor

COMMUNICATION can be said to occur whenever the activities of one animal influence the activities of another animal. Insects thus communicate in connection with all of the major classes of life activity, and they utilize all of the major communicative senses—visual, chemical, tactile, and auditory—in this communication. For purposes of the present discussion, communication among insects can be divided into short range signalling and long range signalling. Included in the first instance are situations in which the individuals involved are in close proximity, generally within range of more than one sense; and in the second instance, situations in which the individuals involved are relatively far apart and within range of a single sense only. Sound operates in both kinds of situations, but arthropod systems of sound communication have reached a high level of complexity and become diverse in function only when the initial assembly or coming-together of the adult males and females has become involved. In most insects this coming-together of the sexes is accomplished primarily as a result of 1) attraction of all the individuals to some feature of the environment (e.g., to a host plant or animal, or to ecological conditions existing only in restricted locations within the range of the species), or 2) the location and behavior of individuals of the previous generation (e.g., factors involved in determining the oviposition site of the females, particularly in species which mate upon emergence). In certain cases, however, communicative devices are known to be involved and to be effective over great distances. Riley (1895) demonstrated that a marked male of the *Ailanthus* silkworm moth, *Philosamia walkeri* Felder, could locate a female of the same species a mile and a half away during one night, apparently by the odor she emitted. More recent experiments reported by Collins and Potts (1932), Dufay (1957), Schwink (1958), and others have given

---

[1] Manuscript received June 1959.
[2] Recordings illustrating this chapter are on Side I, Band 1 of the Demonstration Record.

similar results, showing that male Lepidoptera orient to the odor emitted by sexually responsive females from incredible distances. Travis (1939) found that males of the June beetle, *Phyllophaga lanceolata* (Say), orient to the odor emitted by the females at distances of 15 to 75 feet, depending upon the direction and velocity of the wind.

Visual stimuli operate at long range in the assembly of insects in several ways. Thus, Magnus (1958) found that size, motion, and color are involved in the male-female interactions in the fritillary butterfly, *Argynnis paphia* L., and Crane (1955) and Stride (1958) found that in other species of Lepidoptera the males first react to the females because of their color patterns or motions in flight. Downes (1958), Provost (1958), and others have shown that male Diptera assemble over "marker" objects and perform as groups when so assembled, probably stimulated both by the marker and by each other's individual activities. Such swarms attract the females, and mating frequently takes place within the swarm.

Buck (1935, 1937a, 1937b), Barber (1951), and others have demonstrated that males and females in the Lampyridae or fireflies (Coleoptera) are initially attracted to each other as a result of the light-flashing rhythms of the males, and in some species there is a sequence of interactions between the males and females which involves alternate flashing by both. This light-flashing system is remarkably analogous in many details to certain of the sound-signalling systems that have developed in the Orthoptera, as will be pointed out later.

Auditory stimuli have long been suspected to operate at long range in certain insects, chiefly because of the intensity and remarkably specific nature of song rhythms in sympatric species of Orthoptera and Cicadidae (Davis, 1928; Myers, 1929; Allard, 1929; Faber, 1929, 1932; Fulton, 1932; Pringle, 1954; Alexander, 1957b). Regen (1913) and Duijm and Van Oyen (1948) were among the first to show that the females of certain Orthoptera are attracted by the songs of males of their own species in the absence of other stimuli. Recent reviews by Pringle (1956), Alexander (1957a), and Frings and Frings (1958) have summarized the evidence for both long range and short range sound communication in insects. Information acquired since the publication of these reviews has primarily involved three systems which in terms of complexity, numbers of species, and broadness of the taxonomic categories involved, represent the major systems of sound communication in insects. These three systems are: 1) tegminal stridulation associated with tympanal auditory organs on the front tibiae in the Ensifera (Orthoptera: Saltatoria), 2) tegmino-femoral stridulation and alary crepitation associated with abdominal tympanal auditory organs in the Caelifera (Orthoptera: Saltatoria), and 3) tymbal vibration associated with abdominal tympanal auditory organs in the Auchenorrhyncha (Homoptera: Cicadidae and Cicadellidae). Walker (1957), Perdeck (1957), and Alexander and Moore (1958) have shown that the differences among the songs of sympatric species in each of these three groups are behaviorally significant and are involved in reproductive isolation among such species. The present discussion will be concerned with the significance of this and other new evidence detailing the operation of sound communication in these three groups.

ACKNOWLEDGMENTS

The investigations making this report possible have been supported in part by grants from The Rockefeller Foundation and the Horace H. Rackham School of Graduate Studies of The University of Michigan. Special thanks are due Dr. Thomas E. Moore, Mr. Kenneth C. Shaw, and Dr. Irving J. Cantrall of the University of Michigan for suggestions, criticisms, and many stimulating discussions on the subject of sound communication in insects. Dr. Moore assisted in taking readings in some of the tests reported here, and Mr. Shaw collected some of the insects used, and recorded the female *Pterophylla* sound which appears on the Demonstration Record.

THE OPERATION OF SOUND COMMUNICATION IN THE ORTHOPTERA AND CICADIDAE

In general, the sounds produced by Orthoptera and Cicadidae can be divided into five categories: 1) calling sounds by male[3], 2) calling sounds by females, 3) courtship sounds by males, 4) aggressive sounds by males, and 5) disturbance sounds by either sex or both. The first two of these sounds operate primarily at long range, the second two primarily at short range, and the last may be effective either at long range or at short range in the cases in which it operates as an intra-specific stimulus.

The conditions regulating production of these five kinds of sounds and their functions as communicative devices are diagrammed in Figures 1 and 2. The sequences indicated in Figure 1 are not to be interpreted as always suggesting cause-effect relationships, but primarily as descrip-

---

[3] The variety of stimuli involved in evoking this sound, and its multiple effects, make it a difficult signal to label. The term "calling" has been selected from those in current use by various authors (common, ordinary, usual, spontaneous, indifferent, wonted, attracting, calling) because it is descriptive (implying "signalling," "summoning," "attracting," "drawing attention to by loud sounds," and "causing to assemble," according to various dictionaries), and it can be applied to a variety of species without undue presumption.

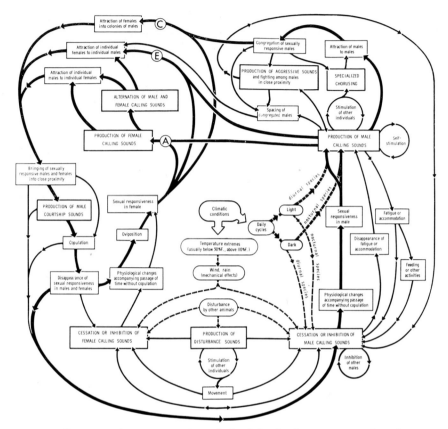

Fig. 1. A diagrammatic representation of the behavioral sequences and cycles associated with sound communication in adult Orthoptera and Cicadidae. Heavy lines
indicate more important sequences, and the symbols (C), (E), and (A) designate
sequences most characteristic of the Cicadidae, Ensifera, and Acridinae, respectively.

tive devices illustrating the sequences in which particular events ordinarily take place. The degree of completeness or incompleteness of
available information with respect to particular portions of the diagram
can be inferred from the specificity or lack of specificity in the terms
employed.

Male Calling Sounds

As shown in Figure 1, these sounds are the only ones which are normally produced by individuals which are completely isolated from all
others. Any sexually mature male in the three groups illustrated in

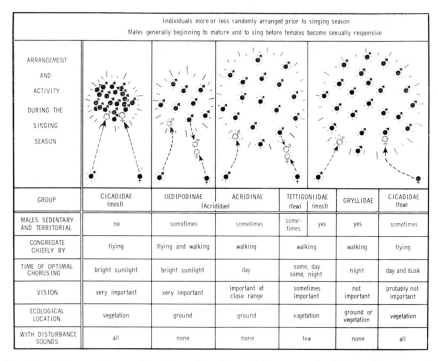

				Individuals more or less randomly arranged prior to singing season			
				Males generally beginning to mature and to sing before females become sexually responsive			
ARRANGEMENT AND ACTIVITY DURING THE SINGING SEASON							
GROUP	CICADIDAE (most)	OEDIPODINAE (Acrididae)	ACRIDINAE	TETTIGONIIDAE (few)	(most)	GRYLLIDAE	CICADIDAE (few)
MALES SEDENTARY AND TERRITORIAL	no	sometimes	sometimes	some-times	yes	yes	sometimes
CONGREGATE CHIEFLY BY	flying	flying and walking	walking	walking		walking	flying
TIME OF OPTIMAL CHORUSING	bright sunlight	bright sunlight	day	some, day some, night		night	day and dusk
VISION	very important	very important	important at close range	sometimes important		not important	probably not important
ECOLOGICAL LOCATION	vegetation	ground	ground	vegetation		ground or vegetation	vegetation
WITH DISTURBANCE SOUNDS	all	none	none	few		none	all

Fig. 2. A diagram illustrating the modes of assembly as a result of the calling songs in various Orthoptera and Cicadidae, and some correlations between behavioral and environmental phenomena.

Figure 1 can be expected to sing [4] at temperatures between 50° F and 110° F (approximately), provided that he 1) has not copulated recently, 2) is not disturbed by the presence of other animals or by the mechanical effects of wind or rain, 3) has not sung for a while, or has not been singing continually for a long period of time just previously, and 4) is located a) in the dark if a nocturnal species, b) in a situation of high light intensity if a diurnal species, and c) in a situation of low light intensity if a crepuscular species. All of these regulating factors combine to cause the males of each species to sing during definite, predictable periods of each day. Light intensity seems to be the most universally important single factor in determining the exact time on each day when different

[4] Because the male calling sounds are rhythmical and repetitious, thus structurally resembling the "songs" of amphibians, birds, and humans (though lacking melody —characteristic of the last two named), they are commonly referred to as "songs," and an individual producing such a sound is said to be "singing." This usage will be employed here. The only other insect sounds known to possess these characteristics are the courtship sounds of various Orthoptera and Homoptera.

species begin song.   Thus, most of the cicadas, meadow grasshoppers, band-winged grasshoppers, and slant-faced grasshoppers sing during the day, and certain species achieve optimal chorusing only in bright sunlight (Alexander and Moore, 1958) .   Some cicadas sing only at dusk for surprisingly brief and definite periods of time, usually less than one hour in length, as for example, *Tibicen auletes* (Germar) and *T. resonans* (Walker) , sibling species occurring in eastern United States.   When the light intensity has dropped to about five footcandles (estimated), these species begin to sing in chorus so suddenly that the noise of their starting resembles the sound of a great wind swelling across the woods.   For a short period of time, cicadas seem to fly in every direction and the woods is literally alive with them.   Then, as the light intensity continues to drop, the sound stops as suddenly as it began, at about the time when the chorus of night-singing Orthoptera is just beginning to develop.

Figure 3 shows the climatic conditions at the times when an isolated, dense colony of a nocturnal, coneheaded grasshopper began singing on several different evenings.   Light intensity was the only factor in which there was no measurable difference from one evening to the next, except on two evenings when the mechanical effects of brisk rain delayed the beginning of song.   Generally, the only other time that such finely tuned inhibition to light intensity as the triggering device in night-singing species is upset is late in the season when these insects are prevented from completing normal daily quotas of song by temperatures below 50° F from shortly after dusk until after dawn.   Under these conditions the inhibition to light intensity is characteristically overcome earlier in the day, and many night-singers can be heard in middle and late afternoon, and rarely even at noon on the brightest days.   Other factors may also enter in, such as the change in the ratio of daylight to dark, and changes in the quality and intensity of light during the daylight hours.   Lutz (1932) has shown that there is a 24-hour cycle of activity in some Gryllidae and Tettigoniidae which persists for a time in the absence of the usual fluctuations in light intensity.   It is likely that in some species the situation is similar to that demonstrated by Buck (1937a) in Lampyridae in which 24-hour cycles in the frequency of flashing by males of a nocturnal species, *Photinus pyralis* L., persist feebly even in continuous light or darkness, but relatively slight changes in light intensity cause increases in light flashing frequency at any time that they occur.

Although night-singing species begin at about the same light intensity from one evening to the next, their choruses generally dwindle noticeably after a few hours of darkness, and frequently one hears few or no individuals after midnight.   Likewise, day-singing species generally stop chorusing, and sometimes stop singing entirely before the light intensity

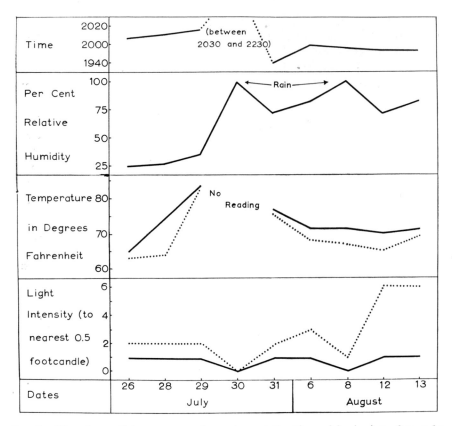

Fig. 3. Climatic conditions on several evenings at the time of beginning of song by an isolated, dense colony of *Neoconocephalus ensiger* (Harris) (Tettigoniidae: Copiphorinae). Dotted lines, in the open; solid lines, near the insects in vegetation.

has dropped to the same level that initiated singing. *Magicicada septendecim* (L.) begins to sing at dawn, and to chorus intensely when the first rays of the morning sun reach down into the trees, but only a few individuals are still singing in late afternoon when the sun is still high (Alexander and Moore, 1958 (Selection 2)). Part of this diminishment of singing volume is undoubtedly due to some of the males finding mates or becoming involved in courtship. Most of it, however, is due to an inability of the individual insects to maintain song during the entire period of the day that climatic conditions remain similar to those responsible for initiating singing (labelled "fatigue or accommodation" in Figure 1), and sound production is accordingly replaced by other activities. It is not unusual to see a male cricket which has been singing steadily for some time in the laboratory suddenly stop stridulating and begin to feed almost simultaneously upon food that was within reach when he began singing. Species such as *Tibicen auletes* and *T. resonans* operate somewhat differently in that individuals are probably able to participate continually in chorusing for a longer period of time than is represented by the proper climatic conditions during each 24-hour period. Whether the particular activity in species which operate within such brief daily periods is sound production, light-flashing, swarming in flight, or other behavior, the insects involved are nearly always crepuscular, and their level of activity is largely determined by changes in light intensity. Most often, such species are active in the evening rather than in the morning, and we can speculate that two advantages are involved: 1) fewer insectivorous birds are active, and 2) pairs entering into and remaining in copula for long periods of time are less vulnerable during the hours of darkness following dusk than they would be during the hours of daylight following dawn.

When cool nights or other disturbing factors prevent them from completing normal quotas of song, male Orthoptera sometimes sing under quite unusual conditions in addition to those already noted above. Thus, a male of *Acheta pennsylvanicus* (Burmeister), which I captured late in the season and was carrying inside my closed fist, produced a normal calling song there until dropped into a cage, where he began to sing again within two or three minutes. A male of *Conocephalus nemoralis* (Scudder) in early November produced a normal calling song almost uninterruptedly while dodging my hand as I made several attempts to capture him. A male of *Orchelimum vulgare* (Harris) sang almost continually for several days after remaining silent for a time in a small vial barely large enough to contain him which I carried in my pocket. A male of *Orchelimum silvaticum* McNeill was watched for several minutes singing normally while perched on a blossom eating a small bee which it had apparently just captured there.

The male calling song in Orthoptera and Cicadidae is the basis of the structure of sound communication in modern species; many of these insects possess no other sound signal. Directly and indirectly, the male calling song exerts many different influences upon the activities of both the males and the females in connection with the process of eventually bringing the adults into close proximity. When a male begins to sing, his sound affects his own behavior directly through the external auditory organs, continually restimulating him and setting the rate of production of certain of the rhythmical units in his song. There is evidence that male Orthoptera produce their rhythmical songs for long periods of time and with their usual precision only if their auditory organs are unimpaired. Deafened male field crickets which have never heard themselves or any other crickets, sing considerably less than non-deafened males and do not sing steadily for long periods of time as do normal males. This phenomenon will be discussed in more detail later when chorusing behavior is analyzed.

The calling song of the male likewise stimulates neighboring males, and males reared in isolation usually sing considerably less than males reared in groups. This has been reported by Haskell (1957) for Acridinae, and has been found to be true with field crickets in our laboratory.

Fulton (1928) showed that neighboring males of the snowy tree cricket, *Oecanthus niveus* (DeGeer), could not synchronize their chirps in chorus after they had been deafened. The starting in quick succession of many males in dense colonies, sometimes in synchrony with each other from the start (Alexander, 1957a), is relatively easy to observe in the field in eastern United States and is the chief reason that one can ascribe definite times of starting to entire colonies in order to make the kind of calculation shown in Figure 3. In the particular colony discussed here, beginning of steady singing by one individual always resulted in continued chorusing from that time, with a dozen or more individuals joining the chorus within a few seconds. There were never more than one or two very brief, irregular, and obviously abortive song starts prior to this time, and on most evenings there were none at all.

The assembly of sexually responsive males enhances chorusing behavior, which is more stable in dense colonies, thus operating as a feed-back mechanism increasing the effectiveness of the colony as an attractant for outside males and females. The obvious formation of colonies of singing males in the field suggests strongly that the male calling song under certain circumstances (such as from a given distance or at a certain intensity) attracts other males. In most Orthoptera, lone males are generally less stationary than males which are incorporated into colonies, frequently shifting locations and singing from different perches on successive evenings. This is especially evident in long-winged individuals capable of flight. Alexander and Moore (1958) demonstrated in the field that the males of two species of 17-year cicadas are attracted by the songs of other males in the same species. Haskell (1957) found that male Acridinae sometimes orient and locomote toward speakers playing back the calling song of the species.

Some of the above effects of the male calling song upon the amount and kind of activity of other males, although suggested by field and laboratory observations, are yet to be clearly demonstrated in the Ensifera. Haskell (1953) failed to observe any reaction to the male calling song in caged male house crickets (*Acheta domesticus* L.), and none was

clear in males of a California species of field cricket tested in our laboratory (Fig. 6) in a situation in which responses to both the calling song
and the courtship song were obvious in females.   More recent experiments have suggested that at certain times males respond to chirps from
the calling song or to aggressive chirps by one or more of several activities, including 1) chirping aggressively once or a few times, 2) making
short dashes, 3) flipping the antennae, or 4) pausing while locomoting
(Alexander, Ms.).   Adjustment of the rhythm of the sound by playing it at half speed or by increasing the speed by about fifty per cent
nullified all response, suggesting that the particular sound of the species
was the stimulus involved.   No response to long-continued playbacks
of steady chirping (calling song) has been evident.

As shown in Figure 2, in most Gryllidae and Tettigoniidae the males
rarely move close enough together in the field to be within range of any
sense other than hearing.   They may remain this far apart through being
repelled by each other's singing, though this has not been experimentally
demonstrated.   The males in these species are quite sedentary in such
colonies, remaining within restricted localities and frequently returning
to the same perch or burrow, and singing most often from that spot.   In
the laboratory, male field crickets become "attached" to introduced
crevices or to burrows which they sometimes hollow out in the sand
under objects.   This occupation of crevices or burrows is characterized
by several behavioral peculiarities: 1) restriction of the total area trav-
ersed by the occupying male, 2) long periods of time spent motionless
in the crevice, 3) repeated movement in and out, and detailed examination of the crevice, 4) distinctive "sallies" outside the crevice at intervals,
during which food and water are consumed and encountered males and
females are fought and courted, respectively, 5) unusually direct returns
to the crevice after being outside, 6) unusually aggressive reactions in encounters with other males, and 7) a decrease in the number of encounters
with other males, frequently leading to virtual isolation for long periods
of time.   Such an occupying male is able to dominate encounters that
he would lose under any other circumstances, and in one series of twelve
encounters during five hours between two males occupying neighboring
crevices, each male won all encounters near his own crevice and lost all
encounters near the other male's crevice.   Temporary isolation enhances
the dominating ability of a male, thus working together in a reinforcing
manner with territorial behavior in effecting the stability of natural
colonies of male field crickets.   A crevice-occupying male does not pursue
males or females far from the crevice.   However, temporary contact
with other individuals frequently results in long-continued production
of the calling song by a territorial male, by causing brief production of

aggressive or courtship sounds through which the male is stimulated, either by external auditory feedback, some kind of internal feedback, or both, to keep chirping and gradually adjust into the calling rhythm. This response would have the desirable effect of calling back the departing female if she is sexually responsive, and possibly also of reinforcing the repellence of the temporarily contacted male. The conditions under which male field crickets are found in the field—permanently located at burrows or crevices, and spaced far enough apart to be within range of hearing only most of the time—seem to be those under which the calling song would be produced during a maximum amount of time and function most efficiently in guiding the sexually responsive females. An isolated male, once started into song, is less likely to be interrupted by outside disturbances than a male in a closely confined group or one in which the individuals are continually contacting each other.

In the Oedipodinae, the males move somewhat closer together than do the males of most Ensifera and Acridinae, within sight of each other, and they are less sedentary and less territorial. The formation of colonies of males interacting with each other and chorusing as a group in these insects is a day-to-day or even hour-to-hour phenomenon, as it is also in *Magicicada* spp., and the appearance of the same individuals in the same places in the same colonies from one day to the next is much less likely than in the Ensifera. Optimal chorusing seems to depend upon the males not only hearing, but seeing each other as well. In certain cicadas (e.g., *Magicicada* spp.), the adult males are drawn into compact masses by their singing, literally piling together and crawling over and around each other continually while chorusing. Both the Cicadidae and the Oedipodinae congregate chiefly through flying, and flying is actually a part of the chorusing rhythm in these insects, providing a visual stimulus along with the auditory stimulus involved (Isely, 1936; Alexander and Moore, 1958). Vision seems important in many aspects of the behavior of these insects which chorus optimally only in bright sunlight and are disturbed into flight by the movement of an observer several feet away. The band-winged grasshoppers (Oedipodinae) flash their brightly colored underwings during characteristic crepitating flights which are usually as distinctive and species-specific in the motion involved as they are in the sounds produced. For example, in the Carolina locust, *Dissosteira carolina* (L.), such a flight usually consists of taking off vertically, hovering while flashing the underwings and crepitating, then suddenly dropping back into the vegetation in almost the same spot from which the flight began. Cantrall (1943) describes the differences between crepitating flight, and flight after being flushed, in several species of Oedipodinae.

A set of observations made by the writer on the behavior of *Chorto-phaga viridifasciata* (De Geer) suggests how sound ordinarily operates in some species of Oedipodinae. As a result of alternate crepitating flights, three males assembled within a few minutes in a sparsely vege-tated, gravelly area where they continued to fly and crepitate a few feet apart for several minutes without dispersing. Once during this time, two of the males landed about six inches apart, and one of them began to stridulate by rubbing his hind femora against the tegmina in the manner best known in the Acridinae. Stridulating intermittently, he moved to the other male by walking and taking short hops. Then he hopped and walked about the other male for about a minute, still stridulating, and occasionally moving his hind legs silently. Eventually the two males moved apart, and shortly afterward, the second male flew away without crepitating. A few minutes later, the first male crepitated, and a female flew into the area and landed about two feet away. Almost immediately, she began to stridulate tegmino-femorally and to walk and hop about. The male then walked toward the female, stridulated, walked again, mounted her, and copulated with her. The third male, meanwhile, had also approached the female, and he sat almost against the copulating pair, occasionally flipping his hind legs silently. This entire sequence took place in less than thirty minutes. All of the sounds were tape-recorded with the microphone inside a parabolic reflector about four feet away.

These observations reveal the close relationship between sound com-munication in the Oedipodinae and the Acridinae, and suggest that the systems utilized by the two groups had a common origin, probably in motions of the hind legs originally having only visual significance dur-ing courtship, or even earlier, only tactile significance after the male had mounted the female. Cantrall (personal communication) has ob-served that soundless stroking and flipping of the hind legs occurs characteristically in a wide variety of Acrididae during encounters be-tween males and during encounters between males and females, both before and after the male has mounted the female. The crepitating flight of the Oedipodinae would appear to be an innovation utilizing sound, motion, and perhaps color in bringing sexually responsive indi-viduals into ranges within which the tegmino-femoral stridulations can operate.

The spacing and behavior of the males in colonies of singing insects have a considerable effect upon the way in which the females are at-tracted. In the cicadas on the left side of the diagram in Figure 2, this is largely accomplished through an attraction of the females into very dense colonies of males, and the sound of the colony is more important for individuals outside the colony than the sound of any individual. Any differential mating in such instances must ordinarily take place with the female within courtship range of a number of males. In the Ensifera, on the other hand, in which the males are more widely spaced and more sedentary, individual females are probably most often attracted to within sight or touch of a single male without coming close to his singing neighbors, and the sound of the individual male is thus relatively more important for individuals outside the colony.

In the Ensifera and Acridinae the males and females congregate chiefly through walking. Vision is important at close range in the Acridinae, as demonstrated by Haskell (1958) who found that blinded females do not copulate. An additional significance for vision in the Acrididae is indicated by the fact that the males of most species take the initiative in courtship, leaping upon the female sometimes from a distance of several inches. In the Ensifera, in which the courting male simply backs under the female or allows her to mount upon his back, vision does not seem to be of much importance, even at close range. Optimal chorusing in most Ensifera occurs at night, and Khalifa (1950) found that the house cricket courts and copulates in total darkness with little or no delay. In the Ensifera the antennae are long, slender, active appendages which literally "trace out" the shape of objects encountered by the insects, while the antennae of Acrididae are short, thick, and much less active.

Although the basic function of the male's calling song is in every case the attraction of sexually responsive females, it seems likely that in most species these sounds actually have a greater variety of effects upon other males which hear them than upon the females. Thus, it appears that in different situations the singing of one male may cause another male to become more active, to become less active, to move toward him, to move away from him, to start singing, to stop singing, or to sing at a different rate or rhythm than he would if he were unable to hear the first male's song. In the Orthoptera and Cicadidae, elaboration of these different "side" effects would seem in every case to depend upon the ultimate enhancement of the primary function of bringing the sexes together, whether this enhancement operates directly or more or less indirectly through adjustments in the social organization of the species. It is possible that the variety and complexity of the effects of the calling song upon other males are responsible for the difficulty in making satisfying, positive demonstrations of function.

Male Aggressive Sounds

When sexually responsive males of the Ensifera are in close proximity, it is not unusual for them to exhibit aggressive behavior, frequently sparring or fighting with the antennae, forelegs, and mandibles, and kicking with the hind legs. Distinctive sounds are produced in this situation by many species, and there is evidence that these sounds affect the outcome of encounters between males, and are at least partially responsible for the later separation of the individuals. At the least, they are reflective of the aggressiveness of a male and his ability to dominate a particular encounter. Thus, when five adult male field crickets were placed together in our laboratory (Alexander, Ms.), the dominant male was the only cricket to chirp in 354 encounters occurring during the first three hours, and he produced aggressive chirps in all of the 223 encounters in which he was involved. The first male to chirp in an encounter with this dominant male later became dominant over him. In subsequent encounters, observed over a period of several weeks, the winning males chirped more often and usually produced more chirps than the loser in encounters in which both individuals chirped. The losing male rarely chirped after any kind of encounter; the winning male almost invariably chirped after combat. Sometimes this chirping immediately following a fight continued, the chirps gradually merging into the calling song, as noted earlier.

Female Calling Sounds

In the Gryllidae, and in most Tettigoniidae, the females are not known to produce any sounds which operate at long range, and in such cases the females simply move toward the singing males until contact is made through some sense other than auditory. In the Caelifera, and in a few Tettigoniidae, the females produce long range calling sounds upon hearing the songs of the males. The sounds of the male and female are usually alternated for some time, and the male may then move to the female, or both individuals may locomote (Figs. 1 and 2). Faber (1932, 1953), Jacobs (1953), Busnel and Loher (1954), Ragge (1955), Haskell (1958), Perdeck (1957), and others have discussed female calling sounds in European species of Acridinae and Oedipodinae, and Allard (1928) and Fulton (1933b) described such a sound for the katydid, *Microcentrum rhombifolium* (Saussure). In our laboratory a caged female of *M. rhombifolium* was noticed to be responding to the ticking song of a male caged nearby but out of sight. At the end of each series of ticks produced by the male, the female shuffled her tegmina, producing a brief lisp or tick that was so precisely timed with the male's tick-series that it seemed almost a part of his sound (Selection 4). Sometimes, immediately following this sound by the female, the male produced a curious, irregular shuffling sound. This sequence was observed and tape-recorded a number of times over a period of two or three weeks. Later

we found that we could cause the female to make her sound and the male
to follow with his shuffling noise by striking two razorblades together
in imitation of the ticking sound of the male. Both Allard and Fulton
noted that the males go to the females in this species when this alternation of sounds is taking place. The male of *M. rhombifolium,* apparently unlike any other Ensiferan, has two quite distinct sounds (Fig.
13) which are both produced by lone males. Possibly this species is
similar to *Chortophaga viridifasciata,* the female locomoting toward the
male as a result of one of his sounds, then producing a sound which
stimulates him to produce his second sound and to locomote toward her.
The similarity between the operation of the male and female calling
sounds in *M. rhombifolium* and the operation of the male and female
flashes in the firefly, *Photinus pyralis* L., is remarkable. In both cases
the actual signals of the male and female are both nondescript, and it
is their timing with respect to each other which carries significance
(Buck, 1935).

Allard (1928, 1929) and Fulton (1933b) reported that females of
other Tettigoniidae also produce soft, nondescript sounds which attract
the males. Ordinarily, female calling sounds in both the Ensifera and
Caelifera are produced only in response to the male calling sound. However, Ragge (1955) and Perdeck (1957) have reported instances in which
female Acrididae produced sounds in the absence of the stimulation of
the male's sound.

Male Courtship Sounds

Once the sexually responsive male and female are within range of some
sense other than auditory, various courtship sequences are provoked,
some involving the production of specialized sounds by the males. In
the absence of outside disturbances or discordances in the interactions
between the two individuals, copulation results. Demonstration of the
actual significance of the specialized sounds produced by the males in
this courtship sequence are even less extant than demonstrations of the
functions of the calling sounds and aggressive sounds. Huber (1955)
and von Hörmann-Heck (1957) believe that only the courtship song will
cause females of *Gryllus bimaculatus* De Geer to assume the copulatory
position. Ghouri and McFarlane (1957), on the other hand, found that
female house crickets copulate with wingless males, and this has been
confirmed in our laboratory by Mr. Kenneth C. Shaw. Perdeck (1957)
and Haskell (1958) both found that silencing male Acridinae lowers
the frequency of successful copulation with sexually responsive females
with which they are caged in close proximity.

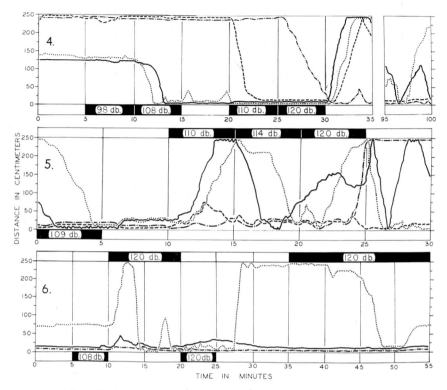

FIGS. 4–6. The effects of playbacks of the male calling and courtship songs upon adult male and female field crickets: Fig. 4—effect of the male calling song upon females; Fig. 5—effect of the male courtship song upon females; Fig. 6—effect of the male calling song (first 35 min.) and the male courtship song (last 20 min.) upon males. See text for further explanation.

In the Gryllinae, courtship singing involves a distinctive and elaborate motion of the tegmina, and it seems possible that the sound produced is most effective only when visual and possibly tactile stimuli are also involved. However, Khalifa's (1950) findings suggest that visual stimuli can be largely eliminated as a necessary factor in the courtship of house crickets.

Figures 4 and 5 show the difference in the responses of four females of a California species of field cricket (presently unrecognized, but near *Acheta pennsylvanicus*) to the calling and courtship sounds, respectively, of males of their own species played to them in the same situation. The females were placed in a cylindrical screen cage about 250 cm long and 10 cm in diameter—essentially a two-dimensional situation as far as direction of locomotion was concerned. A Jensen RP-302 super-tweeter

attached to a Magnecord PT63A2HZ playback amplifier and a Magnecord PT63J tape-recording mechanism was then used to play continuous
tape loops of the sounds shown in Figure 8.   The speaker was located at
one or the other of the ends of the cage, as indicated in Figures 4-6, and
the ends of the cage were rounded so that the orientation of the females
would not diminish as they approached the speaker.   Intensities were
measured at the point nearest to the speaker which could be reached by
the females, using a General Radio Sound Level Meter, Type 1551-A,
with an Amphenol Crystal Microphone, Model 9898.   The cage was
marked off into short lengths for ease of observation, and the movements
of the caged insects were recorded at three-second intervals on especially
prepared graph paper by two observers whose notations were timed and
synchronized by a metronome in the background.   The cage and the
speaker were placed on thick cotton pads to reduce substrate vibration,
and the observers stood behind a low wall to avoid disturbing the animals.   The females used had all mated previously, but they had been
isolated from males for 10 to 14 days previous to the tests.   An important
feature of this setup is that the females could orient directly toward the
speaker from any part of the cage.   Walker (1957) used a similar arrangement, but his rectangular cage was so constructed that the females
could never orient directly toward the speaker, and if they moved toward
the speaker along the screen surface of the cage, their angle of disorienta-
tion became progressively greater.

When observations were begun in each of the present experiments,
the insects had been motionless for some time as is usually the case with
this species during the daytime, and they were located in the positions
shown on the left in each figure.   The end of the cage ordinarily opposite the speaker was purposely made slightly darker than the speaker
end so that the insects would be more likely to move to this end of the
cage in the absence of other stimuli.   Two of the females went to the
dark end of the cage prior to the first test, the other two located near the
center of the cage.   When the calling song (Fig. 8) was played at 98
decibels, a slight increase in activity was apparent in the two females
nearest the speaker.   When the intensity was increased to 108 db, these
two females immediately turned and walked quickly and directly to the
speaker, and remained there as long as the sound was playing.   A slight
increase in activity was noted in the females at the far end of the cage
during this part of the test, but they did not locomote until the intensity
was increased to 110 db at the speaker end of the cage.   At this time,
one of the females oriented and walked directly to the speaker, stopping
near the other two females.   When the intensity was again increased,
this time to 120 db, the fourth female came to the speaker.   When the

sound was shut off, all four females began to move away from the speaker. Their movement an hour later is shown, and the two less receptive females were less active at this time than the two receptive females. The intensities used here are all somewhat higher than those produced by singing males in this species. Several readings for calling and courting *Acheta* males of various species have given ranges of 70-100 db and 50-70 db, respectively, at a distance of about six inches.

Figure 5 shows what happened when the male courtship sound was played to the same females a day later in the same situation. This sound is normally produced only when males and females are in antennal contact, although it is frequently produced by males confined with other males, and even rarely by isolated males (Alexander, Ms.). In this test there was no stimulus available to the females other than the sound and that which their presence provided for each other.

The tests with the courtship sounds were also begun at a time when all of the females had been motionless for a considerable period of time. The less responsive females were located at the speaker end of the cage, one of the two more responsive females was near the speaker end of the cage, and the other was at the end opposite the speaker. When the courtship sound was played at 109 db near the speaker, both of the responsive females moved to the speaker, but without the obvious, quick orientation before starting to locomote, and not in the direct fashion of females responding to the calling song. These two females remained in the general area of the speaker, walking about, for five subsequent minutes when the sound was not playing. The speaker was then moved to the other end of the cage, and the same sound was played, this time at 110 db. All of the females became more active, and the two responsive females came to the speaker, though again they did not remain motionless near it as they had when the calling song was playing, but rather walked about erratically, eventually moving away from the speaker, and then starting to return when the intensity was increased to 120 db. The two less responsive females did not leave the end of the cage opposite the speaker. On two occasions the responding females exhibited a curious kind of behavior which was not noticed during the playing of the calling song or at any other time. When two females came into antennal contact during the playing of the courtship sound, they began to circle each other, each female playing her antennae over the back of the other (Fig. 7) in a manner closely resembling the behavior of a sexually responsive female approaching a courting male from behind. This peculiar behavior was continued for about a minute on both occasions that it was observed. When the sounds were finally discontinued, three of the females became inactive rather

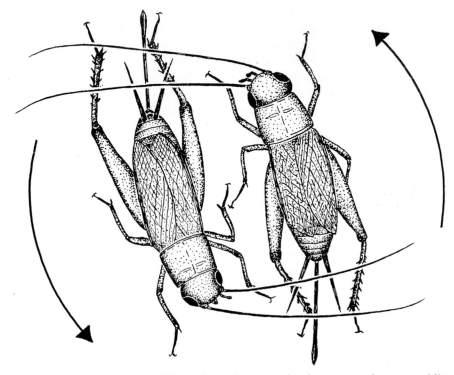

FIG. 7. Circling behavior of female field crickets coming into antennal contact while being stimulated by playbacks of the male courtship song.

quickly, while one female continued to move back and forth in the cage.

Several months after the above tests had been conducted, some unusual observations were made on the behavior of a single pair of field crickets caged alone, which shed light on the results obtained with the playbacks of the courtship sound to caged females. A male and a female of the F_1 hybrid generation from a cross between an *Acheta firmus* (Scudder) male and an unidentified *Acheta* female (pale brown with a striped head, collected on the beach on Grand Isle, Louisiana) were placed together in a cage on the writer's desk with the primary intent of securing eggs to continue the culture. Both individuals had been caged in isolation since maturing. The male had never been observed to stridulate before this time. Upon contact with the female he began to chirp, and to orient his rear end toward the female's head. The female responded to antennal contact with the male by becoming immobile. Each time the male chirped, the female moved forward in the usual manner of sexually responsive females in the presence of courting

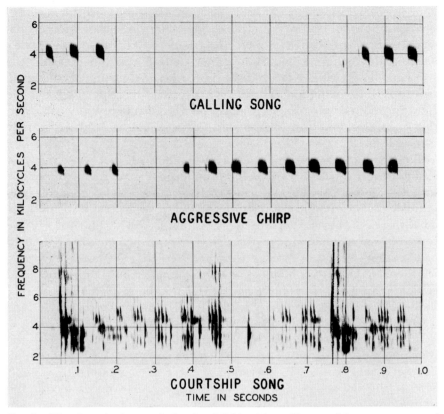

Fig. 8. The three basic sound signals of field crickets, illustrated by spectrograms of tape recordings of *Acheta firmus* (Scudder) (2nd generation reared adults from Grand Isle, Louisiana).

males, and had there been no discordance, she presumably would have mounted and copulated with him. However, the male's chirping was each time brief, and the female's approach was an abrupt jerk forward against him. The result was that each time the pair came into contact, the male oriented, chirped one or twice (not continually, as is usual in *Acheta*), the female jerked forward immediately, and he jerked away at her touch. In 74 consecutive initiations of courtship in this fashion, the female was immobile when the male chirped, she jerked forward at his chirp, and he jerked away if she touched him, or ceased chirping if she did not. Several times the female left the male after such an encounter, and when he chirped next, she was several inches away, twice behind the water vial out of sight and several times facing directly away from the male or at an angle away from him. Nevertheless, each time he chirped, within about one tenth of a second she dashed forward, regardless of the direction she was facing.   After 74 such responses, observed over a period of two days, the female walked up on the male's back for the first time, and although she fell off this time without the spermatophore being attached, she immediately remounted the male and successful copulation occurred.   Thereafter the male produced the courtship sound progressively more perfectly and continuously, and the courtships and copulations were comparable with those usually observed.

This unusual opportunity positively confirmed that the courtship sound alone can cause forward locomotion on the part of a responsive female.   This forward movement results in the female mounting any individual which happens to be in front of her, or at least leads into the mounting act.   Together with the results obtained with playbacks of the courtship sound, these observations suggest that the courtship sound in field crickets does not possess the characteristics of the calling song which make the latter a highly directional stimulus, but that it does have certain unique effects upon the female which increase the likelihood that she will assume the copulatory position and shorten the length of time involved in pre-copulatory maneuvers.

It should be noted that the above results, while in agreement with the conclusions of Huber (1955) and von Hörmann-Heck (1957) concerning European field crickets, are at variance with results obtained by Haskell (1953) with the house cricket.   Haskell suggests that in this species, the calling song causes short bursts of locomotor activity and the courtship sound causes cessation of locomotor activity.   He does not fully explain how these determinations were made, and it seems unlikely that such a great difference exists between species in the same genus which otherwise behave similarly in most respects.

As with the calling songs, there are occasionally species with two or three different male courtship sounds, each characteristic of a particular stage of courtship (Alexander, 1957a; Alexander and Moore, 1958; Alexander and Thomas, 1959).   In crickets the structural changes in the sound produced during the courtship sequence are usually so gradual that one cannot separate the sounds produced into separate entities, but must consider the entire sequence more or less as a unit.   This is well illustrated in the sequence of courtship sounds of *Acheta pennsylvanicus* in Selection 1 (See Alexander, 1957a, for spectrograms).

Immediately following copulation, neither the male nor the female produce calling sounds and neither engages in copulation again for periods of time which vary from a few minutes in some crickets to until oviposition has been accomplished in the Acridinae (Haskell, 1958).

Even in crickets, if the female does not find suitable ovipositing substrate she ceases to copulate after a few days, although she may copulate several times without ovipositing. With the passage of time, and with oviposition of the female, the males and females again become sexually responsive and the cycle involving sound production and specific responses to it begins again. It seems likely that in none of the singing Orthoptera or Cicadidae is a single copulation per female or per male the rule. Field crickets copulate repeatedly at intervals of a few minutes if undisturbed, and on several occasions I have seen male field crickets successfully initiate copulation with a female while one or two spermatophores from previous copulations were still attached to her. In such cases the old spermatophore is either pushed out of the way by the male as he attaches the new spermatophore, or the female pauses after mounting the male with the old spermatophore obviously impeding attachment of the new one, and rubs the old spermatophore off with her hind legs or bites it off with her mandibles.

Disturbance Sounds

Most species of Cicadidae and a few Orthoptera produce characteristic sounds when they are restrained, startled, or otherwise disturbed, generally by visual or tactile stimuli produced as a result of the activities of other animals. Apparently, the production of such sounds, as well as the cessation of production of the calling song by nearby males as a result of disturbance, can through auditory stimulation alone cause other individuals to cease production of the calling song. Almost anyone who has collected Orthoptera or Cicadidae by tracing individual singing males has had the experience of all the singers in an area stopping abruptly when the first individual was captured and silenced or caused to produce the characteristic squawk of restrained individuals of the species. In *Magicicada cassinii* (Fisher), causing one individual to squawk during times when the light intensity is slightly below the chorusing threshold, results in brief production of the calling song by nearby individuals, and this may be reinforced until a large group choruses for several minutes before the sound again dwindles away. It seems at times that causing a single male cicada to fly and to emit the disturbance squawk is the direct cause of an entire treeful taking off and squawking in chain reaction. Whether the stimulus here is visual, auditory, or both remains to be discovered through careful experimentation.

Most male cicadas produce disturbance sounds, and it seems likely that all of the sounds produced by tymbal vibration in cicadas had an origin in sounds produced in this situation. In the Ensifera, on the other hand, there is good evidence that the sound-producing and auditory structures both arose in connection with courtship, and that disturbance sounds in the few species possessing them are secondary. It is interesting that among the Orthoptera, only species which live and sing on vegetation produce disturbance sounds, and in the different species the possession of this response does not seem to be of common origin. Of approximately fifty species of Gryllidae and ninety species of Tettigoniidae tape-recorded and handled by the writer, only the following four species of Tettigoniidae have been observed to produce this response: *Neoconocephalus exiliscanorus* (Davis) (Copiphorinae), *Aglaothorax armiger* Rehn and Hebard (Decticinae), *Pterophylla camellifolia* (Fabricius) and *Liparoscelis nigrispina* Stal (Pseudophyllinae). Only a few individuals of the first species named have produced this sound when handled, but they did so readily and for several seconds continuously each time. The last three species are all large, flightless, slow-moving, sedentary night-singers, suggesting a possible correlation with susceptibility to predation.

THE IMPORTANCE OF RHYTHM PATTERN IN INSECT SOUNDS

The most important parts of the structure of insect sounds, in terms of specific effects upon the behavior of individuals which hear them, are their rhythm patterns (Walker, 1957; Perdeck, 1957; Haskell, 1958; Alexander and Moore, 1958). Examination of all the different kinds of sounds known to be produced by insects reveals that the male calling songs are the most intense, the most distinctive, the most rhythmical, the most complex, and the most long-continued of all insect sounds. This is not surprising if we consider the kinds of selective forces that must have been acting upon them as a result of the fact that they operate at great distances and generally represent the initial contact between adult males and females. Increases in intensity have probably been generally favored because they increase the range and thus the effectiveness of the sounds in the assembling function. Increases in the amount of time spent in song by individual males and the development of specificity with respect to the time of day or night that the males of particular species sing and the females are responsive also increase the chances that the two sexes will get together. In groups in which individual males (rather than choruses) attract individual females, selection should operate primarily in increasing the total amount of time spent in song by individual males. Thus, the success of a sedentary, territorial, relatively isolated male of an ensiferan species in attracting females (and thus transmitting genetic material to subsequent generations) depends largely upon his prowess as an individual singer. Not only the rhythm pattern and intensity of his song are important, but also the amount of time that he can produce the song during particular parts of each 24-hour period. In groups in which the attractive function primarily involves the singing behavior of the colony (chorus) rather than the singing behavior of individual males, it is most important that the individuals become synchronized with each other in terms of the daily singing period. This has been effected primarily through 1) increased specificity to daily cycles of light intensity, and 2) increased sensitivity to sound production and other activities of the other individuals in the species (such as flying as a part of the singing rhythm in *Magicicada* spp.) . The culmination of this trend, illustrated by *Tibicen auletes* and *T. resonans,* has resulted in a very much shortened daily period of song, but one in which nearly every individual becomes active at the same time. In these species, the success of an individual male depends largely upon his ability to conform and thus become a part of the colony. The male most likely to copulate is one which reacts to changes in light intensity and other climatic conditions, and to the other males, in the same way that the other males react to climatic conditions and to each other.

If more than one species lives in a particular area, one would expect a selective advantage to be attached to the development of structural differences in the songs of different species and to a corresponding specificity of response in the females. Any increase in the number of sympatric species utilizing sound as a primary assembling mechanism in a particular area, owing to this pressure for divergence in song patterns, should result eventually in a trend toward greater complexity, causing an increase in the number of potentially significant structural features. The kind of song possessed by a particular species would then depend chiefly upon two aspects of its history: 1) the kind of song possessed by its immediate ancestor (and the limitations imposed by the kind of apparatus acquired through heredity) , and 2) the sound environment in which it has developed as a species. Since most of the intense selection should operate with respect to the calling song, we should expect that the structure of other sound responses possessed by the species would be more or less reflective of the structure of the calling song. All of these suppositions appear to be correct, and because of this, any reconstruction of the evolution of structure in insect sounds is most profitably centered around the male calling songs. As might be expected, parallel evolution in song rhythm patterns seems to have taken place in different sound environments—geographic areas within which all of the singing species are directly or indirectly interacting with one another and have been during most or all of their history as sound-communicating species. For example, although I am not apt to confuse the songs of different species of cicadas in eastern United States with each other, I did confuse the songs of Ceylonese cicadas recorded by J. W. S. Pringle with those of some of the species occurring in eastern United States before becoming aware that the sounds I was hearing were not the songs of cicadas from eastern United States. Certain of the songs of Mexican and southwestern United States Orthoptera form close parallels in rhythm pattern with the songs of more or less unrelated species in eastern United States with which they are allopatric and have been for thousands of years. As further evidence of the fact that the evolution of rhythm patterns in the calling songs has proceeded more or less independently in different geographic areas, one can locate the entire range of structural complexity in insect sounds—from the simplest possible patterns, almost non-rhythmical, to the most complex ones known in the world—in the calling songs of the 250 or so species of singing Orthoptera and Cicadidae in eastern United States. The publication of comparative studies of the sounds of all the species living together in different geographic areas of the world is a desirable undertaking which would be of considerable value to those interested in the evolution of communicative mechanisms. Such studies should include not only the structure of the sounds, but also degrees of sympatry among species, both in terms of macro- and micro-distribution, and in terms of seasonal and daily singing periods. No such comparative study has yet appeared for any region, utilizing modern recording and analyzing equipment in the descriptive aspects. The studies of Fulton (1932, 1951), Faber (1929, 1932, 1953), Pierce (1948), and Pringle (1955) are contributions in this direction (See also, Alexander and Borror, 1956).

Most insects are able to deliver not just one but a number of rhythms in their different sound responses, as is well illustrated in the subtle modifications in the sounds of *Acheta pennsylvanicus* and in the repertoires of other species accompanying this paper. The basic rhythm in all insect sounds, including the different sounds in the repertoires of single species, is a pulse rate depending upon the rate of oscillation or vibration of the sound-producing apparatus—the tymbals in cicadas, the tegmina in Ensifera, and the tegmino-femoral and alary apparatus in Caelifera. The pulse in an insect's sound may be considered comparable to the "phoneme" in human language (Hockett, this publication). Thus a single pulse is in most cases meaningless, and pulse-groups of different lengths and patterns have differences in their significance. Most insect "languages" possess only a single phoneme, but in the courtship song of Gryllinae (Fig. 8) there are variations in intensity and uniformity within the pulses and also in the spacing of pulses which suggests that it would be more accurate to speak of two or three different kinds of phonemes. Let us consider the first two field cricket sounds shown in Figure 8 in terms of their structural relationships and their specific effects upon the females.

The calling song of a chirping field cricket contains one kind of pulse or phoneme and one morpheme—the multi-pulse chirp. This sound affects the behavior of a sexually responsive female in the following respects: 1) she orients toward the source with a high degree of accuracy, and 2) she locomotes steadily in a fairly straight line (if there are no obstructions) toward the source of the sound. There may be other effects, but these have not been demonstrated. The courtship song differs from the calling song in the following respects: 1) the dominant frequency is lost and each pulse is less intense and more "ragged"— less obviously a single, intense unit (transient), 2) each pulse group contains about twice as many pulses delivered at about twice the rate as compared with the calling song, probably because in the courtship song the stridulatory apparatus is engaged during both the opening and the closing of the tegmina but only during the closing in the calling song, and 3) between the pulse groups there occurs a distinctive, intense, single pulse, slightly separated from the others. This courtship song affects the behavior of a sexually responsive female in the following re-spects: 1) she locomotes in short, irregular dashes forward, 2) she orients to the touch of another individual and walks up on that individual if possible.

These lists of effects are probably both incomplete and improperly categorized. Thus, a female approaching a calling male might also mount more readily than she would upon a silent male, but this situation would be difficult to produce since a calling male begins to court upon contact. On the other hand, the females in the test described earlier (Fig. 4) became motionless in the area of greatest intensity of the calling song, suggesting that a female touching a calling male might in some circumstances remain immobile in contact with him until he began courting. This response, whether by a male, a female, or a nymph, in-duces courtship in a calling male.

In the list of effects suggested above, the chief variation in the reaction of the female is her ability to orient directionally to the source of the calling song with a high degree of accuracy. Likewise, in comparing the structure of the two sounds it is obvious that the chief difference which separates the calling song from the softer, creakier, more nondescript courtship song is the superimposition of discreteness in the character of the pulses and the pulse intervals. The evolution of an increasing ability to produce intense, clear chirps not only increased the male's range of effectiveness, but also introduced characteristics which allowed the increasingly sensitive auditory organs of the female to become more effectively directional at a greater distance.

One obvious structural difference between the courtship and calling songs illustrated in Figure 8 remains totally unexplained. The courtship song actually possesses two kinds of pulses or phonemes—the ordinary, less distinctive pulse produced in groups, and the distinctive, isolated pulse produced between groups. What is the significance of the rhythm created by the introduction of this distinctive pulse? It appears gradually as the male changes to the courtship song, and it occurs regularly only after the rhythm has been fully developed. In chirping species, the rate of delivery of this lone pulse sometimes corresponds to the rate of delivery of the chirps or pulse groups in the calling song. Without it there would be no characteristic in the courtship song comparable to the chirp rate in the calling song, since the pulse groups frequently run together and are never as discrete as in the calling song. Unfortunately, we do not yet know the significance of the chirp rate in field crickets, although it is usually species-specific with some overlap between species. Walker (1957) showed that the chirp rate in the calling song of the tree cricket, *Oecanthus niveus,* is significant. The females responded to pulseless, artificial "chirps," but not as well as they did to the natural, pulsed chirps, and they failed to respond at all to continuous trills in which the pulse rate was identical to that in the chirp. However, the distinctive pulse described above is sometimes as evident in the courtship of trilling field crickets as in the courtship of chirpers.

There is obviously much to be learned concerning the significance of subtle modifications and differences in the sound "languages" of crickets, which may be considerably more complex and varied in their specific functions than we have been able to demonstrate thus far.

THE EVOLUTION OF RHYTHM IN CALLING SONGS

A cursory survey of the rhythm structure in the calling songs of several species of Orthoptera and Cicadidae will give some idea of the kinds of patterns which are significant, and of how complex patterns have evolved from simpler ones.

Simple succession of oscillations of the sound-producing apparatus

Fig. 9. The calling songs of five species of tree crickets (Oecanthinae), illustrating simple trills—continuous in the first two species and broken in the last three species. Top to bottom: Franklin Co. O., 21 Sept. 1954; Raleigh, N. C., 8 Aug. 1955; Franklin Co. O., 28 July 1954; Franklin Co. O., 23 Aug. 1954; Franklin Co. O., 28 July 1954. (Ordinate, kc/sec.) .

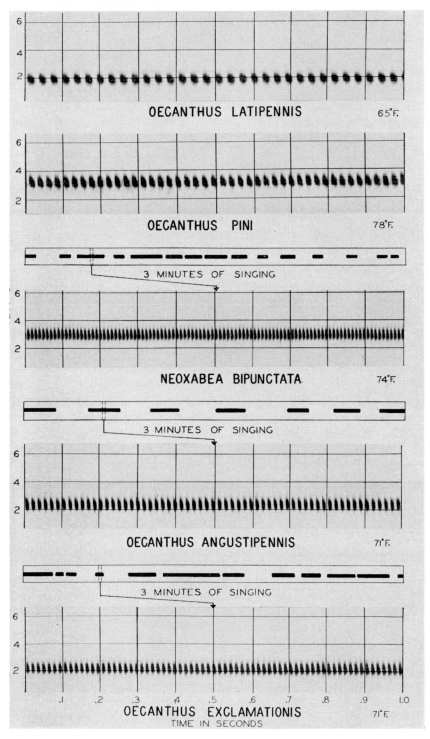

OECANTHUS LATIPENNIS 65°F.

OECANTHUS PINI 78°F.

3 MINUTES OF SINGING

NEOXABEA BIPUNCTATA. 74°F.

3 MINUTES OF SINGING

OECANTHUS ANGUSTIPENNIS 71°F.

3 MINUTES OF SINGING

OECANTHUS EXCLAMATIONIS 71°F.
TIME IN SECONDS

result in simple "trills" such as those illustrated by the songs of several species of tree crickets in Figure 9. These sounds contain but a single rhythm element of sufficient uniformity to be considered potentially of much behavioral significance, and this is the basic pulse rate. As shown in Figure 9, differences in pulse rate are the chief interspecific variables in this type of song. Successions of pulses may be produced more or less continually as in the songs of *Oecanthus latipennis* Riley and *O. pini* Beutenmuller, or in bursts of irregular length and spacing as in the other three species illustrated, without changing the fundamental nature of the sound. Walker (1957) found that females of species with irregularly broken trills responded as well to continuous trills as to broken trills. These trills represent the simplest and most common kind of calling song occurring in both Orthoptera and Cicadidae.

The calling song of *Acheta pennsylvanicus* (Selection 1) and the *Acheta* calling song illustrated in Figure 8 are chirping songs, representing the next step in evolution toward greater complexity in rhythm pattern. Figure 10 illustrates chirping songs of species in the six subfamilies of crickets found in eastern United States. In these songs behavioral significance could possibly be attached not only to the pulse rate, but also to the chirp rate, to the length of the chirp relative to the length of the chirp interval, or even to the regularity of the chirp interval. Thus, the number of potentially significant characters has tripled or quadrupled with this simple change of making the length and spacing of pulse groups more uniform. The songs in Figure 10 can also be distinguished from one another on the basis of characteristics which are probably of little importance to the insects themselves, such as frequency or cycles per second (in crickets the dominant frequency corresponds to the number of teeth of the stridulatory vein struck per second), and structure (e.g., number of toothstrikes) in the individual pulses. Some of the katydid songs illustrated in Figure 12 are made up of similar, simple groupings of pulses.

Progressing toward increasing complexity, we can find songs in which the pulse groups themselves are grouped, as in the three songs illustrated in Figure 11. In these songs there are interspecific differences in the length of the pulse groups, in the length of the secondary groupings, and in the pulse rate. Again the number of characteristics of potential behavioral significance has increased.

Fig. 10.   Chirping, calling songs in six different subfamilies of crickets. Top to bottom: *Gryllotalpinae*, Champaign Co. O., 24 Aug. 1954; *Oecanthinae*, Erie Co. O., 26 July 1955; *Eneopterinae*, Dyar Co. Tenn., 24 Sept. 1955; *Gryllinae*, Florida laboratory culture; *Trigonidiinae*, Lenoir, N. C., 2 Aug. 1955; *Mogoplistinae*, Raleigh, N. C., 8 Aug. 1955. (Ordinate, kc/sec.) .

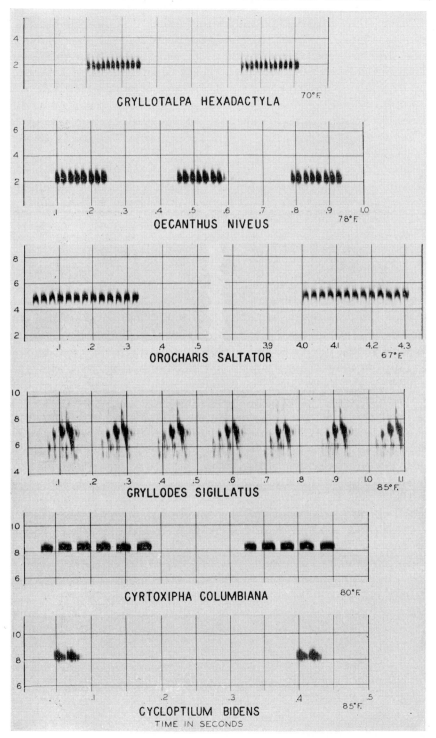

GRYLLOTALPA HEXADACTYLA   70°F.

OECANTHUS NIVEUS   78°F.

OROCHARIS SALTATOR   67°F.

GRYLLODES SIGILLATUS   85°F.

CYRTOXIPHA COLUMBIANA   80°F.

CYCLOPTILUM BIDENS   85°F.
TIME IN SECONDS

The rhythm patterns illustrated in Figures 9-11 are all reversible patterns—that is, they could be played backward and still have about the same structure, and probably about the same effect upon the insects which respond to them. However, in several subfamilies of Orthoptera and Cicadidae there have developed patterns of a "program-like" or irreversible nature, more like the bird song patterns discussed and illustrated elsewhere in this publication. Some of the patterns illustrated in Figure 12 are of this nature. Thus, the three-pulse phrase of *Amblycorypha oblongifolia* (De Geer) begins with a long-drawn-out pulse in which the toothstrike rate is gradually accelerated in a peculiar fashion. The phrases of *Conocephalus nemoralis* (Scudder), like those of most meadow grasshoppers, are composed of two parts, or two pulse rates, giving the effect of a series of ticks followed by a buzz. The song of *Orchelimum volantum* McNeill demonstrates still another kind of irreversible pattern, introducing a gradual change in pulse rate as each phrase is terminated.

An extreme in this tendency toward the development of more and more complex song patterns is exhibited by the male calling song of *Amblycorphla uhleri* Stal, illustrated in Figure 14. This song is probably the most complicated insect sound known in the world. It is composed of several different kinds of pulses, including some made by striking only one tooth of the stridulatory vein at a time. It has at least three different pulse rates, and it incorporates both gradual increases and gradual decreases in intensity. All of these characteristics are delivered in about the same way each time an individual sings, in a complicated sequence lasting up to a minute and a half and rarely less than 40 seconds. Variations in the length of the entire sequence are due to differences in the length of the various parts, rather than to the omission of particular parts of the song. The behavioral significance of different parts of the song represents a still unsolved problem. However, there are indications that this species and others in the genus, as also with the meadow grasshoppers (Conocephalinae), have isolated different functions of the calling song into separate and different rhythms which are produced in sequence in each repetition of the calling song. For example, in the meadow grasshopper songs which consist of a series of ticks followed by buzzes, the ticks are frequently left out at night, and when two males are in close proximity an unusually large number of ticks is produced, with the buzzes sometimes left out completely.

FIG. 11. The calling songs of three species of katydids (Decticinae), illustrating secondary groupings of pulses. Top to bottom: Pocohontas Co. W. Va., 11 Aug. 1955; Franklin Co. O., 27 July 1954; Franklin Co. O., 15 June 1954. (Ordinate, kc/sec.) .

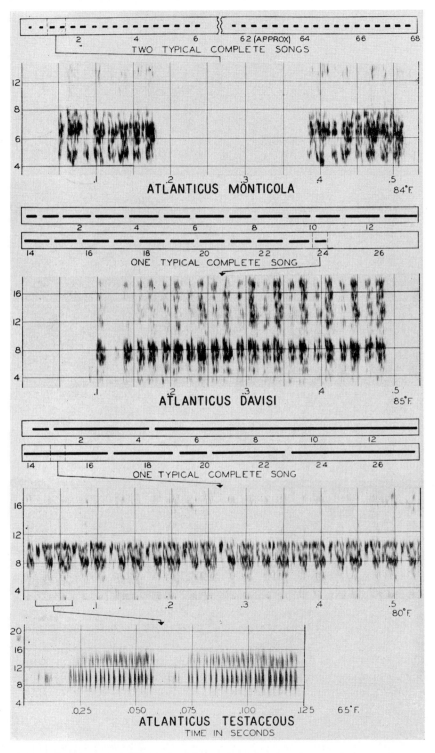

ATLANTICUS MONTICOLA
84°F.

ATLANTICUS DAVISI
85°F.

ATLANTICUS TESTACEOUS
65°F.

TIME IN SECONDS

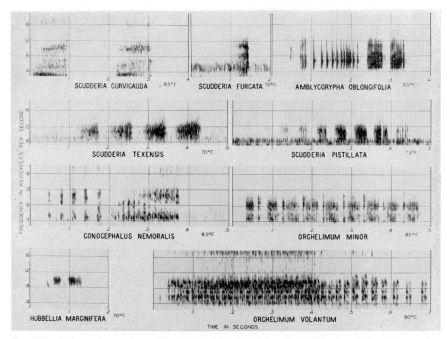

FIG. 12. Phrases from the calling songs of several species of Tettigoniidae, illustrating various degrees of complexity. Top to bottom: *(left)* Franklin Co. O., 8 Aug. 1954; Franklin Co. O., 23 Aug. 1954; Franklin Co. O., 17 Sept. 1954; Raleigh, N. C., 8 Aug. 1955; *(center)* DuPage Co. Ill., 18 Aug. 1954; *(right)* Carroll Co. O., 14 Aug. 1954; Champaign Co. O., 24 Aug. 1954; Hocking Co. O., 4 Sept. 1954; Pickaway Co. O., 26 Sept. 1954.

This would suggest that a visual stimulus is essential in the production of the ticks, as has also been suggested for the very similar song of *Magicicada cassinii* (Alexander and Moore, 1958). It is possible that the ticking part of the song of a meadow grasshopper is connected chiefly with the function of spacing of individual males and the buzzing represents the female-attracting part of the sound. In *M. cassinii,* both parts of the song are apparently essential to synchronization in chorusing which in turn is essential to success of the song chorus in attracting outside individuals.

Figure 15 shows the details of structure in the songs of ten species of cicadas. All of the *Tibicen* songs are illustrated by brief sections taken out of the middle of the songs, which in this genus are characterized by an initial swell in intensity accompanying the gradual introduction of the superimposed fluctuations in intensity (or disconnected pulse groups in some species) in the different songs, and then a corresponding de-

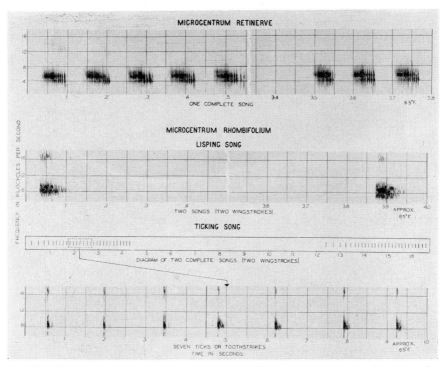

FIG. 13. The songs of two species of katydids (Phaneropterinae), showing the relationship of the lisping and ticking songs of *M. rhombifolium* to the calling song of *M. retinerve*, the only sympatric species in the same genus. Top to bottom: Pickaway Co. O., 10 Sept. 1954; Franklin Co. O., 21 Sept. 1954.

crease in intensity accompanied by the dying out of the superimposed rhythm elements as the sound terminates. The total song pattern in such species lasts from ten seconds to a minute or more, depending upon the species. In *Okanagana* and *Diceroprocta* species there is no such rise and fall in intensity, and the individual phrases, such as in the song of *O. rimosa* (Say), are repeated more or less continuously for long periods of time without change.

One of the most intriguing questions in the study of the evolution of song patterns, in insects as well as in amphibians and birds, is that of how differences in the song patterns of different species arise in the first place. It is not always necessary when new species develop for a completely new song pattern to appear. For example, in the genus *Nemobius*, there are several pairs of sibling species in which the male calling song of one species is almost identical to the male courtship song in the other species (Alexander, 1957c; Alexander and Thomas, 1959). Here, there

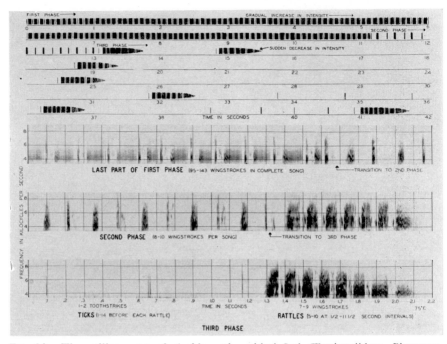

FIG. 14. The calling song of *Amblycorpha uhleri* Stal (Tettigoniidae: Phaneropterinae): diagram of a typical, complete song and spectrograms of portions of each phrase and each transition between phrases (Hocking Co. O., 3 Sept. 1954).

appears to have been just an alteration of the situation in which the male of one species produces a particular sound, and an alteration of the response of the females (and the males) to that particular sound. We may note that the male courtship sound is the only sound other than the calling song which is occasionally distinctive and repetitious enough, especially in crickets, to be involved in such a change in function. This phenomenon is probably not very common, and in most cases it appears that new song patterns have developed as species have multiplied.

It is important to remember that differences in rhythm pattern can arise in the calling songs of incipient species without any change in the external sound-producing apparatus. When differences in the sound-producing apparatus do appear in closely related species, they seem generally to be incidental to the significant song differences. For example, differences in pulse rate in simple trills in the Ensifera can arise in at least three different ways without requiring a change in the stridulatory apparatus: 1) a change in the actual speed of wing motion (distance moved per unit time), as in *Atlanticus testaceous* (Scudder) and *A.*

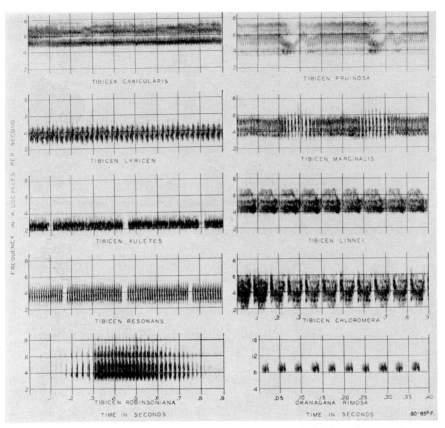

FIG. 15. Sections from the calling songs of ten species of cicadas. See text for explanation. Top to bottom: *(left)* DuPage Co. Ill., 26 Aug. 1954; Hocking Co. O., 4 Sept. 1955; Hocking Co. O., 12 July 1955; Harnett Co. N. C., 10 Aug. 1955; Adams Co. O., 9 July 1954; *(right)* Pickaway Co. O., 10 Sept. 1954; Lawrence Co. O., 4 Sept. 1955; DuPage Co. Ill. 20 Aug. 1954; Hocking Co. O., 4 Sept. 1954; Ashland Co. O., 26 July 1955.

davisi Rehn and Hebard (Fig. 11), 2) a change in the length of the stroke of the wing without any particular change in the actual speed of its movement, as in *Nemobius carolinus* Scudder and *N. melodius* Thomas and Alexander (See Alexander, 1957c), and 3) the introduction of "wing hold" intervals of variable length between pulses as in *Nemobius tinnulus* Fulton and *N. allardi* Alexander and Thomas (Alexander and Thomas, 1959).

There is little evidence as to how the differences in song patterns of sibling species are inherited. Fulton (1933a) found that hybrids between *Nemobius tinnulus* and *N. allardi* (formerly considered erroneously under the name, *N. fasciatus* (De Geer)—cf. Alexander and Thomas, 1959) had pulse rates intermediate between those of the parent species, and that backcrosses moved the pulse rate of the F_2 generation partway toward that of the parent used in the backcross. Alexander (1957b) reported that a presumed hybrid between two chirping species of *Acheta* (*pennsylvanicus* (Burmeister) and *fultoni* Alexander) had the pulse rate of one parent, the chirp length of the other, and a chirp rate intermediate between the two. Perdeck (1957) found that hybrid males between *Chorthippus biguttulus* L. and *C. brunneus* Thunb. had song patterns with intermediate characteristics.

When one begins to compare the songs of sibling species in groups which possess highly complex songs, the problem of origin of differences becomes a great deal more puzzling. Figure 16 and Selection 5 compare the songs of two species of katydids which are both presently considered under the specific name, *Amblycorypha rotundifolia* (De Geer), and which will be referred to here as the "rattler" and the "clicker," respectively. These two species are thus far completely inseparable on a morphological basis. There is little doubt as to their distinctness. They have different geographic ranges, the clicker being a southern species ranging north in eastern United States into southern Ohio, and the rattler being a northern species extending southward to the southern border of the Appalachian Mountains. Their ranges overlap about 200 miles across the Appalachians, and their general distribution is very similar to that of other pairs of closely related species of Ensifera in eastern United States (Alexander, 1957b, and unpublished data; Alexander and Thomas, 1959). In the field the two species mature at the same time of year, sing at the same time in the evening, and in their overlap zone they frequently occur together in the same habitats, individually intermixed together in colonies. When placed next to each other in the laboratory in large cages, each containing about 25 males, the two species chorused independently of each other, indicating that each was unaffected by the singing of the other.

Figure 16 shows pen and ink diagrams of typical complete song patterns of these two species, then successive elaborations on spectrograms of parts of the patterns. In each case the pattern is complex and irreversible. The song of the rattler is composed of groups of similar pulses which become progressively longer, finally terminating with a single, long pulse group usually followed by one to three short pulse groups. All of the

Fig. 16. The calling songs of two sibling, sympatric species presently included under the name, *Amblycorypha rotundifolia* (De Geer) (Tettigoniidae: Phaneropterinae) (Hocking Co. O., Aug. and Sept. 1954). From Selection 5. (Ordinate, kc/sec.).

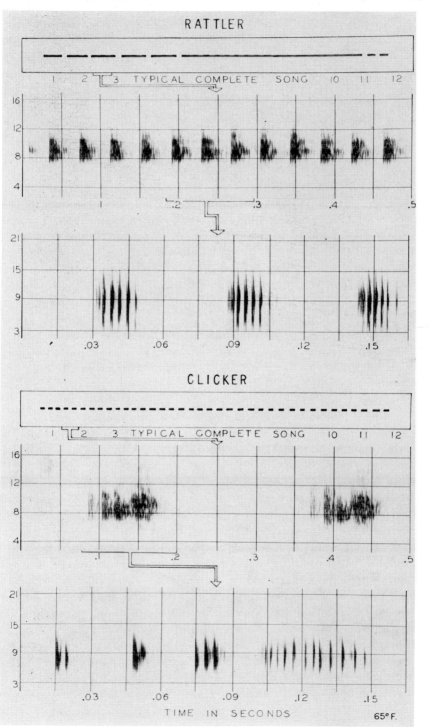

RATTLER

TYPICAL COMPLETE SONG

CLICKER

TYPICAL COMPLETE SONG

TIME IN SECONDS

65°F.

pulses in this song are alike, and each contains six to eight toothstrikes. In the clicker, on the other hand, the successive pulse groups in the song are of about the same length though there is a slight reduction in the rate at which they are produced as the song progresses. Each pulse group is in itself an irreversible pattern composed of three or four pulses, of which the last is much longer (contains more toothstrikes) than the first two or three.

To the human listener, these songs appear to bear no relationship to each other. However, a closer examination reveals that they have many similar structural characteristics. Each song is composed of groups of pulse groups, and the structure of the individual toothstrikes appears to be identical. Furthermore, the songs are about the same length, they are produced in chorus in the two species in the same way, and they are produced at intervals of similar length in the singing of lone males. The stridulatory apparatus in the two species appears to be identical. Since we know nothing of the behavioral significance of different parts of the sounds, it is useless to speculate concerning which of their differences are significant to the individuals of the two species. The origin and development of complex song differences in very closely related species such as these pose some interesting questions.

The only instance in which the song patterns of different species of insects are known to the writer to be identical is the case of three bush katydids in eastern United States, Scudderia furcata Bruner, S. cuneata Morse, and S. fasciata Beutenmuller. The males of these species all produce simple, one-pulse lisps (Fig. 12). However, they are in the group (Phaneropterinae) in which the females of many species produce answering sounds. It would be particularly interesting to investigate the timing of the responses of the females of these three species to the male's sound.

It has been suggested that because the calling songs of insects (and other animals) operate as they do, and because there has been such intense selection for specific distinctiveness, it follows that these sounds are poor indicators of phylogenetic relationships. However, it should be pointed out that even the simplest insect sound (for example) has more than one structural characteristic, and not every one of these will be of equal value to the animal in terms of behavioral significance. In most cases, the songs of sibling species of insects are widely divergent with respect to one or a few characteristics only, and when all structural features are taken into account one cannot escape placing the songs where they belong phylogenetically. Even in the extreme case in *Amblycorypha* cited above, and in the case of the seventeen-year cicadas in which the songs seem at first totally unrelated and sympatry is as nearly complete as it could be (Alexander and Moore, 1958), a careful analysis of the songs leads one inevitably to the conclusion that the species involved are closely related. When more than one kind of sound is produced by a species, a comparison of all the different sounds and the situations in which they are produced is the most reliable method of using this facet of the animal's behavior to help in determining relationships. Thus, Alexander (1957c) found that two species of *Nemobius* with calling songs that at first did not appear to be closely related had certain peculiarities of starting and stopping that suggested a close relationship, and this hypothesis was borne out by comparing the courtship sounds and later the specimens when the species responsible for the sounds were identified.

THE EVOLUTION OF SPECIALIZED CHORUSING BEHAVIOR

Along with the development of rhythmical units in the songs of individual insects, there have developed certain characteristic tendencies for the neighboring males in colonies to synchronize, alternate, or combine in some unusual fashion, the individual phrases or pulses of their songs. This results in an intensification of the total sound produced by the colony and in most cases causes a concomitant emphasizing of particular elements of rhythm which would otherwise be obscured in direct proportion to the number of individuals singing at once. Such specialized chorusing has obviously arisen many times, and similar forms of chorusing behavior have developed in insects with sound communication systems of separate origin, indicating a strong selective advantage and an origin in basic patterns of behavior common to most or all singing insects.

The simplest kind of chorusing behavior consists merely in the starting of song by a large number of individuals in a colony in response to hearing the starting of song by other individuals. This results in bursts of singing separated by nearly or entirely silent intervals. Such behavior probably occurs in most or all singing insects to some degree, and in eastern United States is most clearly exemplified in species of *Atlanticus, Amblycorypha, Neoconocephalus*, the flight-crepitating Oedipodinae, and the Cicadidae.

Synchronization of Song Phrases

This behavior occurs in one form or another in both Orthoptera and Cicadidae. Fulton (1928, 1934) demonstrated synchronization in *Oecanthus niveus*, and discussed it in several other species. Field observations and tape recordings in our laboratory verify that it occurs in the following species in eastern United States: *Oecanthus niveus* (De Geer) (Gryllidae: Oecanthinae); *Cyrtoxipha columbiana* Caudell, *C. gundlachi* Saussure (Gryllidae: Trigonidiinae); *Neoconocephalus nebrascensis* (Bruner), *N. caudellianus* (Davis), *N. exiliscanorus* (Davis), *Pyrgocorypha uncinata* (Harris) (Tettigoniidae: Copiphorinae); *Orchelimum vulgare* (Harris), *O. glaberrimum* (Burmeister) (Tettigoniidae: Conocephalinae). Faber (1953) lists several species of European Orthoptera which chorus in this fashion. Allard (1946) reported synchronized chorusing in *Magicicada cassinii,* and this was verified experimentally by Alexander and Moore (1958).

By listening to tapes played back at reduced speeds and by examining spectrograms it can be determined that in the crickets and katydids which synchronize, one individual starts his phrase just after the beginning of a phrase by the other individual with which he is synchronizing. Thus, one individual becomes a sort of leader, the other a follower. That the two individuals do not bear identical relationships to each other in this interplay is illustrated by the fact that silencing of the leader almost always causes the follower to stutter or stop, while silencing the follower rarely has an effect upon the leader.

An interesting similarity already mentioned occurs between the songs of *Orchelimum vulgare,* a meadow grasshopper, and *Magicicada cassinii,* a cicada. Both of these species have songs composed of a series of ticks followed by a buzz, or in other words, a slow pulse series followed by a rapid pulse series. Both species synchronize in chorus on sunny, still days in dense colonies, and in both cases the synchrony is largely a matter of synchronizing the two different parts of the songs. Thus, all the individuals tick together, then they all buzz together. A noteworthy difference is that in *cassinii,* short bursts of flight occur between buzzes and usually during part of the ticking, while *vulgare* does not fly during song, though it does sometimes walk or turn about while ticking. Alexander and Moore (1958) suggest that in *cassinii,* synchrony is probably a combination of the effects of visual and auditory stimuli, with the visual stimuli largely connected to the short flight bursts between buzzes. In *vulgare,* there seems to be a connection between ticking and visual stimulation, but synchrony can occur when the individuals are not within sight of each other and are not moving about at all.

In some meadow grasshoppers, a peculiar form of alternation sometimes occurs between neighboring males which are singing in very close proximity. In a quart jar containing two males of *Orchelimum agile* (De Geer) it was noticed in our laboratory that while the sound being produced was much like that produced by a single male singing alone, one male did all the buzzing while the other produced all the preliminary ticks. Two such groups of males were tape-recorded and observed on several different days, and each time this peculiar chorusing was maintained for long periods of time. The males were caged much closer together than is normal for singing males in the field. At particular times, different individuals were producing the different parts of the song, this perhaps depending upon which one started singing, or the relative positions of the two males in the cage.

Alexander and Moore (1958) reported a similar response under unusual conditions with *Magicicada cassinii*. A tape recording of the calling song of this species was played to males in nearby trees, which were not normally singing because of unfavorable weather conditions. When the first half of a phrase was played and then the sound was abruptly cut off, the males finished the phrase, but then dwindled off without chorusing through another phrase. When the second half of the song phrase was played, and the sound was abruptly stopped afterward, the insects chorused the first half of their normal song phrase and then dwindled off without finishing the phrase in chorus.

Alternation of Song Phrases

This behavior is well illustrated by *Pterophylla camellifolia* (Selection 4). An individual of this species singing alone delivers song phrases at a rate of four to six in five seconds at 80° F. However, when two individuals are singing near each other, each delivers phrases slightly more than half this fast, and the two alternate phrases so that about the same rhythm is produced by two males singing together in alternation as by a single male singing alone. When a large number of these katydids are close enough together while singing to react to each other, the result is a sort of synchronized alternation in which each male is in alternation with the neighbor he hears most clearly and also in synchrony with other males alternating with his neighbor. The result is a great, pulsing sound which fills the air for hours when there is no interrupting wind or rain. In eastern United States this kind of chorusing has been recorded only in the Appalachian Mountains where the woods are continuous for considerable distances and support tremendous populations of this species.

Alternation of song phrases occurs also in one form or another in many Acridinae, and in *Amblycorypha oblongifolia* (De Geer), *Orocharis saltator* (Uhler), *Microcentrum rhombifolium* (Saussure), and doubtless in many other species in at least a rudimentary form (Fulton, 1934). In some Oedipodinae there is a sort of chain reaction in flight crepitation in which one individual crepitates, his nearest neighbor follows immediately, a third individual or group of individuals follows the second, and a wave of sound and flight is thus generated, sometimes for a considerable distance and involving large numbers of individuals (Isely, 1936).

It is important to remember that in any species exhibiting at one time or another some degree of specialized chorusing, optimal chorusing may occur only under very special conditions, such as on clear, calm days (*Magicicada cassinii*) or on calm, warm nights (*Pterophylla camellifolia*), and only when large, dense colonies are involved. In some species, such as *Oecanthus niveus* and *Neoconocephalus nebrascensis*, it is unusual to hear individuals singing out of hearing range of all others, and thus synchrony can be detected almost every time one listens to singing individuals. On the other hand, singing males may be very close together, even in these species, and still not always sing in perfect synchrony. It is likely that whether or not two individuals in close proximity are synchronizing or alternating depends upon the intensity with which each insect hears his own sound as compared to the intensity with which he hears the sounds of other individuals. By means of a sound level meter, we have found that a tree cricket stridulating with his tegmina at a 90° angle produces the most intense sound almost directly behind him, while the auditory organs are located on the front tibiae. Thus, it would not be unusual for an insect to be in a position such that he could hear a neighbor more intensely than he could hear himself, and under such conditions he presumably would continually adjust the time of production of his own phrases according to his neighbor's singing rate rather than according to the rate at which he would sing if alone. It is clear that synchronization and alternation involve continual adjustment of each individual rhythm unit over long periods of time rather than simply the adjustment to a general rate of singing similar or identical in different individuals. If the intensities with which each of two individuals singing in close proximity is receiving his own sound and that of his neighbor are enough alike, or if each individual hears his own sound more strongly than that of his neighbor, then each may either alternately respond to his own song and to that of his neighbor, or fail to synchronize or alternate at all until the situation changes.

In eastern United States, all of the species exhibiting specialized chorusing live on vegetation, not one of the approximately 43 species which live on the ground synchronizing or alternating the calling song in chorus. Among the crickets, only night-singing species which live in trees or tall shrubs synchronize. Among the Tettigoniidae, all species which synchronize in chorus (except for the meadow grasshoppers and their special kind of synchronization) live either in trees or in bushes or tall weeds, and all are strictly night-singers. As mentioned earlier, certain correlations between habitat and time of singing are also evident (Fig. 2). All tree-inhabiting Ensifera in eastern United States are strictly night-singers, singing in the daylight hours only late in the season when the nights are consistently so cold that they cannot sing at their normal daily intervals. The correlation between habitat or height from the ground and time of singing is so consistent that within species groups there are differences in the time of singing associated with species differences in habitat. *Oecanthus pini* Beutenmuller lives in pine trees and it sings only at night. The other four or five species in the *Oecanthus nigricornis* group sing both day and night and live on weeds and grasses, usually less than four feet above the ground.

The significance of all these rather peculiar correlations between habitat and singing behavior is largely undemonstrated. There would seem to be a distinct advantage in loud, sedentary, chorusing species performing only at night, and thus being less susceptible to predation by birds. The relationship between song rhythm and habitat may be affected by whether or not the species can fly, and whether or not it does fly in connection with assembly through sound communication. There may be some significance in the fact that the sound of a calling male perched up on vegetation is carried more directly to other males and to females, even if the females are on the ground, than the sound of a male calling from dense ground cover when other males and females are also on the ground.

Busnel (1954), in dealing with 22 species of European Orthoptera, has correlated the production of simple, intense, continuous calling songs with low population densities and few acoustical obstacles in the species environment (e.g., vegetation-inhabiting Tettigoniidae), and the production of complex, soft, intermittent calling songs with high population densities and many acoustical obstacles in the species environment (e.g., ground-inhabiting Acridinae). These generalizations are far too simple to apply to the singing insects of eastern United States. For example, they do not take into account phylogenetic relationships, and Busnel's classification significantly places all the Acridinae in one group and all the Tettigoniidae in the other group. In the eastern United States one can take just the fifty-odd species of Tettigoniidae which live on herbaceous vegetation and find both simple and complex, soft, intermittent sounds (*Atlanticus, Scudderia, Amblycorypha* spp.), both soft and intense, simple, continuous sounds (*Conocephalus, Orchelimum, Neoconocephalus* spp.), both simple and complex, intense, intermittent sounds (*Scudderia, Microcentrum, Amblycorypha* spp.), and many other combinations of song types which, in addition, do not obviously correlate with variations in population density. Conversely, one can find a particular song type in all kinds of ecological locations, such as simple, intense, continuous trills in ground-inhabiting *Acheta* spp., herb-inhabiting Oecanthinae, and treetop-inhabiting Oecanthinae. When a large number of species and situations are considered, it is obvious that correlations between different types of song must take into account not only habitat and population density, but also phylogenetic relationships, present and past "sound environments," modes of assembly, susceptibility to predation, sedentariness of the singing males, and probably many more obscure factors. No simple comprehensive generalization appears possible at this stage in our knowledge.

The Origin of Specialized Chorusing Behavior

In terms of the production of song, an individual male can be regarded as composing two feedback circuits, one of them completely internal and the other partly external, involving feedback through the auditory organs. It is the influence of the external circuit upon particular units in the song patterns of males of different ages, different histories, and different species that is involved in the origin and evolution of specialized chorusing behavior. That the internal circuit can operate alone under certain circumstances is demonstrated by the production of the normal, rhythmical song in deafened individuals of *Oecanthus niveus* and *Acheta pennsylvanicus*. The significance of the external circuit, on the other hand, is demonstrated by all kinds of specialized chorusing behavior and also by the failure of deafened individuals of the above species to produce song uninterruptedly for as long periods of time as do non-deafened individuals.

Specialized chorusing has arisen whenever the males of a species have begun to respond to the phrases of their neighbors in a fashion similar to their responses to auditory feedback in their own songs. On the basis of the way that singing males respond to each other, chorusing insects can be divided into two groups: 1) those in which neighboring individuals merely stimulate each other into song (and perhaps keep each other singing over relatively long periods of time) without any interplay with respect to individual rhythm units in the song, and 2) those in which there is in addition a continual interplay between neighboring individuals (synchronization or alternation) with respect to the rate or rhythm of production of the individual phrases in their songs. The second group seems to include every species in which the normal calling song contains a precise or highly uniform chirp or phrase rate within the range of two to five per second; the first group probably includes all other singing species, or in other words, all species which have no precise rhythm unit within this range in the calling song.

Auditory feedback is a necessary coincident to the possession of auditory organs in sound-producing animals, even in cases such as that suggested for some cicadas by Pringle (1954) in which the auditory organs are rendered partially insensitive during sound production. It is also an appropriate mechanism for relieving a singing individual from the disturbing influence of other stimuli in the immedate surroundings, and as such its influence has apparently been elaborated in most singing insects in connection with selection for the ability to produce sound uninterruptedly for long periods of time. Auditory feedback can operate most efficiently in long-continued singing when successive rhythm units are delivered with a high degree of regularity. Constancy of rhythm pattern is also an important characteristic in rendering insect songs distinctive and recognizable to the members of the species. Thus, the independent appearance of similar forms of specialized chorusing behavior in different groups of singing insects seems based upon the re-inforcing interaction between 1) the development of regularity in the rate of production of phrases delivered within a range susceptible to successive stimulation through auditory feedback, and 2) an elaboration of the influence of external feedback. Whenever the sexual behavior and the particular song pattern of a species combine to make a chorusing colony a more efficient assembling mechanism than a non-chorusing colony, then the colony itself begins to operate as a feedback mechanism, continually enhancing by its own operation, its stability and its effectiveness as an attracting force. Under these conditions, it might be expected that relatively great alterations might occur in the assembling behavior and also in the song pattern and the conditions under which it is produced if these alterations increase the overall likelihood of optimal chorusing occurring. *Magicicada cassinii* perhaps represents an extreme in the elaboration of specialized chorusing behavior. There is evidence that in this species there is a great difference in the effectiveness of synchronized choruses as compared with non-synchronized choruses or partially synchronized choruses in assembling the males and females (Alexander and Moore, 1958).

The two most obvious ways in which specialized chorusing functions are by 1) emphasizing particular elements of rhythm which would otherwise be obscured in direct proportion to the number of individuals singing at once, and 2) intensifying the total sound produced by a colony, thus increasing the range of its effectiveness. However, if the interactions between individual males are comparable to successive induction—of antagonistic spinal reflexes in vertebrates (Sherrington, 1947) and of sequences of different kinds of complex activities in aphids (Kennedy, 1958)—then it is apparent that just as a single individual with efficient

auditory feedback is a more stable sound-producing unit than a male
lacking auditory feedback, a pair or group of chorusing males is a more
stable sound-producing unit than a single male alone, not only because
more individuals are involved, but also because of the successive induction of phrase production from individual to individual. Several observations on the responses of singing males of various species to artificial
sounds and other unusual situations suggest that this analogy is a
proper one.

Two mechanisms which appear to be operative in both synchronization and alternation can be described as 1) a stimulation to produce
sound upon hearing a particular kind of phrase, and 2) an inhibition
of sound production for a species-specific interval after hearing a particular kind of phrase. These two mechanisms are both demonstrated
in the reactions of a male katydid, *Pterophylla camellifolia,* to a typewriter tapped in imitation of his song and as various kinds of deviations
from it. A male of this species, normally a night-singer, was noticed to be
singing consistently during the day when someone was typing in the
neighboring room. To see if the typewriter was influencing the katydid,
it was tapped in imitation, and the katydid slowed his rate of phrase
production immediately in alternation with the typewriter taps.   The
katydid was then placed near the typewriter, and several hours of his
reactions to various typewriter sounds were noted and recorded over a
period of several days.   The katydid could be stimulated into song at
any time by the typewriter, even at times when he repeatedly stopped
singing a few phrases after the typewriter had been discontinued.   His
rate of production of pulses within phrases could not be altered even by
gross changes in the rate of pulse production in the typewriter phrases,
but if the typewriter pulses were produced very slowly, he responded to
each as if it were a complete phrase.   When the typewriter was tapped
continuously at a very rapid rate, he did not produce a phrase until after
the typewriter stopped, and then his phrases were produced more rapidly
than usual for a time.   This fits with the suggestion of successive induction very well, as does the fact that two katydids singing in alternation
usually produce phrases together at a combined rate slightly faster than
either would if singing alone.   A katydid sings sooner after being
stimulated by a phrase produced by another katydid than he does after
being stimulated by a phrase he himself has produced, and it can be seen
that this is essential for alternation, for if this interval were of the normal
length, the second katydid would not sing soon enough to inhibit the
production of the second phrase by the first individual.   Presumably,
if the typewriter had been tapped continuously for a very long period of
time, the katydid would not have sung at all afterward.   Unfortunately,

the significance of this was not clear to us at the time, and such a test was not performed.

The inhibitory effect of hearing a phrase which begins just before the affected individual would have begun a phrase himself in normal singing is further demonstrated by interactions between males of different species caged in close proximity. Fulton (1934) discussed this in describing the interaction between males of *Orchelimum militare* Rehn and Hebard and *O. bradleyi* Rehn and Hebard. A single caged male of *Neoconocephalus exiliscanorus* in our laboratory synchronized with loud buzzes produced by the mouth at both slightly slower and slightly faster rates than he was singing when alone. When the artificial noise ceased he reverted quickly to his original rate. Much like the *Pterophylla* male he could change his singing rate only slightly, then, if the stimulating sound was further altered, he would stutter irregularly a moment and stop, or revert to his original rate, the particular reaction apparently depending upon the intensity of the imitation. When continual noises lasting several seconds were produced near his cage, this male produced phrases during intervals of silence between them, and remained silent during the prolonged noise.

Observations such as the above lead one to wonder if there has not been, in the evolution of interaction sequences of communicative nature, selection in some cases toward signals of "optimal" length. If this were true we might expect, for example, that the number of ticks per series ordinarily produced in the song of *Microcentrum rhombifolium* (Fig. 13, Selection 3) results in a more intense and more effectively timed response in the female than much shorter or longer series. Perdeck (1957) found that the rate of alternation of males with males versus males with females in *Chorthippus* species differs, providing a means of sex recognition.

THE ONTOGENY OF INSECT SONGS

Nearly all of the sound-producing insects, even those with complex calling songs such as *Amblycorypha uhleri*, overwinter in the egg stage and have no contact between individuals of any age from one generation to the next. Under such conditions, the faithful transmission from generation to generation of song patterns as complex as some of those described in this paper is quite a remarkable phenomenon. An individual in such species must be able to reproduce the calling song of his species without ever having heard any part of it produced by any individual other than himself. In species with simpler songs, as already pointed out, an individual can produce the normal calling song without having heard even himself. Walker (1957) has shown that virgin female tree crickets (Oecanthinae) orient and move toward the songs of their own males without having previously heard the sound and without previous contact with the males, and Haskell (1958) has demonstrated that subjecting young females of *Chorthippus parallelus* (Zett.) to various sounds during the last nymphal instars failed to change their response to the calling song of males of their own species or to make them responsive to any other sound.

There is little information available as to how the song patterns of insects develop in the individual. It is probable that the song is never produced perfectly and completely the first time the sound-producing apparatus is moved. A male field cricket in our laboratory was reared in isolation and then placed with a receptive female and another male which had already copulated several times. The courtship song in field crickets, as already discussed, is quite different from the calling song and involves a different position and kind of motion of the tegmina. Although both males immediately showed interest in the female, the previously isolated and unmated male obviously had some difficulty in developing the correct rhythm of vibration of the tegmina. After several seconds of starts and stops and almost soundless shuffling of the tegmina, the correct motion seemed to appear rather suddenly, and he began to actively court the female, which in this case had already entered into copulation with the other male. A similar case was discussed above in connection with the effects of the courtship song upon females in field crickets.

Kramer (1958) suggests that the initial imperfection in the singing of male crickets may be associated with the development of pigmentation in the wing muscles, but this does not seem likely since male field crickets do not begin chirping movements of the tegmina, even in aggressive contacts, until about three days after maturing, and Kramer points out that in cockroaches the pigmentation of the wing muscles develops during the first 72 hours after the molt to adulthood. Furthermore, imperfect chirping occurs temporarily in crickets which have been adult two weeks or more if they have not chirped previously.

Although most rhythm elements in insect sounds appear to be relatively inflexible, certain species have units in their songs which are at least temporarily modifiable to some degree. Thus, the phenomena of synchronization and alternation require temporary modifications in an individual's song pattern. Pierce (1948) reported that he was able to change the number of pulses per phrase emitted by a caged male of *Pterophylla camellifolia* after he had gotten the animal to respond to artificial stimulation of its sounds, simply by changing the number of pulses in the stimulating sound. It is well-known that in this species there is a considerable amount of variation in the number of pulses per phrase in the songs of individuals located in different colonies. It is also noticeable that the individuals in any given, dense colony are likely to be producing the same number of pulses per phrase, especially late in the night when they have been chorusing together for some time, and when the climatic conditions are conducive to perfection in chorusing. In our laboratory, the caged *Pterophylla* responding to the typewriter produced only two-pulse phrases, after producing a few one-pulse phrases when first starting to sing, as is usual in this species. However, when we stimulated him into song with three-pulse typewriter phrases, we were able to get him to sing three-pulse phrases consistently in alternation with the typewriter. After he had started alternating, it was usually difficult to change him from a two-pulse phrase to any other kind of phrase, but this could be done most easily by interspersing the typewriter phrases in such a way as to interfere with the rhythm of alternation, and by continuing to produce three-pulse phrases with the typewriter as this was done. Once he had changed to three-pulse phrases, he usually kept this kind of song going until two-pulse phrases were produced with the typewriter, which generally caused him to change immediately back to two-pulse phrases. Occasionally we were able to change him back and forth from one- to two-pulse phrases and from two- to three-pulse phrases, and vice versa, tapping out only one kind of each phrase at a time. This showed that he was responding to each individual phrase as it was produced. On one day we successfully altered his singing so that for a short time he consistently produced four-pulse phrases. We were never able to induce five-pulse phrases. There was some indication that it was easier to alter this male's singing after he had been subjected to phrases with unusual numbers of pulses over a period of several days, but this remains to be checked more carefully.

These experiments raise some interesting questions. For example, is the number of pulses per phrase sung by a lone male determined in part by sounds he hears early in his adult life, or is this genetically determined? The fact that even an old male's phrase length can be temporarily altered in spite of his continual tendency to slip back into a two-pulse phrase and to sing a two-pulse phrase when alone suggests that environmental influences may have been involved in the establishment of his normal phrase length. This species has two populations, northern and southern, respectively, which meet and apparently interbreed across a narrow zone in the Appalachian Mountains. The southern population produces three- to seven-pulse phrases, most often four- to six-pulse phrases. The northern population produces one- to five-pulse phrases, most often two- to three-pulse phrases. There is also a difference in the pulse rate within phrases.   In the area in which these forms appear to intergrade, the pulse number per phrase is more variable than anywhere else in the range, with seven-, eight-, and nine-pulse phrases common, and occasional individuals producing pulses continually in series of 25 to 30 without pausing.   Whether this particular erratic behavior is due entirely to the genetic make-up of the hybrids or is largely a product of the behavioral interactions among the genetically different individuals maturing in this area remains to be discovered.   Here again we may wonder what effect repetitions of song involving auditory feedback may have on the influence of the internal circuit.   Is there a difference in the relative influence of these two circuits in the singing of individuals subjected to different noises early in their adult lives?   For example, deafened males of the snowy tree cricket, *Oecanthus niveus,* sing normally but less if they are deafened after singing for some time, but several males deafened as nymphs never sang in our laboratory after maturing.

SOME GENERAL COMPARISONS

Apparently, only the vertebrates and the arthropods have evolved systems of sound communication.   The arthropods were probably the first animals to utilize sound as a communicative mechanism—certainly the first to utilize it as an air-borne signal.   The rudiments of modern orthopteroid sound communication can be traced to behavior patterns occurring in the Paleozoic orthopteroid ancestor, and the antiquity of arthropods and the extent of specialized sound production in modern species suggests that it probably originated much earlier.

Sound communication has arisen independently hundreds of times in the arthropods and today occurs in tens of thousands of species—far more than in all other kinds of animals combined.   There is evidence for special sound-producing apparatus and special auditory organs in hundreds of families of insects involving nearly every pterygote order.

The most complex arthropod sound signals involve fewer dimensions than the more complex vertebrate signals (for example, rhythmic fluctuations in frequency—melodies—are lacking), but within the dimensions utilized, a high degree of intricacy and efficiency is realized.   The auditory sense is probably exceeded in the complexity and multiplicity of its functions as an intraspecific communicative device in arthropods only by combinations of tactile apparatus, and by the visual sense in connection with rhythmic "dances."

LITERATURE CITED

Alexander, R. D. 1957a. Sound production and associated behavior in insects. Ohio Jour. Sci. *57:* 101–113.

——. 1957b. The taxonomy of the field crickets of the eastern United States (Orthoptera: Gryllidae: *Acheta*). Ann. Ent. Soc. Amer. *50:* 584–602.

——. 1957c. The song relationships of four species of ground crickets (Orthoptera: Gryllidae: *Nemobius*). Ohio Jour. Sci. *57:* 153–163.

——. (Ms.) Aggressiveness, territoriality, and sexual behavior in field crickets.

——, and D. J. Borror. 1956. The songs of insects: calls of the common crickets, grasshoppers, and cicadas of Eastern United States. Ithaca, N.Y.: Cornell Univ. Press: 29 min., 40 species.

——, and T. E. Moore. 1958. Studies on the acoustical behavior of seventeen-year cicadas (Homoptera: Cicadidae: *Magicicada*). Ohio Jour. Sci. *58:* 107–127.

——, and E. S. Thomas. 1959. Systematic and behavioral studies on the crickets of the *Nemobius fasciatus* group (Orthoptera: Gryllidae: Nemobiinae). Ann. Ent. Soc. Amer. *52:* 591–605.

Allard, H. A. 1928. Remarkable musical technique of the larger angular-winged katydid. Science *67:* 613–614.

——. 1929. Physiological differentiation in over-wintering individuals of certain musical Orthoptera. Canad. Ent. *61:* 195–198.

——. 1946. Synchronous singing of 17-year cicadas. Proc. Ent. Soc. Wash. *48:* 93–95.

Barber, H. S. 1951. North American fireflies of the genus *Photuris*. Smithsn. Inst. Misc. Coll. *117:* 1–58.

Buck, J. B. 1935. Synchronous flashing of fireflies experimentally induced. Science *81:* 339–340.

——. 1937a. Studies on the firefly. I. The effects of light and other agents on flashing in *Photinus pyralis*, with special reference to periodicity and diurnal rhythm. Physiol. Zool. *10:* 45–58.

——. 1937b. Studies on the firefly. II. The signal system and color vision in *Photinus pyralis*. Physiol. zool. *10:* 412–419.

Busnel, R. G. (ed). 1954. Colloque sur l'acoustique des Orthoptères. Compte rendu des réunions tenues au laboratoire de physiologie acoustique de l'Institute National de la Recherche Agronomique a Jouy-en-Josas du 5 au 8 Avril 1954. Inst. Rech. Agron. 7, Rue Keppler, Paris, 1-448.

——. 1956. Etude de l'un caracteres physiques essentiels des signaux acoustiques reactogenes artificiels sur les Orthopteres et d'autres groupes d'insectes. Insectes Soc. *3:* 11–16.

——, and W. Loher. 1954. Memoire acoustique directionelle du male de *Chorthippus biguttulus* L. (Acrididae). Compt. Rendus Soc. Biol. Paris. *148:* 993.

Cantrall, I. J. 1943. The ecology of the Orthoptera and Dermaptera of the George Reserve, Michigan. Univ. Mich. Mus. Zool. Misc. Pub. *54:* 1–182.

Collins, C. W. and S. F. Potts. 1932. Attractants for the flying gypsy moth as an aid in locating new infestations. U.S. Dept. Agric. Tech. Bull. *336:* 1–43.

Crane, Jocelyn. 1955. Imaginal behavior of a Trinidad butterfly, *Heliconius erato hydara* Hewitson, with special reference to the social use of color. Zoologica *40:* 167–196.

Davis, W. T. 1928. Cicadas belonging to the genus *Diceroprocta* with descriptions of new species. Jour. N.Y. Ent. Soc. *36:* 439–458.

Downes, J. A. 1958. Assembly and mating in the biting Nematocera. Proc. Xth Internatl. Cong. Ent. (1956) 2: 425–434.

Dufay, C. 1957. Sur l'attraction sexuelle chez Lasiocampa quercus L. (Lep., Lasiocampidae). Bull. Soc. Ent. France. 62: 61–64.

Duijm, M. and Truus van Oyen. 1948. Het sjirpen van de zadelsprinkhaan. Levende Natuur 51: 81–87.

Faber, A. 1929. Die Lautäusserungen der Orthopteren. (Lauterzeugung, Lautabwandlung und deren biologische Bedeutung sowie Tonapparat der Geradflügler). Vergleich. Untersuch. I. Ztschr. f. Morph. u. Ökol. der Tiere 13: 745–803.

————. 1932. Die Lautäusserungen der Orthopteren. II. (Untersuchungen uber die biozönotischen und vergleichend-physiologischen Probleme der Orthopterenstridulation. Methodik der Bearbeitung und Auswertung von Stridulationsbeobachtungen. Einzeldarstellungen). Ztschr. f. Morph. u. Ökol. der Tiere 26: 1–93.

————. 1953. Laut—und Gebärdensprache bei Insekten. Orthoptera (Geradflügler). Teil I. Stuttgart: Gesellshaft der Freunde und Mitarbeiter des Staatl. Museums für Naturkunde. 1-198.

Frings, H. and M. Frings. 1958. Uses of sounds by insects. Ann. Rev. Ent. 3: 87–106.

Fulton, B. B. 1928. A demonstration of the location of auditory organs in certain Orthoptera. Ann. Ent. Soc. Amer. 21: 445–448.

————. 1932. North Carolina's singing Orthoptera. Jour. Elisha Mitchell Sci. Soc. 47: 55–69.

————. 1933a. Inheritance of song in hybrids of two subspecies of Nemobius fasciatus (Orthoptera). Ann. Ent. Soc. Amer. 26: 368–376.

————. 1933b. Stridulating organs of female Tettigoniidae. Ent. News 44: 270–275.

————. 1934. Rhythm, synchronism, and alternation in the stridulation of Orthoptera. Jour. Elisha Mitchell Sci. Soc. 50: 263–267.

————. 1951. The seasonal succession of orthopteran stridulation near Raleigh, North Carolina. Jour. Elisha Mitchell Sci. Soc. 67: 87–95.

Ghouri, A. S. K. and J. E. McFarlane. 1957. Reproductive isolation in the house cricket (Orthoptera: Gryllidae). Psyche 64: 30–36.

Haskell, P. T. 1953. The stridulation behaviour of the domestic cricket. Brit. Jour. Animal Behaviour 1: 120–121.

————. 1957. Stridulation and associated behaviour in certain Orthoptera. I. Analysis of the stridulation of, and behaviour between, males. Brit. Jour. Animal Behaviour. 5: 139–148.

————. 1958. Stridulation and associated behaviour in certain Orthoptera. 2. Stridulation of females and their behaviour with males. Animal Behaviour 6: 27–42.

Hörmann-Heck, Sibylle von. 1957. Untersuchungen über den Erbgang einiger Verhaltensweisen bei Grillenbastarden (Gryllus campestris L. X. Gryllus bimaculatus de Geer). Ztschr. f. Tierpsychol. 14: 137–183.

Huber, F. 1955. Sitz und Bedeutung nervöser Zentren für Instinkhandlungen beim Männchen von Gryllus campestris L. Ztschr. f. Tierpsychol. 12: 12–48.

Isley, F. B. 1936. Flight-stridulation in American acridians (Orthop.: Acrididae). Ent. News. 47: 199–205.

Jacobs, W. 1953. Verhaltensbiologische studien an feldheuschrecken. Ztschr. f. Tierpsychol. Beiheft I: 1–228.

Kennedy, J. S. 1958. The experimental analysis of aphid behaviour and its bearing on current theories of instinct. Proc. Xth Internatl. Cong. Ent. (1956) 2: 397–404.

Khalifa, A. 1950. Sexual behaviour in Gryllus domesticus L. Behaviour 2: 264–274.

Kramer, Sol. 1958. Pigmentation in the thoracic musculature of cockroaches and related Orthoptera and the analysis of flight and stridulation. Proc. Xth Internatl. Cong. Ent. (1956). *1:* 569–579.

Loher, W. 1957. Untersuchungen über den Aufbau und die Entstehung der Gesänge einiger Feldheuschreckenarten und den Einfluss von Lautzeichen auf das akustische Verhalten. Ztschr. f. Vergleich. Physiol. *39:* 313–356.

Lutz, F. E. 1932. Experiments with Orthoptera concerning diurnal rhythm. Amer. Mus. Novitates. *550:* 1–24.

Magnus, D. B. E. 1958. Experimental analysis of some "overoptimal" sign-stimuli in the mating-behaviour of the fritillary butterfly *Argynnis paphia* L. (Lepidoptera: Nymphalidae). Proc. Xth Internatl. Cong. Ent. (1956) *2:* 405–418.

Myers, J. G. 1929. Insect singers: a natural history of the cicadas. London: George Routledge and Sons, Limited. 1-304.

Perdeck, A. C. 1957. The isolating value of specific song patterns in two sibling species of grasshoppers (*Chorthippus brunneus* Thunb. and *C. biguttulus* L.). Behaviour *12:* 1–75.

Pierce, G. W. 1948. The songs of insects with related material on the production, propagation, detection, and measurement of sonic and supersonic vibrations. Cambridge, Mass.: Harvard Univ. Press. 1-329.

Pringle, J. W. S. 1954. A physiological analysis of cicada song. Jour. Expt. Biol. *31:* 525–560.

————. 1955. The songs and habits of Ceylon cicadas, with a description of two new species. Spolia Zeylonica *27:* 229–238.

————. 1956. Insect song. Endeavour *15:* 68–72.

Provost, M. W. 1958. Mating and male swarming in *Psorophora* mosquitoes. Proc. Xth Internatl. Cong. Ent. (1956) *2:* 553–561.

Ragge, D. R. 1955. A note on female stridulation in the British Acridinae (Orthoptera, Acrididae). Brit. Jour. Animal Behaviour *3:* 70.

Regen, J. 1913. Uber die Anlockung des Weibchen von *Gryllus campestris* L. durch telephonisch übertragene Stridulationslaute des Männchens. Ein Beitrag zur Frage der Orientierung bei den Insekten. Pflügers Arch. f. die gesam. Physiol. *155:* 193–200.

Riley, C. V. 1895. The senses of animals. Nature *52:* 209–212.

Schwink, Ilse. 1958. A study of olfactory stimuli in the orientation of moths. Proc. Xth Internatl. Cong. Ent. (1956) *2:* 577–582.

Sherrington, C. S. 1947. The integrative action of the nervous system. 2nd ed. Univ. Press., Cambridge. 1-433.

Stride, G. O. 1958. On the courtship behavior of a tropical mimetic butterfly, *Hypolimnas misippus* L. (Nymphalidae). Proc. Xth Internatl. Cong. Ent. (1956) *2:* 419–424.

Travis, B. V. 1939. Habits of the June Beetle, *Phyllophaga lanceolata* (Say), in Iowa. Jour. Econ. Ent. *32:* 690–693.

Walker, T. J. 1957. Specificity in the response of female tree crickets (Orthoptera, Gryllidae, Oecanthinae) to calling songs of the males. Ann. Ent. Soc. Amer. *50:* 626–636.

Selection 1. The repertoire of a male field cricket, *Acheta pennsylvanicus* (Burmeister) (Gryllidae: Gryllinae), played at normal speed, then at one-fourth speed (Franklin Co. O., June, 1954).

Selection 2. The repertoires of the males of the seventeen-year cicadas, *Magicicada septendecim* (Linnaeus) and *M. cassinii* (Fisher) (Homoptera: Cicadidae) (Brood XIII, DuPage Co. Ill., June 1956).

Selection 3. The repertoires of the male and the female of the katydid, *Microcentrum rhombifolium* (Saussure) (Tettigoniidae: Phaneropterinae) (Ann Arbor, Michigan, August, 1958).

Selection 4. The repertoires of the male and the female of the katydid, *Pterophylla camellifolia* (Fabricius) (Tettigoniidae: Pseudophyllinae) (Franklin Co. O., August 1954; Raleigh, N. C., August 1955; Pocohontas Co. W. Va., August 1955 (3); Ann Arbor, Michigan, August 1958).

Selection 5. The calling songs of two sympatric katydids presently recognized under the specific name, *Amblycorypha rotundifolia* (De Geer) (Tettigoniidae: Phaneropterinae), played at normal speed, then at one-fourth speed. (Hocking Co. O., August and September, 1954).

Sound Production And Underwater Communication In Fishes [1,2]

WILLIAM N. TAVOLGA

Department of Animal Behavior, American Museum of Natural History, New York

INTRODUCTION

T HE FACT THAT fishes make sounds and also have excellent hearing has been known for a long time. Many prominent biologists, including J. L. Agassiz (1850), G. H. Parker (1918) and Karl von Frisch (1938), have investigated these and associated problems. Only within the last twenty years, however, has equipment been developed to the point that has permitted adequate detection, recording and analysis of underwater sounds. Ever since the development of Sonar, during World War II, there has been an increase in interest in underwater sounds of various animals. Numerous reports sponsored by the Office of Naval Research have listed measurements of underwater noise levels and catalog-like descriptions of various sounds. Kellogg (1953) compiled a preliminary but highly useful bibliography including the O.N.R. reports which had been declassified at that time and also some significant earlier works.

The status of investigations of fish sounds is, at present, still primarily descriptive. Fish and her co-workers (1952, 1954) have been cataloging underwater sounds and identifying the sound-makers. Recently, Moulton (1958) has added to the list of known sonic species. Wherever possible, the biological significance of the sounds was also investigated.

Aside from the problems of Sonar operators and the direct interest of the Navy in underwater sounds, the two main questions which stimulate biologists are: How do fishes produce sounds? and: What are the functions of the sounds and their relationship to normal behavior?

Anatomical studies of Tower (1908), Burkenroad (1931), and others have provided a partial answer to the first question. The descriptions of sound-production mechanisms by Fish (1954) have made it eminently

---

[1] Manuscript received March 1959.
[2] Recordings illustrating this chapter are on Side I, Band 2 of the Demonstration Record.

clear that the morphology of sonic organs varies greatly from one family of teleosts to another.

Answers to the second question, however, are highly speculative, for the most part, and very little experimental work has yet been done in this area. Many species of fish reported as capable of sound production do so when out of water, when handled, or when electrically shocked. It is questionable, then, that all species potentially capable of sound emission will do so under normal circumstances.

If communication is defined broadly, then any movement of the water medium initiated by an individual's behavior is potentially, at least, of communicative value. Schneirla (personal communication) defines communication as "the influence of one individual's behavior and processes related to behavior on the behavior of that individual and other individuals." He separates the "communication" from the "stimulus" in that the former is the behavior which produces the latter. Sound is often arbitrarily considered as that range of frequencies which corresponds to the hearing spectrum of the human ear. In regard to underwater communication, however, this spectrum has been extended to include the ultra-sonic range by the work of Kellogg (1958) and Schevill and Lawrence (1956) on echo-ranging in cetaceans. The extensive investigations of Dijkgraaf (1949) on sense receptors in fishes have shown the responsiveness of the lateral line and cutaneous tactile organs to low frequency (sub-sonic) vibrations and, indeed, to any pressure changes or displacements in the water medium.

Sudden movements under water, movements of bone joints in swimming and feeding, and the impact of jaws and teeth upon each other during feeding certainly produce a variety of sounds. Such sounds are often produced incidentally to other behaviors and do not involve specialized sonic organs, yet they may be of communicative value by evoking responses from other individuals appropriate to the presence of food, predators, etc. It is from such communication that specialized sound-producing and sound-receiving equipment and specific behavioral responses may have evolved.

The communicative value of sounds produced by specialized swim bladder mechanisms is probably highly specific. In the Family Sciaenidae, for example, large choruses of drum, croakers, sea trout, etc., are well known to be associated with spawning areas and seasons. Often only the males are capable of sound production, thus emphasizing the relationship to reproductive behavior (Smith, 1905).

In one of the few experimental studies on the significance of fish sounds, Moulton (1956) found that the "staccato" call of the sea robin, *Prionotus,* can be stimulated in the field by playback of recordings of the call or by playing artificial approximations. Other signals can be used to suppress the normal calls. He suggests that in this form, the "staccato" call may function in species discrimination and, possibly, may be related to breeding behavior.

The present report is not intended to be a complete review on the subject of fish sounds. It is intended to present some specific examples of types of mechanisms and attendant behaviors involved in sound production, to indicate possible approaches to studies in this area and to report on some recently acquired data. The last of these consists of several recordings which were made during the summer of 1958 at the Cape Haze Marine Laboratory, and the Marineland Research Laboratory in Florida. Samples of these recordings are included together with the results of spectrographic analyses. Four types of sound production will be described and discussed, wherever possible, with reference to the role such sounds might play in underwater communication.

ACKNOWLEDGMENTS

This project was aided by a contract between the Office of Naval Research, Department of the Navy, and the American Museum of Natural History, N. Y., Contract No. Nonr 552 (06) NR 104-322.

Laboratory and field work facilities were generously provided by the Cape Haze Marine Laboratory, Placida, Florida, through the courtesies of Dr. Eugenie Clark, Director, and Mr. Oley Farver; and by the Marineland Research Laboratory, Marine Studios, St. Augustine, Florida, through the helpful cooperation of Mr. F. G. Wood, Jr., Curator, and Mr. Clifford Townsend. The instrumentation and technical problems were undertaken by Mr. Robert Laupheimer, of the Institute of Mathematical Sciences, New York University, and Mr. Nathaniel Tillman, of the Department of Electrical Engineering, the City College, N. Y. Many helpful comments and criticisms of the manuscript were given by Dr. Lester R. Aronson, Chairman, Department of Animal Behavior, the American Museum of Natural History, N. Y.

EQUIPMENT

The hydrophone that was used for detection of underwater sounds was a Barium Titanate transducer (Model LF-400; Chesapeake Instrument Corporation, Shadyside, Maryland). A low-noise transistor amplifier was designed for this transducer by Mr. Robert Laupheimer. This instrument had a voltage gain of about 1500X and its output was fed into a tape recorder. A portable, battery-powered Magnemite (Amplicorp.) tape recorder was used with a tape speed of $7\frac{1}{2}$ inches per second.

Among the advantages of fidelity and sensitivity, this equipment was portable and could even be used in a small rowboat.

In addition to the basic techniques of sound recording and analysis described in earlier sections of this volume by Borror and Kellogg, there are some problems which are peculiar to underwater sound detection and, especially, with respect to the low frequency sounds described here. In much of the work done on underwater sounds the hydrophones used contained a Rochelle salt crystal as the sensitive element. This is true of the U. S. Navy QBG hydrophone which at one time was the standard sound receiver and producer in echo-ranging equipment (Sonar). This instrument is now often available on the public market as surplus or obsolete equipment. Although quite sensitive to frequencies of 1000 cps. and over, its response to lower frequencies attenuates rapidly. It has the additional disadvantage of being bulky and heavy. Smaller units containing crystals usually have the sensitive element in mineral oil with a rubber diaphragm at one end or side. Through a trial and error method, I have found that a ceramic tube of barium titanate possessed a low frequency response suitable for detection of the sounds reported here. Although smaller units were tried, the minimum size of such a tube with adequate low frequency response was found to be about 5″ in height and 3″ in diameter. The unit, as assembled by the Chesapeake Instrument Corporation, was coated with neoprene on the outer surface and capped with steel and rubber at the ends. The response of this hydrophone was ± 2db from 10 to 12000 cps, and essentially flat up to 1000 cps. The voltage output (re: 1 v./μbar) was from −93 to −95 db in a sound field of one microbar. From the calibration curves supplied by the manufacturer, and information on the voltage gain of the amplifiers used, the amplitude of the detected sounds can be measured and calculated. It should be understood, however, that such measurements have little or no significance unless the distance of the sound producing animal from the hydrophone is known, as, for example, under laboratory conditions.

The portable, battery-powered tape recorder has an advantage in addition to small size and portability. The 60 and 120 cps hum inherent in all line powered equipment is absent here. Despite the best of filtered power supplies, this low frequency noise is detectable and, especially in the case of low intensity and low frequency fish sounds, this is sufficient to interfere with recording and analysis. The impedance mismatch and lack of sufficient gain in this recorder made a preamplifier necessary between the hydrophone and the recorder input. In such an instrument, an input transformer is necessary to provide a balanced input for the hydrophone and also to match the high impedance (over 50,000 ohms) of the hydrophone to the transistors. Shielding and the quality of the transistors is important since the high gain involved means that noise must be minimized. Such an instrument was designed specifically for this equipment by Mr. Robert Laupheimer.

In the analysis of the sounds, both an oscilloscope and sound spectrograph were used. The dominant frequencies could usually be determined on an oscilloscope by matching against known frequencies. The sound spectrograph (Kay Electric Co.) was used as described by Borror in a previous section. For aid in the analysis of low frequencies the playback tape speed was sometimes doubled thus decreasing the range of the full width of the spectrograph paper to 4000 cps. In addition a scale magnifier, available as an accessory to the Kay Sonograph, was used to magnify any given 800 cps range to full scale.

Using the hydrophone as a speaker to play back various sounds to fishes proved to be difficult. Below frequencies of about 1000 cps, some distortions of the sounds began to appear, and below 500 cps, a pure sine wave begins to sound like a buzz. This is true of all types of hydrophones that the author is familiar with. Moulton (1956) experienced the same difficulty with his equipment. At the present time, I am not aware of the existence of a hydrophone of reasonable cost and portability which can adequately reproduce low frequency sounds under water.

EXAMPLES OF SOUND MECHANISMS AND ATTENDANT BEHAVIOR

Example 1

In the sea bass family, Serranidae, the swim bladder is a thin-walled, non-muscular structure, which functions only indirectly in sound production. Any blow against the body of the fish resonates within the bladder as within a drum. The sound, thereby, becomes amplified and extended in duration. The common sea bass, or black bass (*Centropristes striatus*) produces sounds when prodded or when electrically shocked. These sounds have been described by Fish (1954). The drum-like thumps are produced by the pounding of the opercula against the cleithra and other pectoral supporting bones. Moulton (1958) described such vibrant grunts from specimens of the Nassau grouper (*Epinephalus striatus*) and the rock hind (*E. adsencionis*).

The black grouper, *Mycteroperca bonaci*, produces similar sounds when disturbed, except that they regularly occur in rhythmical groups of four or five. The selection included on the accompanying record (Selection 1) is a series of sounds made by a small specimen (about 8″ in length) in a large aquarium. At first the sounds were elicited by

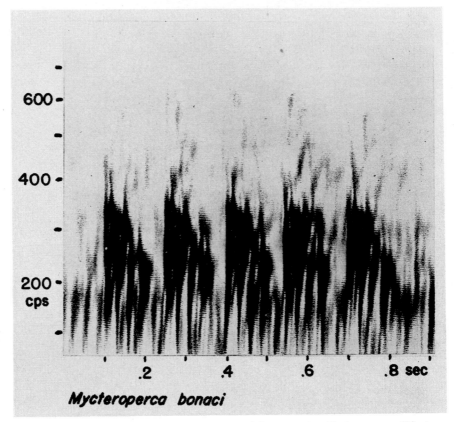

FIG. 1. A group of five "drum-beats" produced by a captive black grouper (*Myctero-perca bonaci*) when prodded lightly. From Selection 1.

prodding the animal with a long stick, but after a few such stimulations just the approach of a foreign object within a few inches was sufficient to evoke sound production.

Figure 1 is a spectrogram of one group of five sound beats made by the specimen whose sounds are recorded on the accompanying disc. The dominant frequency is about 250 cps, i.e., the frequency at which the sound energy is highest, and the component frequencies range from 100 to over 400 cps. The harmonic character of the sound is not clear from the spectrogram, but there are indications of an overtone about 100 cps. above the dominant. Each of the five drum-like beats is a complex of five sound pulses with both the dominant and overtone dropping in pitch rapidly with each pulse. The presence of these pulses may indicate one of three possible interpretations. 1) Each pulse represents a separate blow of the operculum, and the change in frequency may be the result of changes in muscle tensions or impact force. 2) The five pulses within a period of 110 milliseconds actually represent a pulse repetition frequency of 45 cps. This may be the fundamental resonating frequency of the swim bladder. 3) The 45 cps resonance may be the result of reverberations within the aquarium. Although my own preference inclines toward the second of the above hypotheses, there is, at the present time, no direct evidence to support any one of these interpretations. Future investigations are planned involving the use of aquaria lined with sound absorbing materials to reduce reverberations.

A total of eight specimens, all ranging in size from 7″ to 8″ in standard length, were tested for sound production in three types of aquaria: a wooden tank constructed of marine plywood, coated with fiberglass resin on the inside, measuring 9′ by 4′ and 8″ deep; a five-gallon glass and steel aquarium; and a concrete tank approximately 6′ by 4′ and 3½′ in depth. Variations due to differences in the aquaria were primarily in the intensity of the sounds detected. Reverberations within the wooden tank produced the loudest sounds, but spectrograms showed no significant frequency variations when compared with sounds produced in the concrete or glass aquaria. Variations in dominant frequency and in the pulse rate were in the order of ±20 cps for the former and ±5 cps for the latter. The five-beat combinations were most frequent, with four-or six-beat sounds occurring at about a 10% frequency. Occasional single beats were heard. The duration of each beat averaged 110 milliseconds, ±10 milliseconds, and the repetition rate of the beats was remarkably constant at 150 (±10) milliseconds from the beginning of one beat to the start of the next.

Thus far, the only interpretation of the function of these sounds is that they are some mechanism of defense against noxious stimuli. In an aquarium, these fishes usually hide behind rocks or in corners from which they dart out rapidly to pick up food. This is also true of specimens observed in the field. In aquarium conditions the sounds are produced most regularly when the specimens were lightly touched with a stick, but occasionally the close approach by another fish would elicit drum-beats. At times a number of sea catfish were kept in the same tank with a black grouper. The latter would usually produce a group of the drum-beats when approached or nudged by one of the catfish, at which the catfish would immediately veer off and move away.

In the clear waters about Bimini, in the Bahamas, Moulton (1958) was able to observe and listen to specific individuals. His data indicates that the groupers of the genus *Epinephalus* produce essentially the same type of sound as in *Mycteroperca*. These sounds were also, as in *Myc-*

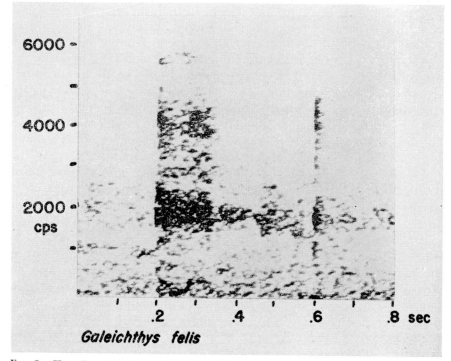

FIG. 2. Two "creaking" sounds produced by the sea catfish *(Galeichthys felis)* during movement of pectoral fin spines. From Selection 3, in which the spine of a dead animal was artificially moved.

teroperca, elicited by an approach of a foreign object such as a hydrophone.

Example 2

The following example is one in which the sound production involves considerable specializations in the swim bladder and associated structures, but here again the swim bladder functions as a resonator for the sounds which themselves are produced by other organs. Two species of marine catfish were used in this study; the sea catfish, or hardhead, *Galeichthys felis;* and the gaff-topsail catfish, *Bagre marinus.*

Sounds of Galeichthys felis. Selection 2 on the record is an example of a series of sounds produced by a sea catfish *(Galeichthys felis)* when it was freshly captured and hanging on the end of a line. The recording was made out of water, using a dynamic microphone. Two distinct kinds of sounds can be heard: a high-pitched creak, and a lower pitched grunt.

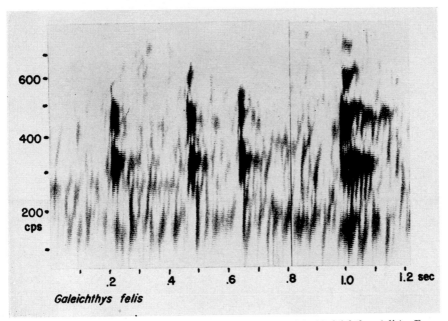

FIG. 3. Four "grunting" sounds produced by the sea catfish *(Galeichthys felis)*. From Selection 2, in which the animal was freshly captured and hanging, in air, on a fishing line.

The creaking sound is produced when the enlarged first pectoral spines are moved within their sockets and the sound can be duplicated in a dead animal by artificially twisting these spines. This is demonstrated in Selection 3. A sound spectrogram of a long and short creak are shown in Figure 2. The fundamental frequency is at 2000 cps with a trace of a harmonic at 4000 cps. Both natural sounds and artificially produced ones exhibit the same spectral characteristics but differ in duration. The sounds produced by a living animal are characteristically 30 to 50 milliseconds.

The mechanism involved in the production of the creaking sound is the rubbing of the dorsal tuberosity at the base of the first pectoral spine against the inside of its socket formed by the cleithrum. This sound and its means of production have been described in detail by Burkenroad (1931) and, for related species, by Sörensen (1894). To my knowledge, this sound is produced only when the animal is out of water. Its adaptive function, if any, is doubtful.

Selection 2 also includes several grunts, the spectrograms of which are shown in Figure 3. In these sounds the major portion of sound energy is at 300 and 450 cps. Occasionally, as in the last of the sounds shown on

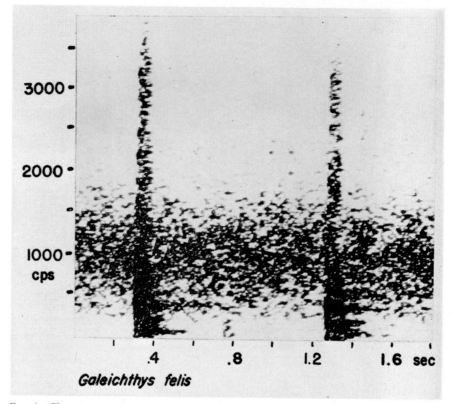

FIG. 4. Two "grunts" produced by the sea catfish *(Galeichthys felis)*. From Selection 4, in which a single captive specimen was prodded under water.

Figure 3, three additional harmonics can be demonstrated: a fundamental at 150 cps, and two faint ones at 600 and 750 cps. In a single individual the pitch may vary as much as 20 cps at the dominant frequencies. The durations vary from 30 to 100 milliseconds, with an average of 45 milliseconds.

A similar grunt is produced by *G. felis* under water. Selection 4 contains some examples of recordings made in an aquarium when the specimen was prodded. Figures 4 and 5 show spectrograms of these sounds. In Figure 4 the band of dotted traces running across the spectrogram was made by background noise. The sounds made by the fish are harsh and appear almost non-harmonic, with component frequencies up to 4000 cps. Figure 5 shows the same sound with the first 800 cps magnified, and a frequency-amplitude section taken at the point indicated by the arrow. The lowest distinct frequency is 300 cps, and

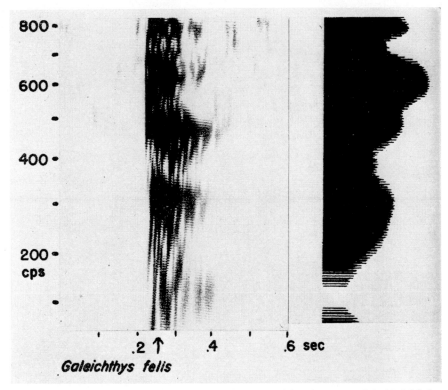

FIG. 5. A "grunt" such as shown in Fig. 4 produced by the sea catfish *(Galeichthys felis)*. From Selection 4, in which a single captive specimen was prodded under water. Only the low frequency components of this sound are shown here, accompanied by a frequency-amplitude section (on the right) taken at the point indicated by the arrow.

harmonics continue upward at approximately 150 cps intervals. The theoretical fundamental at 150 cps is absent. The section (Fig. 5) shows the 600 cps band to be strongest, with the others relatively weaker. The average duration of these sounds was 110 milliseconds, varying from 100 to 150 milliseconds.

Selection 5 was a recording made of a group of nine catfish in an aquarium. These animals were not disturbed in any way, and the soft grunts that can be heard were being produced spontaneously while they were swimming together in a loose school. The amplitude of these sounds was considerably lower than the previous ones, therefore there is an increased amount of background noise as a result of necessary additional amplification. The spectrogram (Fig. 6) contains four such grunts, visible as darker, vertically arranged blotches. It is probable that

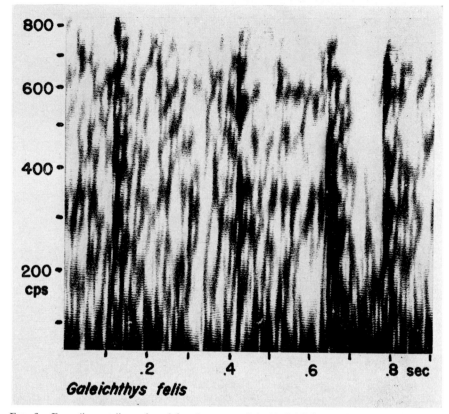

FIG. 6. Four "grunts" produced by the sea catfish *(Galeichthys felis)*. From Selection
5, in which nine captive animals were swimming undisturbed in an aquarium.
There is considerable background noise in this recording because the low intensity
of the sounds made the use of high gain necessary.

at least two different animals have their sounds represented here. In
an analysis of 50 such sounds, the component frequencies again began
at about 300 cps, with harmonics at 150 cps intervals. This lowest frequency varied from 250 to 350 cps, with corresponding variations in the
harmonics. Durations ranged from 20 to 40 milliseconds (ave. 28).

Galeichthys felis is an extremely abundant species, and large numbers
can be found in any of the inland waterways and bays along the coast of
Florida. The sample recording on Selection 6 was made on the night of
July first, 1958, in Gasparilla Sound. The boat was permitted to drift
along the length of a deep channel near the Cape Haze Marine Laboratory. Selection 7 was recorded on the night of August 10th, 1958, in the

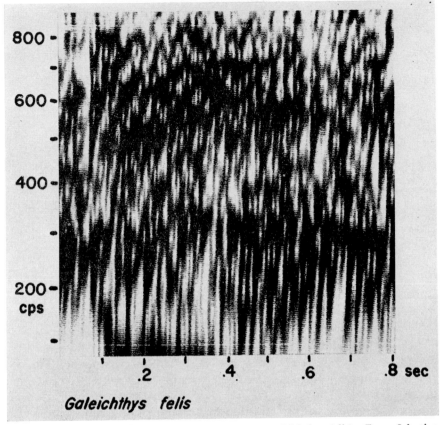

Galeichthys felis

FIG. 7. The "percolator" noise of the sea catfish (*Galeichthys felis*). From Selection 6, recorded on the night of July 1, 1958, in Gasparilla Sound, Florida.

Intracoastal Waterway at Marineland, Florida. Kellogg (1955) described and recorded a similar chorus of catfish from Homasassa Springs, Florida. His comparison of these sounds to the "bubbling of a giant percolator" is very apt. The number of animals involved in these choruses can be estimated only crudely at hundreds, or possibly thousands, of individuals. A spectrogram (Fig. 7), made from Selection 6, appears, at first, like indeterminate, random noise, and individual calls can hardly be distinguished. The predominance of frequencies around 300 cps, and at roughly harmonic intervals above, indicates that the individual grunts which comprise the chorus are fundamentally similar to those described above from captive specimens.

Mechanism of sound production in Galeichthys felis. The swim blad-

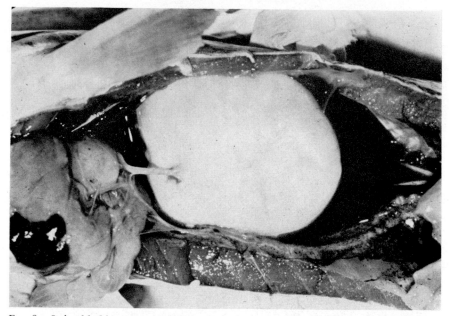

Fig. 8. Swim bladder of *Galeichthys felis*. The viscera have been reflected anteriorly and the pneumatic duct can be seen.

der in *G. felis* is composed of a soft, fibrous connective tissue (Fig. 8). It is ovoid in shape with a straight, flattened margin anteriorly and coming to a rounded apex posteriorly. A thin pneumatic duct connects the ventral surface to the anterior-dorsal wall of the cardiac stomach. The bladder is never strongly distended, and puncturing its wall results in little or no collapse. There are no muscles within the bladder wall nor inserting on it. No red glands are present. Internally, there is a large anterior chamber, and a smaller posterior chamber (Fig. 9). The latter is divided by a sagittal and two additional transverse septa. All the chambers are connected by dorso-lateral passage-ways through the traverse septa. This internal architecture is strongly reminiscent of a series of sound-absorbing and directing baffles within a loud-speaker enclosure. The posterior chamber is attached to the dorsal body wall loosely, but the anterior chamber is firmly knitted to a thin shelf of bone formed by the fusion of several transverse vertebral processes (the "elastic spring" of Sörensen, 1894). A pair of tough, flat tendons extend from the lateral-anterior ends of the above shelf mesiad to a thick, peg-like ventral protuberance from the basioccipital bone. A detailed anatomical description for a number of species can be found in a work by Bridge and Haddon (1893).

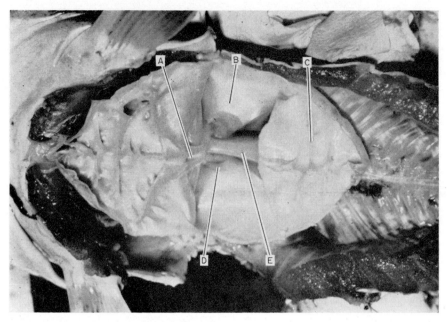

Fig. 9. Swim bladder of *Galeichthys felis*. The ventral face of the bladder has been cut away and reflected anteriorly (to the left).
  A. Entrance of pneumatic duct.
  B. Anterior chamber. The smooth expanse indicated is where the dorsal surface of the swim bladder is attached firmly to the thin shelf of bone formed by the transverse process of the fourth vertebra (see C in Fig. 10).
  C. Posterior chambers (3 pairs).
  D. Location of tripus.
  E. Median eminence formed by the basioccipital bone.

The swim bladder in this species, as in most siluroids, is closely involved with the Weberian apparatus of the specialized skull structure. The osteology of this species has been described in detail by Merriman (1940), and the relationships and possible functions of the Weberian apparatus were discussed by Sörensen (1894).

Burkenroad (1931) surmised that the mechanism of sound production in *G. felis* was essentially the same as that described for other siluroids by Sörensen (1894). This consists of two groups of muscles that originate from the skin just behind the cranium and on either side of the vertebral column, and insert on the thin shelves of bone ("elastic springs") which form the dorsal support of the bladder. Indeed, small patches of skin at the points described are seen to vibrate in synchronization with the grunts.

In my own dissections, I have been unable to find any muscles in this

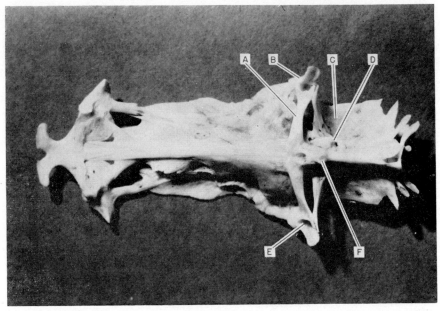

Fig. 10. Skull and anterior vertebral complex of *Galeichthys felis* (ventral view).
 A. Median arm of the post-temporal bone.
 B. Lateral arm of the post-temporal bone.
 C. Thin shelf of bone derived from the transverse process of the fourth vertebra. This is the "elastic spring" which forms the dorsal support of the swim bladder.
 D. Tripus. A portion of the Weberian apparatus.
 E. Socket formed by the two arms of the post-temporal for the reception of the dorsal spine of the cleithrum.
 F. Median eminence formed by the basioccipital bone.

region whose fibers run dorso-ventrally, and the electrical stimulation of any of the muscles dorsal to the swim bladder failed to elicit any sounds. However, stimulation of the muscles which elevate the pectoral girdle produce a distinct thumping sound. The dorsal end of the cleithrum fits into a deep socket formed by the two arms of the post-temporal bone (Figs. 10 and 11). It is my present interpretation that the sounds are produced by the sudden elevation of the cleithrum in its socket. This forces the post-temporal to pound against the front edge of the bony sheet extending over the dorsal surface of the bladder. The vibration of this "elastic spring" against the tension of the tendons along the anterior face of the bladder sets the air within in motion.

As described earlier, catfish grunts have been detected under four different circumstances: 1) out of water, hanging on a fish line; 2) irritated or frightened specimens; 3) small, captive group under undisturbed

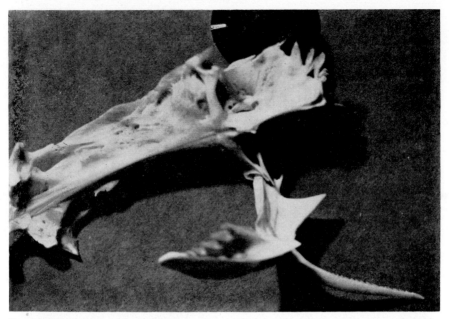

Fig. 11. Skull and right pectoral apparatus of *Galeichthys felis*. This shows how the dorsal spine of the cleithrum fits into the socket of the post-temporal bone.

conditions; 4) large choruses in the field. Harmonic analysis showed that the sounds produced in all these cases are basically the same, therefore it is most probable that the same sound producing mechanism is involved in each. Differences are primarily of duration and intensity. The calls of longer duration, as in 2 above, are also louder and it may be that a more vigorous impact of the sound producing mechanism results in a resonance of longer duration as well as of greater amplitude.

Behavior and sound production in Galeichthys felis. During the daylight hours, field recordings indicate that few, if any, catfish make sounds, although there is little doubt that they are present, since they can be captured at any time of the day. As dusk sets in, large aggregations can easily be located with the listening gear. Selection 6 was recorded at night while drifting along a channel with a depth of twenty feet or more. The largest concentrations of the sounds were in the deepest areas, whereas at depths of ten feet or less, the numbers of catfish sounds became reduced. In very shallow water of two or three feet over grassy flats, the catfish chorus could only be heard faintly from a distance. At low tides, such concentrated choruses were very distinctly limited to deep spots.

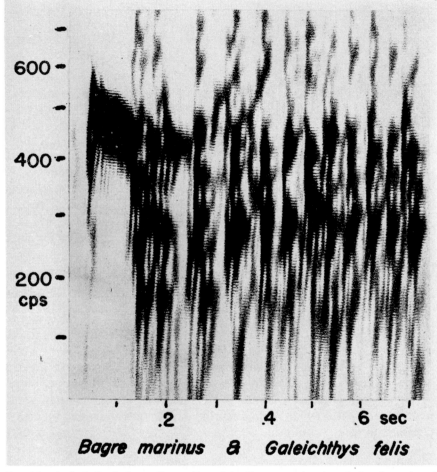

Fig. 12. A "yelp" of the gaff-topsail catfish *(Bagre marinus)* and the "percolator" noise of the sea catfish *(Galeichthys felis)*. From Selection 8, recorded on the night of July 1, 1958, in Gasparilla Sound, Florida. The sound of *B. marinus* is represented on the extreme left of the spectrogram.

The long, loud grunts, of 100 milliseconds or over, were elicited only under duress, whereas the short grunts were produced spontaneously in captive animals only if there were several together in an aquarium. The "percolator" sound of the large choruses appears to consist of large numbers of animals producing the short grunts at frequent intervals.

The relationship of this chorus of sounds with reproductive behavior is doubtful: first, because such choruses can be heard outside of the usual breeding season, which, on the west coast of Florida, ends in July (Merri-

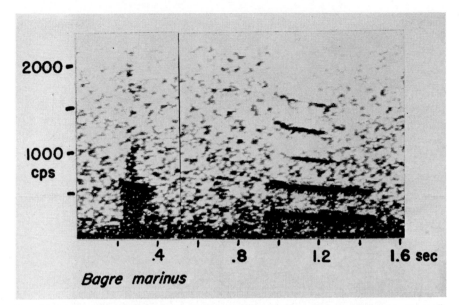

FIG. 13. A "yelp" (on left) and a "sobbing" sound (on right) produced by the gaff-topsail catfish *(Bagre marinus)*. From Selection 9, in which five animals were swimming undisturbed in an aquarium.

man, 1940); and second, because this species spawns in single pairs, or at most in small groups, rather than in large schools. Both sexes produce sounds and participate in the choruses.

On the basis of the present evidence, my tentative interpretation of the function of these choruses is that they aid in the formation of night schools. Similar choruses of large schools have been reported for a South American characin by Von Ihering (1930).

Sounds of Bagre marinus. The closely related gaff-topsail catfish also produces creaking sounds and grunts when it is captured, but its most distinctive sound is a high-pitched tone of descending pitch resembling a yelp or a sob. Selection 8 was recorded at the same time as Selection 6. Mixed with the predominating *Galeichthys,* occasional higher pitched sounds can be heard over the din. Figure 12 is a spectrogram of a portion of this recording and it shows one such "yelp" at the extreme left. The remainder of the spectrogram shows the typical grunts of a chorus of *Galeichthys.*

The identification of these yelps as originating from individuals of *Bagre marinus* was based on the observation of captive specimens. Single specimens were silent, but when two or more were placed in the same

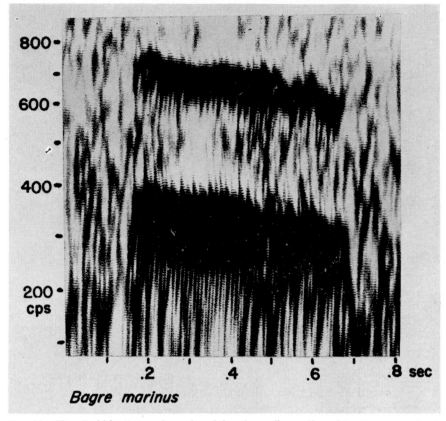

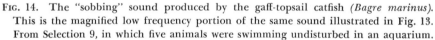

FIG. 14. The "sobbing" sound produced by the gaff-topsail catfish *(Bagre marinus)*. This is the magnified low frequency portion of the same sound illustrated in Fig. 13. From Selection 9, in which five animals were swimming undisturbed in an aquarium.

aquarium spontaneous sounds could be detected such as those in Selection 9. In this recording there were five animals. Two types of sound can be heard in this recording: a long sob-like note of descending pitch; and a short, high-pitched note resembling a yelp or bark. Figure 13 shows spectrograms of both these sounds. There was considerable background noise in this recording and it shows on the spectrogram in the form of small scattered speckles becoming more concentrated toward the baseline. The right hand portion of Figure 13 shows the sob-like sound, and Figure 14 has the same sound on a magnified scale. The fundamental frequency begins at 350 cps and descends to 275 cps toward the end. Four harmonics are present. About 80% of the sound energy is in the first two harmonics, i.e. the fundamental, and the next

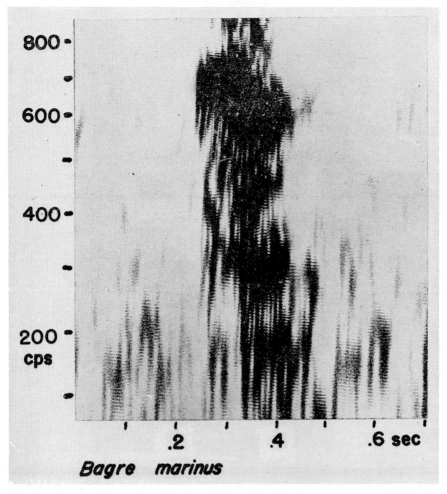

FIG. 15. The "yelp" produced by the gaff-topsail catfish *(Bagre marinus)*. This is the magnified low frequency portion of the same sound illustrated in Fig. 13. From Selection 9, in which five animals were swimming undisturbed in an aquarium.

tone beginning at 700 and descending to 550 cps. There was a variation of only ±10 cps in the fundamental in different calls. The duration of these calls varied from 420 to 550 milliseconds (ave. 490 ms.).

The short yelp-like sound has a strongly dominant frequency descending rapidly from 700 to 600 cps (Fig. 13, left; Fig. 15). This tone appears to be a harmonic of lower frequencies, but the large amount of variation in the spectrograms of this sound make the analysis of this sound uncertain. This dominant frequency varies (at its beginning)

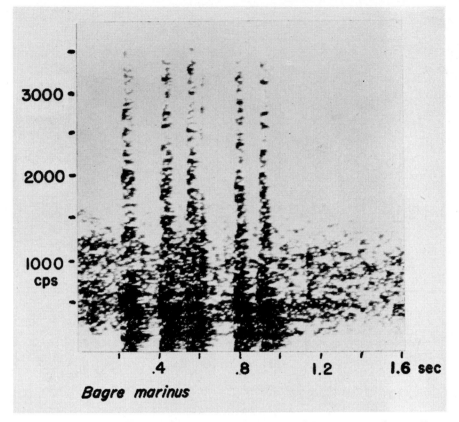

Fɪɢ. 16. Five "grunts" produced by the gaff-topsail catfish *(Bagre marinus)*. From Selection 10, in which a single captive specimen was prodded.

from 400 to 850 cps, and overtones are often absent. Durations also vary greatly from 110 to 200 milliseconds.

Returning to Figure 12, the extreme left shows a "yelp" recorded in the field. The dominant frequency, the duration, and the descending character of the pitch make it highly probable that this sound was produced by the same species, i.e. *Bagre marinus*. Individuals of this catfish are known to mix with schools of *Galeichthys felis,* and in captivity specimens of both species swim together readily.

When disturbed or prodded, individuals of *Bagre marinus* produce short grunt-like sounds. These are demonstrated on Selection 10, and spectrograms of these sounds are shown in Figures 16 and 17. These sounds are practically identical to those produced under similar circumstances by *Galeichthys felis* (Selection 4; Figs. 4 and 5).

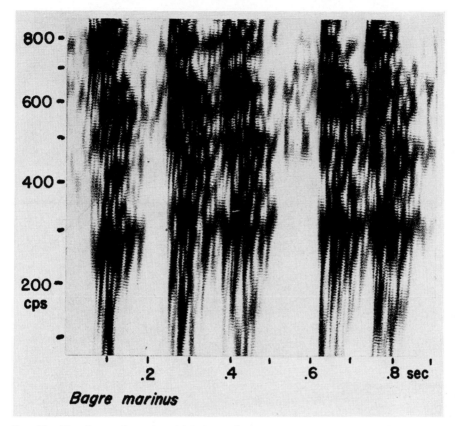

Fig. 17. Five "grunts" produced by the gaff-topsail catfish *(Bagre marinus)*. This is the magnified low frequency portion of the same sounds illustrated in Fig. 16. From Selection 10, in which a single captive specimen was prodded.

Mechanism of sound production and attendant behavior in Bagre marinus. The skeletal apparatus of the gaff-topsail catfish is basically the same as in *Galeichthys.* In *Bagre,* however, the socket into which the dorsal spine of the cleithrum fits is deeper, the spine itself is longer and more loosely fitted. The posterior chambers of the swim bladder are larger and the walls possess numerous small pockets on the inside (Fig. 18). The internal architecture of the swim bladder appears constructed to minimize sound reflections more efficiently than in *Galeichthys.*

It is probable that these differences in the structure of the sound producing apparatus can account for differences in the quality of the sounds emitted by the two species of catfish. The smoother inner walls

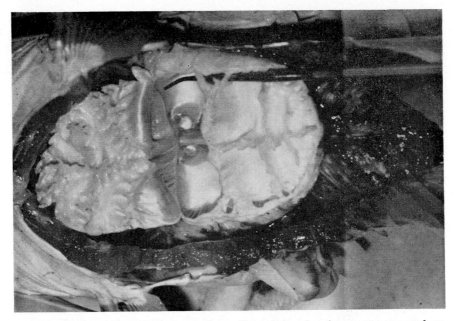

FIG. 18. Swim bladder of *Bagre marinus*. Ventral face has been cut away and reflected anteriorly. Compare with Fig. 9 and note the relatively smaller anterior chamber and the greater complexity of folds and pockets in the ventral and lateral walls. The probe indicates a passageway connecting the anterior and posterior chambers.

of the swim bladder in *Galeichthys* might cut down the clarity of overtones, while these would be enhanced in *Bagre*. The skeletal differences are such as to allow a greater freedom of movement of the cleithral spine within its bony scabbard in *Bagre,* and this may account for the increased variations in pitch and duration in sounds produced by this species.

In *Bagre marinus,* the long, descending sobs and yelps appear to be associated with schooling or social behavior in some way. Although this species does not form large schools as does *Galeichthys,* it frequently swims in small groups and also joins with schools of the latter. Both males and females produce essentially identical sounds. Spawning in *B. marinus* occurs in May and June on the Florida west coast (Merriman, 1940).

The short, grunt-like sounds produced in response to prodding are similar in the two species, and these can be considered as the basic type from which other sounds can be derived. The "percolator" grunts in *Galeichthys* are shortened and rapidly repeated versions of this "fright" sound. By a lengthening and a clarification of the harmonic com-

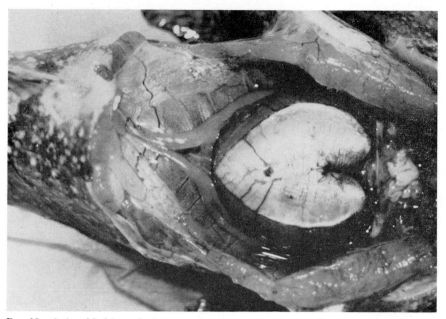

FIG. 19. Swim bladder of *Opsanus beta*. Ventral surface is composed of fibrous connective tissue. The intrinsic "drumming" muscles are on the lateral faces.

ponents, the "sobs" or "yelps" of *Bagre* can be obtained. Following this hypothesis further, it appears that a comparison of the sounds produced by these two species shows a divergence from a common ancestry as well as a probable ontogenetic differentiation. This difference in the sounds of significance in social behavior arises concomitantly with differences in morphology and behavior. A future investigation of the development of social behavior and sound production suggests itself at this point.

Example 3

A third type of sound production is illustrated by the toadfish, *Opsanus*. Two species have been used in this report: *O. tau*, whose range extends from Maine to Florida along the Atlantic coast; and *O. beta*, a Gulf of Mexico species.

Mechanism of sound production in the toadfish, Opsanus. Excellent descriptions of the mechanisms involved have been reported by Tower (1908) and Fish (1954). Here the swim bladder is an independent sound making organ. It is thin-walled, tightly distended and possesses its own intrinsic musculature along the lateral walls (Figs. 19 and 20). Branches of the vagus and occipito-spinal nerves lead to these muscles

FIG. 20. Swim bladder of *Opsanus tau*. Compare with Fig. 19, and note the deeper anterior cleft and different distribution of the "drumming" muscles.

and the stimulation of the nerves, even in a swim bladder completely removed from the body, results in grunt-like sounds. The bladder is heart-shaped. Internally the walls are smooth, and the interior is divided into two chambers by a thin, membranous transverse partition. Red glands are present along the ventral margin of the partition. The latter has a small aperture surrounded by a sphincter, connecting the two chambers. Vibration of the musculature sets this membrane in motion by changing air pressures within the chambers. It is possible that the membrane acts as a vibrating string or drum head and determines the harmonic character of the sounds produced. The function of the opening in this membrane during sound production is not known, nor is it known if it is open or closed. A California species, *Porichthys notatus,* has a similar sound producing apparatus and its anatomy and sonic behavior has been described by Greene (1924). A scorpaenoid fish (*Sebasticus marmoratus*) also has a sound-making swim bladder like that of the toadfishes (Dôtu, 1951).

"Boat-whistle" sounds of Opsanus beta. The toadfish is best known for a sound which has been variously described as a far-off boatwhistle, a hoot, a boop, etc. This sound is sometimes loud enough to be heard

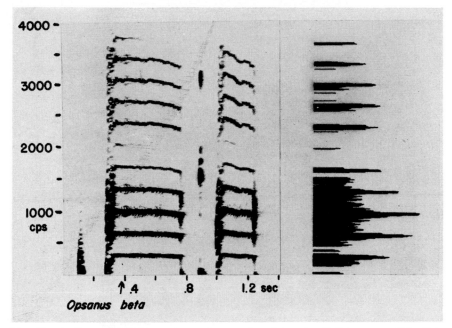

FIG. 21. A "boat-whistle" sound complex produced by the Gulf coast toadfish *(Opsanus beta)*. From Selection 12, recorded on the night of June 14, 1958, near the dock at the Cape Haze Marine Laboratory, Florida. A frequency-amplitude section (on the right) was taken at the point indicated at the arrow.

by the unaided ear out of water. Selection 11 is a recording made in the Gulf of Mexico, in about 20 feet of water, just outside of Big Gasparilla Pass. This pass is located a few miles south of the Cape Haze Marine Laboratory. The recording was taken on the morning of July 29th, 1958. The hoot-like sounds were produced by individuals of *Opsanus beta,* the Gulf species of toadfish. Background noise consists mainly of crackling crustaceans. Since the hoots were probably emitted at irregular intervals, and since the boat was drifting with a strong flood tide, it is impossible to estimate the numbers of animals involved in this chorus. In most cases, each "boat-whistle" consisted of two hoots, with the second one the slightly shorter of the two. This sound has been described in an earlier report (Tavolga, 1958a).

Sounding toadfish were more scattered in the shallow waters of Gasparilla Bay, and a single specimen was heard calling from beneath the laboratory dock. The next sample, Selection 12, was taken on the night of June 14th, 1958. On this night the tide was quite low, the water was clear, and, with the aid of a submarine light suspended from

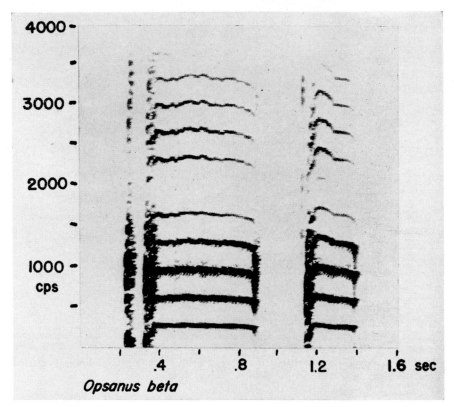

FIG. 22. A "boat-whistle" sound complex produced by the Gulf coast toadfish (*Opsanus beta*). From Selection 12, recorded on the night of June 14, 1958, near the dock at the Cape Haze Marine Laboratory, Florida.

the dock and guided by the sound, the individual toadfish was sighted. The hydrophone was placed within about three feet of the animal.

Figure 21 shows a spectogram of one of the above "boat-whistles." Together with a frequency-amplitude section taken at the point indicated by an arrow, Figure 22 shows another such call. Figure 23 is the low frequency portion taken from the same call. The entire sound is a complex of both low-pitched grunts and harmonic tones, and, for descriptive purposes, it can be separated into the following "notes."

A) A non-harmonic low grunt with its base frequency below 100 cps. This grunt begins the entire complex. Its component frequencies rarely go above 1500 cps, but, occasionally, as high as 3500 cps (Fig. 14). Its duration is 50 milliseconds (range: 35 to 55). A space of about 50 milliseconds usually follows.

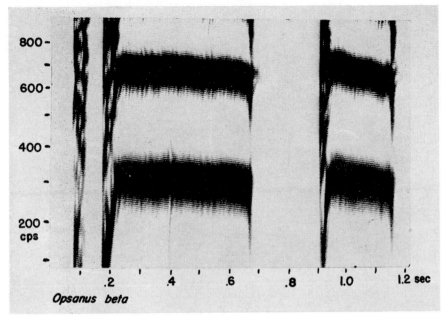

FIG. 23. A "boat-whistle" sound complex produced by the Gulf coast toadfish *(Opsanus beta)*. This is the magnified low frequency portion of the same sound illustrated in Fig. 22. From Selection 12, recorded on the night of June 14, 1958, near the dock at the Cape Haze Marine Laboratory, Florida.

B) A second non-harmonic grunt immediately precedes the "hoot" proper. Its frequency components regularly run as high as 3500 cps or over. Its duration is about the same as "A."

C) With no pause, "B" leads into the hoot-like harmonic portion of the sound complex. The fundamental frequency of this tone is 350 cps, and up to ten additional harmonics can be detected, i.e. up to 3850 cps. It should be noted that determination of frequency from sound spectrograms are all rough approximations. More exact measurements were made with an oscilloscope. Amplitudes of the various component frequencies are consistently different at the different harmonic levels (Fig. 21, left). The 1050 cps frequency is strongest, although in some calls, the 700 cps harmonic may be equivalent. The harmonic at 2100 cps is always extremely weak and in many calls it is completely absent. The top harmonic at 3850 cps is also sometimes absent, and is shorter in duration than the rest. Oscilloscope determinations of the fundamental frequencies of calls from the same individual show a variation of ± 10 cps. Different individuals, however, vary from 320 to 360 cps. The duration of this section of the call averages 440 milliseconds. From

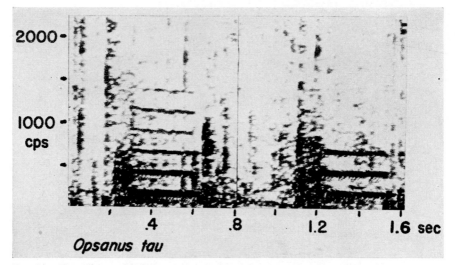

FIG. 24. Two "boat-whistle" sounds produced by the Atlantic toadfish *(Opsanus tau)*. From Selection 14, recorded on August 11, 1958, in Matanzas Inlet, Florida. There is considerable background noise in this recording.

the same individual durations as short as 400 milliseconds and, rarely, as long as 650 milliseconds, have been recorded. There appears to be as much variation in this parameter among different specimens. This portion of the sound complex ends with a slight descent in pitch and, sometimes a non-harmonic cut-off. An interval of 100 to 150 milliseconds follows.

D) This is a short grunt which is non-harmonic and resembles "A." In about 60% of the calls, this portion is absent.

E) Here again is a grunt which is almost identical with "B," and, like "B," it immediately precedes a harmonic tone.

F) Although basically similar to "C," this sound differs in two respects. Its duration is usually less than that of "C," i.e. averaging 410 milliseconds (range: 400 to 415 ms). It also shows a more rapid descent in pitch to about 50 cps below the starting point. The fundamental frequency is always identical to the "C" portion of the sound complex, and the harmonic components are also the same. Occasionally this portion of the sound complex is absent, in which case "D" and "E" are also lacking.

"Boat-whistle" sounds of Opsanus tau. The hoots of this species are well known, and they have been described from underwater recordings by Fish (1954) and Tavolga (1958a). The example presented here

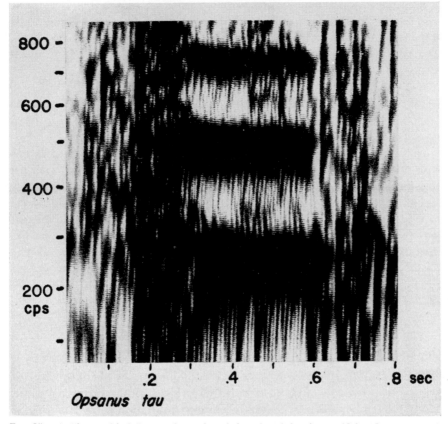

FIG. 25. A "boat-whistle" sound produced by the Atlantic toadfish (*Opsanus tau*). This is the magnified low frequency portion of the second of the two sounds illustrated in Fig. 24. From Selection 14, recorded on August 11, 1958, in Matanzas Inlet, Florida.

(Selection 13) was recorded on the afternoon of August 11th, 1958, in the Intracoastal Waterway, about two miles north of Marineland, Florida. Despite the background noise, a large chorus of toadfish can be distinguished and, in contrast to those of *O. beta*, these hoots seem to be lower in pitch and they are all single. Selection 14 was made the same day in Matanzas Inlet, about three miles north of Marineland. In this one, the toadfish were more scattered and as the boat slowly drifted with the tide, the hydrophone was lowered to within a few inches of the bottom (about six feet). The animal recorded here was probably very close to the hydrophone, but since the water was too murky it was impossible to say how close.

Figure 24 shows spectrograms of two calls recorded in Selection 14, and Figure 25 shows an enlarged portion of the second of these calls. The large amount of background noise makes these spectrograms less clear. The portions of each sound complex can be classified in the same way as in *O. beta* above.

A) This element is usually absent in *Opsanus tau*.

B) As in *O. beta,* an initial non-harmonic grunt immediately precedes the hoot, but here this grunt differs in being significantly longer in duration, i.e., 130 to 150 milliseconds.

C) The fundamental frequency of the hoot in *O. tau* is 250 cps. Five additional harmonics at 250 cps intervals can be present, with the top frequency of 1500 cps. This particular call is unusual, however, since in the majority of cases only frequencies of 250, 500, and 750 cps can be detected. In several instances, only the 250 cps fundamental was present. From 50% to 75% of the sound energy is at the fundamental. This fundamental frequency varies with different individuals to the extent of ±20 cps. The duration of this hoot in the present recordings averaged 380 milliseconds, with a range of from 330 to 460 ms. These were considerably shorter than the sounds recorded at the same locality about a year earlier (Tavolga, 1958a).

The secondary hoots, as in *O. beta,* are absent in all the calls of *O. tau* that were heard.

Other sounds of Opsanus beta and Opsanus tau. Toadfish are also known to produce sounds of a grunt-like or growl-like character (Fish, 1954). Such sounds are generally emitted in response to prodding or electric shock.

Selection 15 includes a recording of a small *O. beta* (about four inches in length). This animal was in a five-gallon glass aquarium and hiding in a small conch shell. A second toadfish was placed in the tank and soon approached the resident who began to produce these sounds. Spasmodic contractions of the entire animal and gaping of the mouth accompanied each sound. At the begining of this sample, each grunt is followed by a long, fading growl resembling a drum roll. In the latter portion of the sample, this growl is absent.

Figure 26 is a spectrogram of such a grunt, together with a portion of the following growl. A frequency-amplitude section was taken at the point indicated by an arrow. The sound appears to be non-harmonic, but careful study of the spectrograms and oscilloscope tracings revealed that there is a fundamental frequency at about 100 cps, and this frequency is also the dominant one in terms of intensity. At the beginning of the grunt, frequencies as high as 1000 cps are present. Figure 27 is a

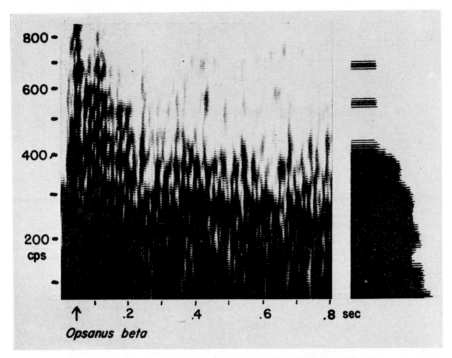

FIG. 26. A "grunt" and "growl" produced by the Gulf coast toadfish (*Opsanus beta*). From Selection 15, in which the sound maker was stimulated by the intrusion of another toadfish. A frequency-amplitude section (on the right) was taken at the point indicated by the arrow.

spectrogram of a grunt toward the end of Selection 15. The sound shown here is about 200 milliseconds in duration, and is almost identical with the first 200 milliseconds in Figure 25.

Selection 16 is a recording of a large specimen of *O. beta* who was being prodded with a stick. This was recorded in a large wooden tank. Similar recordings were made in glass aquaria with fiberglass sound absorbent batting lining the inside walls and floor. No difference in the character of the sounds could be detected. It is evident that the drum-like resonance of these sounds is supplied by the swim bladder of the animal itself.

Selection 17 contains sounds produced by a seven-inch specimen of *Opsanus tau*. These animals did not at first respond to prodding by making sounds, so electric shock was used. After a few stimuli, sounds were produced at the close approach of the electrode with no current applied. The spectrogram in Figure 28 shows these sounds to be virtually identical to those of *O. beta* except in being slightly shorter, i.e.

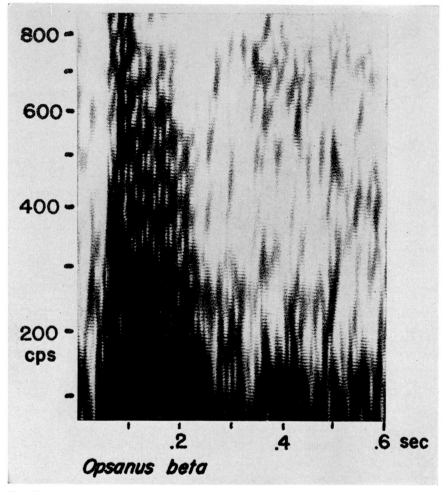

FIG. 27. A "grunt" produced by the Gulf coast toadfish *(Opsanus beta)*. From Selection 15, in which the sound maker was stimulated by the intrusion of another toadfish.

about 150 to 180 milliseconds. This difference in duration may be because of the different methods used in stimulating sound production.

Comparison of Opsanus beta and tau in sound production and behavior. It is evident that the low-pitched grunts and growls are basically the same in the two species, and that these sounds are elicited by irritating stimuli. Often they are associated with the characteristic aggressive gaping behavior.

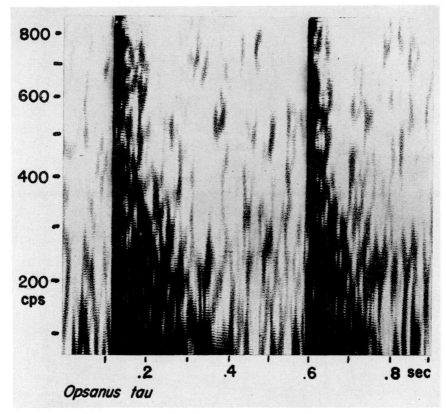

FIG. 28. Two "grunts" produced by the Atlantic toadfish *(Opsanus tau)*. From Selection 17, in which a captive specimen was prodded after several previously administered electric shocks.

Aside from differences in duration and repetition, which would be under central nervous control, the difference in fundamental pitch is highly consistent and significant. This is likely to be a function of the swim bladder construction. The bladder in *O. tau* has a deep anterior fold which penetrates to almost half the length of the organ (Fig. 20) while in *O. beta* this fold is scarcely one-third the length of the bladder (Fig. 19). The intrinsic swim bladder musculature in *O. beta* extends further ventrad than in *O. tau*. Whether these or other differences are significant or not in altering the quality of sounds is not known.

In my experience, no captive toadfish of either species has ever produced the "boat-whistle" sound. Fish (1954) had a freshly captured individual of *O. tau* who did so once in an aquarium. It appears that the production of this sound is not readily available for experimental work at the present time. On the basis of my experiences in recording and listening to toadfish in Gasparilla Sound, some inferences can be made bearing on the relationship of the sounds to behavior.

It has been suspected that the "boat-whistle" sounds are in some way related to reproductive behavior. Both sexes have the same apparatus for sound making, and, indeed, there are no discernible sex differences in the production of grunts and growls from captive individuals. Fish (1954) reported that in the few cases where a given hooting specimen was tracked down and captured, these were all males. In my own experience, I have captured two known sound makers and both of these were males. In the latter case, these animals were collected in August, one in 1957 and one in 1958. Both were dissected and found to have regressed and exhausted testes with no motile sperm. Some of the largest choruses of both *O. beta* and *O. tau* that I have recorded were during the summer months in Florida, where the normal breeding season of both species ends in April (Breder, 1941). On this basis it seems unlikely that the "boat-whistle" is a mating call.

The toadfish tends to be territorial in habit. The individual recorded in Selection 12, for example, had been known and heard as a resident under the laboratory dock for at least three months prior to his capture. Although he did not remain in a single hiding place for more than a day or so at a time, he was within hearing distance of the dock all this time. He was observed to change hiding places frequently, moving from one shell to another, excavating depressions under various bits of litter and junk in the vicinity. In drifting along the channel in Gasparilla Sound with the listening gear, separate toadfish could be heard hooting from spots separated by not less than about fifty or 75 feet.

Opsanus beta also tends to be more active at night. Captive individuals moved about and fed more actively at night. At night in the Sound, the boat-whistles were much more frequently repeated by individuals and more different sound sources could be heard. Just outside Gasparilla Pass, in the Gulf, a regular daily migration appeared to take place. At night the majority of calling toadfish were situated along the edge of an abrupt slope where the water depth changes from 10 feet to over 20 feet within a short distance. During the day, however, few or no toadfish could be heard in this area, and the majority of sound makers seemed to have moved a quarter to a half a mile further out over predominately sandy bottom into deeper water. This "migration" was not correlated with tidal movements.

At the present time it can only be said that the "boat-whistle" sound probably play some role in territorial behavior and, possibly, with species discrimination. We must await some method whereby these calls can be regularly elicited from captive individuals, and many additional field observations are needed in order that some definite conclusions can be reached on the function of these sounds.

Example 4

The case where there appears to be the clearest relationship between a specific behavior and the production of sound is in the gobiid fish, *Bathygobius soporator*. A similar situation is present in a few species of Blenniidae. Curiously, in these forms the mechanism of sound production is not known, and there are no obvious structural modifications or adaptations toward this end. The major portion of this section especially in regard to *Bathygobius*, has been published elsewhere (Tavolga, 1956, 1958b, 1958c).

Sounds produced by gobiid and blenniid fishes. The dull thumps heard on Selection 18 are sounds produced by a male *Bathygobius soporator* during courtship behavior. Figure 29 is a spectrogram of two such sounds. No trace of any harmonic can be detected either in spectrograms or in oscilloscope tracings. The section on the left of Figure 22 shows that the sound energy is strongest in the 100 to 200 cps range. Freqencies as high as 1000 cps can sometimes be detected at the beginning of each sound. Durations range from 150 to 350 milliseconds, averaging 255 milliseconds. Spectrograms show these sounds to be extremely variable.

Selection 19 contains a similar series of thumps, but these were produced by a male blenniid fish, *Chasmodes bosquianus*, during courtship. The spectrograms of these sounds (Fig. 30) are virtually identical with the above.

The sound pressures for these thumps at 6-8 inches ranged from 0.001 to 0.002 dynes/cm² for *Bathygobius*, and 0.005 to 0.008 dynes/cm² for *Chasmodes*. In terms of decibels above human auditory threshold, these figures would be equivalent to about 20 db and 30 db, respectively. In my previous reports (Tavolga, 1958b and c), the same data were in error to the extent of two decimal places as a result of miscalculations.

Two other species of blenniid fish were found to produce basically similar sounds: *Hypleurocheilus geminatus* and *Hypsoblennius hentz*. In these, the thumps were fainter in intensity than in *Chasmodes*, also they were produced only sporadically during courtship. In every case, the sound was synchronized with a snapping sidewise shake of the head of the male. A fourth species, *Blennius marmoreus* was tested but no sounds could be detected, although active courtship was observed.

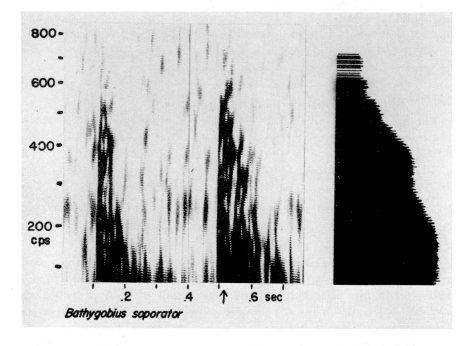

FIG. 29. Two "thumps" produced by a male *Bathygobius soporator* while he was courting a gravid female. From Selection 18, recorded in a small aquarium. A frequency-amplitude section (on the right) was taken at the point indicated by the arrow.

Mechanism of sound production in gobiid and blenniid fishes. In *Bathygobius,* the emission of each thump is synchronized with a quick downward snap of the head and the ejection of water jets from the dorsal regions of the opercular openings. In the blennies, the sounds are made with an accompanying quick sidewise shake of the head. As adults, these species possess no swim bladder, nor are there known to be any organs which have any sound-producing function.

The absence of any air-filled resonating chamber explains the non-harmonic character of the sounds. Similar, if not identical, thumps can be produced under water by any sudden movement. It is quite possible that simply the quick head movement creates a shock wave which registers as a thump-like sound. Of course there is the possibility that there are some skeletal movements which are more directly responsible for the sounds, but on the basis of the presently available evidence the simplest explanation can be taken as a tentative working hypothesis. In connection with this it is noteworthy that although males of *Blennius*

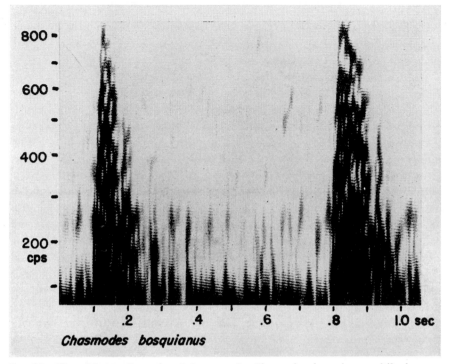

FIG. 30. Two "thumps" produced by a male *Chasmodes bosquianus* while he was courting a female. From Selection 19, recorded in a small aquarium.

marmoreus did not produce detectable sounds during courtship, there were spasmodic tremors of the entire body of the male at this time. Undoubtedly vibrations were being produced here but they would be at a sub-sonic frequency and below the sensitivity of the equipment.

Behavior and sound production in gobiid and blenniid fishes. In *Bathygobius* and in the three species of blennies mentioned above, sound production is clearly an important portion of prespawning behavior. Only males have been detected as producing these sounds and only during courtship of a female. In many species of territorial fishes where the male takes an active part in pursuing and courting a female, the courtship behavior includes a variety of vigorous movements as well as color changes. In the gobies and blennies the male actively waves his body and fins, and usually butts and nips the female. A quick head movement is also present, and it is during this action that detectable sounds are produced. It may be that initially, both in ontogeny and in phylogeny, the sounds were purely incidental to the movement as far as their effect upon the female was concerned. This may still be true of many species, but in one, *Bathygobius soporator,* experimental evidence has shown that the sounds themselves have a value in enhancing the efficiency of prespawning behavior.

Experiments involving the playback of sounds to *Bathygobius* (Tavolga, 1958b) showed that males would approach the transducer which emitted recordings of their own courtship "grunts" and various imitations as well. Females approach such sound sources also, but only if there was another goby in the vicinity to act as a visual stimulus. The selectivity and discrimination of the responses appear to be low. Any sounds which show a slight resemblance to the normal grunt of a male goby will elicit positive responses. The effect of the sounds upon males increases their activity and, probably, their level of responsiveness. Orientation and approach toward the sound source tends to increase the probability that several animals will compete for a given female. The females are also stimulated to more activity and responsiveness, and encounters with males become more likely. It should be noted that sound reception is only one of three sense modalities involved in the initial phase of prespawning behavior in *Bathygobius.* Visual and olfactory stimuli operate simultaneously or in sequence with the auditory to increase the probability of successful pairing and spawning (Tavolga, 1956).

DISCUSSION

At present, three types of classification of fish sounds can be utilized: 1) morphological—classification of mechanisms by means of which sounds are produced; 2) functional—categories of sounds; and 3) behavioral— the roles of various sounds in communication. Fish (1954) used a combination of 1) and 3). Her two main categories were "biological" and "mechanical" sounds. Her distinctions between the two were that "biological" sound is ". . . often purposeful, which originates in the body of the fish itself by means of either internal or external organs," whereas "mechanical" sound ". . . is incidental to swimming, feeding, collision, or other activity of the fish." Within these two categories, the classification was based on the sound producing organs. The distinction between purposeful and non-purposeful is, on the face of it, teleological and such a distinction is undesirable on grounds too numerous to mention here. Perhaps the implication was that some sounds have adaptive value while others do not. In such a case, if either body movements or tooth-gnashings can be shown to serve as stimuli on the behavior of other individuals, then the sounds and their mechanisms must be shifted from the "mechanical" to the "biological" category. It must be emphasized that the detection and analysis of fish sounds, and even the anatomical study of the sonic organs, cannot provide sufficient data for interpretations as to the adaptive and communicative value of the sounds.

A classification on purely morphological grounds eventually becomes a listing of sound-producing organs. Except in the Ostariophysi, sonic organs are widely divergent and often totally unrelated in phylogeny. It appears that such a classification would be primarily useful in comparisons between closely related forms where anatomical differences can be related to functional, ecological and phylogenetic factors.

Lists of various sounds with descriptions including frequency range, harmonic analysis, intensity, etc. are potentially useful for identification purposes in the field—especially for the Sonar operator. Such a classification has no relationship to the phylogenetic or behavioral aspects of the sounds. There is a correlation, however, with the structure of sonic organs. Sounds produced with the aid of the swim bladder are usually low-pitched, grunt-like, and most of them possess several harmonics above a fundamental in the 100 to 300 cps range. Stridulatory sounds are usually non-harmonic and contain a considerable amount of energy in the high frequencies. There is a possible relation here to the sensitivity of the receptor organs. Members of the Ostariophysi evidently have the highest auditory acuity (Dijkgraaf, 1949), and this acuity appears to be the result of the Weberian apparatus which couples the vibrations of the air in the swim bladder to the inner ear in a manner analogous to the function of the auditory ossicles of mammals. Members of the Gobiidae, however, respond only to frequencies below 500 cps and within this range their discriminatory capacity is very poor (Dijkgraaf, 1949; Tavolga, 1958b). The importance of the lateral line system and possibly cutaneous tactile receptors in low frequency reception is undoubtedly greater in the Gobiidae than in fishes with swim bladders. Griffin (1955) remarked that a fish is, in a sense, "transparent" to underwater sound and an air-filled chamber serves as an acoustical discontinuity. One might expect, then, that elaborate sound-producing and sound-receiving organs would be likely to occur in the same species, and that behavioral responses to sounds in such forms would be of considerable adaptive importance. One would not expect a situation such as in the Gobiidae and Blenniidae, where there is no air chamber and no evident sonic organ yet sound production and reception play an important role in a specific portion of pre-spawning behavior.

In a sense, the above situation might appear paradoxical, but it points up the importance of considering even "incidental" or "mechanical" sounds as having a potential value in communication. The responsiveness of fishes to conditioning and their readiness to learn and form associations from experience are well known and numerous experiments have been reported in which this ability is utilized to get at problems involving perception, sensory physiology, and various behavioral questions.

A tentative classification of fish sounds might be set up on a behavioral basis. Of necessity, such sounds that can be elicited only by electrical shock must be omitted from a behavioral classification. Electrical shock, although it may at times produce a "fright" or "alarm" response, may stimulate nerves and muscles directly and it is doubtful that the reaction of an animal to such a stimulus is even reflexive. In other words, electrical shock produces a neuro-muscular response but not necessarily a behavior. Sounds produced under any sort of duress, such as prodding, are difficult to classify. It is not clear, for example, whether the sounds of the black grouper (described earlier in this report) are to be considered as an "alarm" or "fright" response, or a defensive "warning" behavior. In the absence of further information, it would be best to describe such responses in operational terms—i.e., sounds produced in response to prodding or to approach of another animal. Some of the catfish sounds described here would also fall into this category. The communicative value of these sounds is as yet unknown.

Further classification on a behavioral basis emphasizes the present lack of sufficient information on the relationship of fish sounds to behavior. The function of the night-time choruses of catfish in social behavior, i.e., schooling, is far from certain. The territorial value of the toadfish "boat-whistles" is doubtful, and indeed, information on territorial behavior in this genus is very sparse. The reports of so-called breeding choruses of many sciaenids still require confirmation that the sounds are directly related to spawning behavior. A single instance of fish sounds used in orientation was described by Griffin (1955). The possibility that echo-location was actually being utilized in this case was discussed and tentatively concluded. For the present, it is probably premature to erect any such behavioral classification of fish sounds.

LITERATURE CITED

Agassiz, J. L. 1850. (no title). Proc. Amer. Acad. Arts and Sci. 2: 238.

Breder, C. M., Jr. 1941. On the reproduction of *Opsanus beta* Goode and Bean. Zoologica. 26: 229–232.

Bridge, T. W. and A. C. Haddon. 1893. Contributions to the anatomy of fishes. II. The air bladder and Weberian ossicles in the siluroid fishes. Phil. Trans. Roy. Soc. London, Ser. B. *184:* 64–333.

Burkenroad, M. D. 1931. Notes on the sound-producing marine fishes of Louisiana. Copeia. 20–28.

Dijkgraaf, S. 1949. Untersuchungen über die Funktionen des Ohrlabyrinths bei meeresfischen. Physiol. Comp. Oecol. *2:* 81–106.

Dôtu, Y. 1951. On the sound producing mechanisms of a scorpaenid fish, *Sebasticus marmoratus.* Kyushu Imp. Univ., Dept. Agri. Bull. Sci. *13:* 286–288.

Fish, M. P. 1954. The character and significance of sound production among fishes of the western North Atlantic. Bull. Bingham Oceangr. Coll. *14:* 1–109.

————, A. S. Kelsey, Jr., and W. H. Mowbray. 1952. Studies on the production of underwater sound by North Atlantic coastal fishes. Jour. Mar. Res. *11:* 180–193.

Frisch, K. von. 1938. Uber die bedeutung des sacculus und der Lagena für den Gehörsinn den Fische. Ztschr. f. Vergleich. Physiol. *25:* 703–747.

Greene, C. W. 1924. Physiological reactions and structure of the vocal apparatus of the California singing fish. Amer. Jour. Physiol. *70:* 496–499.

Griffin, D. R. 1955. Hearing and acoustical orientation in marine animals. Deep Sea Research. 3 (Sup): 406–417.

Ihering, R. von. 1930. Sur la voix des poissons d'eau douce. Compt. Rendus Soc. Biol. Paris. *103:* 1327–1328.

Kellogg, W. N. 1953. Bibliography of the noises made by marine organisms. Amer. Mus. Novitates. No. *1611:* 1–5.

————. 1955. Sounds of sea animals. Vol. II. Florida. Folkways Record Album No. FPX 125; Science series, Folkways Records and Service Corp. New York.

————. 1958. Echo ranging in the porpoise. Science. *128:* 982–988.

Merriman, D. 1940. Morphological and embryological studies on two species of marine catfish, *Bagre marinus* and *Galeichthys felis.* Zoologica. 25: 221–248.

Moulton, J. M. 1956. Influencing the calling of sea robins (*Prionotus* spp.) with sound. Bio. Bull. *111:* 393–398.

————. 1958. The acoustical behavior of some fishes in the Bimini area. Bio. Bull. *114:* 357–374.

Parker, G. H. 1918. Hearing in fishes. Copeia, *1918:* 11–12.

Schevill, W. E. and B. Lawrence. 1956. Food-finding by a captive porpoise (*Tursiops truncatus*). Brevoria. No. *53:* 1–15.

Sörensen, W. 1894. Are the extrinsic muscles of the air bladder in some siluroidae and the "elastic spring" apparatus of others subordinate to the voluntary production of sounds? Jour. Anat. and Physiol. *29:* 109–139, 205–229, 518–552.

Tavolga, W. N. 1956. Visual, chemical and sound stimuli as cues in the sex discriminatory behavior of the gobiid fish, *Bathygobius soporator.* Zoologica. *41:* 49–64.

————. 1958a. Underwater sounds produced by two species of toadfish, *Opsanus tau* and *Opsanus beta.* Bull. Mar. Sci. Gulf and Carribean. *8:* 278–284.

————. 1958b. The significance of underwater sounds produced by males of the gobiid fish, *Bathygobius soporator.* Physiol. Zool. *31:* 259–271.

————. 1958c. Underwater sounds produced by males of the blenniid fish, *Chasmodes bosquianus.* Ecology. *39:* 759–760.

Tower, R. W. 1908. The production of sound in the drumfishes, the sea robin and the toadfish. Ann. N.Y. Acad. Sci. *18:* 149–180.

CAPTIONS TO SELECTIONS ON DEMONSTRATION RECORD

Selection 1. The black grouper *(Mycteroperca bonaci)*. Groups of "drum-beat" sounds produced by a captive specimen who was prodded.

Selection 2. The sea catfish *(Galeichthys felis)*. "Grunts" and "creaks" produced by a freshly captured specimen hanging from a fishing line. Recorded out of water.

Selection 3. The sea catfish *(Galeichthys felis)*. "Creaks" produced by artificially moving a pectoral spine of a dead specimen. Recorded out of water.

Selection 4. The sea catfish *(Galeichthys felis)*. "Grunts" produced by a single captive specimen being prodded under water.

Selection 5. The sea catfish *(Galeichthys felis)*. "Grunts" produced by a group of nine captive specimens swimming undisturbed in an aquarium.

Selection 6. The sea catfish *(Galeichthys felis)*. "Percolator" noise produced by a chorus of catfish. Recorded in Gasparilla Sound, Florida, on the night of July 1, 1958.

Selection 7. The sea catfish *(Galeichthys felis)*. "Percolator" noise produced by a chorus of catfish. Recorded in the Intracoastal Waterway, near Marineland, Florida, on the night of August 10, 1958.

Selection 8. The gaff-topsail catfish *(Bagre marinus)* and the sea catfish *(Galeichthys felis)*. "Yelps" of *B. marinus* are mixed with the predominating "percolator" noise of *G. felis.* Recorded in Gasparilla Sound, Florida, on the night of July 1, 1958.

Selection 9. The gaff-topsail catfish *(Bagre marinus)*. "Yelps" and "sobs" produced by a group of five specimens swimming undisturbed in an aquarium.

Selection 10. The gaff-topsail catfish *(Bagre marinus)*. "Grunts" produced by a single captive specimen being prodded under water.

Selection 11. Gulf coast toadfish *(Opsanus beta)*. Chorus of "boat-whistle" sounds recorded just outside of Big Gasparilla Pass, Florida, on July 29, 1958.

Selection 12. Gulf coast toadfish *(Opsanus beta)*. "Boat-whistle" sounds from individual near the dock at the Cape Haze Marine Laboratory, Florida, on the night of June 14, 1958.

Selection 13. Atlantic toadfish *(Opsanus tau)*. Chorus of "boat-whistle" sounds recorded in the Intracoastal Waterway about two miles north of Marineland, Florida, on August 11, 1958.

Selection 14. Atlantic toadfish *(Opsanus tau)*. "Boat-whistle" sounds recorded in Matanzas Inlet, three miles north of Marineland, Florida, on August 11, 1958.

Selection 15. Gulf coast toadfish *(Opsanus beta)*. Sounds produced by a specimen in an aquarium in response to the approach of an intruding toadfish.

Selection 16. Gulf coast toadfish *(Opsanus beta)*. Sounds produced by a captive specimen being prodded under water.

Selection 17. Atlantic toadfish *(Opsanus tau)*. Sounds produced by a captive specimen being prodded under water after several previously administered electric shocks.

Selection 18. Goby *(Bathygobius soporator)*. Low "thumps" produced by a male during courtship of a gravid female in an aquarium.

Selection 19. Blenny *(Chasmodes bosquianus)*. Low "thumps" produced by a male during courtship of a female in an aquarium.

The Influence Of Sound On The Behavior Of Amphibians and Reptiles [1, 2]

CHARLES M. BOGERT

Curator, Department of Amphibians and Reptiles,
The American Museum of Natural History, New York City

Contents

[1] Manuscript received February 1960.
[2] Recordings illustrating this chapter are on Side I, Band 3 of the Demonstration Record.

INTRODUCTION

When aroused by an interplay of internal and external stimuli a sexually mature male treefrog emits a call that is apparently audible to females in the vicinity. It may even be audible to females at distances of a kilometer or more. The call is repeated as often as the frog shunts the air from its inflated vocal sac back to its lungs and re-expels it. The sound, or some peculiar characteristic of it, elicits a positive motor response in the receptive female that leads to a sequence of interactions in the behavior of the two sexes. Ordinarily the sequence terminates in the oviposition and the fertilization of the eggs, and the departure of the female from the spawning site. Do the male's vocalizations qualify as communication? His mating calls unquestionably attract the female, even though her response may depend upon recent ovulation. The mating call may not only orient and attract the female. It may simultaneously advertise the presence of the male to other males, eliciting a negative response that discourages their approach.

Whatever semantic or biological problems remain to be solved, it is evident that the treefrog's call is one of several stimuli employed in numerous stereotyped patterns of behavior characteristic of anuran reproductive activities. The male treefrog does not utter its mating call with forethought, design, or intention. His vocalizations do not constitute speech or even remotely resemble the articulations human beings employ to convey ideas or information. Nevertheless, the sounds that frogs and many other animals produce can be interpreted as being "useful" to the individual or to the species in its natural environment. Sound is often an element in reproductive or defensive behavior, and the importance of it in the lives of several groups of animals is reflected in the diversity as well as the complexity of mechanisms largely or completely devoted to sound production.

Animals produce sounds in astonishingly varied ways, from the simple tapping on the tunnel walls of some termites, through the relatively simple stridulations of insects, to the complex and sometimes bizarre vocalizations of the vertebrates. Sounds or noises seemingly produced fortuitously, by the wing movements of birds and insects, for example, or the locomotion, feeding or breathing of numerous terrestrial vertebrates, may have behavioral significance. When sound emanates from specialized structures, some functional significance is commonly apparent or becomes so when the behavior of the animal is thoroughly investigated.

Because it is sometimes difficult to assess the significance of sound as an element in the behavioral pattern of individual species, specialists may not fully agree in their interpretations. But few students of evolution doubt that such elaborate and distinctive structures as the tympanic organs of cicadas, the syrinx of birds, the vocal apparatus that incorporates highly modified hyoid bones as a resonator in some howler monkeys, or the amazing growth of interlocking segments on the tail of rattlesnakes, stem directly from the advantages conferred on these animals by their acquisition of mechanisms of sound production during the course of their descent from their respective ancestors.

Whether sound is employed in the maintenance of territories, the attraction of mates, or in echo-location, the apparatus for its production arose because it enhanced the chances for the survival of individual members of the population so endowed. Most mechanisms producing sound in animals presumably evolved, or became modified, along with other elements of their behavior. The origin of mechanisms for sound production and their integration in the behavioral patterns of individual species are surely the outcome of progressive changes in the genotypes resulting from natural selection in succesive generations. If the origin and evolutionary development of a structure as complex in growth and structure as the snake's rattle (Klauber, 1956) seem inexplicable in such terms, it will be recalled that selection, in the words of Fisher, "is a device for generating a high degree of improbability" (Pittendrigh, 1958).

To be effective the apparatus animals employ in producing the sounds associated with such phenomena as territoriality, breeding aggregations, or behavior largely limited to the population of the species, is dependent upon coordinated specializations in other structures, notably phonoreceptors. Echo-location in bats and porpoises scarcely could have evolved without more or less simultaneous and integrative adaptations of the ear, along with various other components of the nervous system. The behavior and morphology of other creatures often reflect their utilization of sound, which like other elements of the external environment, has affected trends in their evolution and morphology.

It is difficult or virtually impossible to trace the modifications in behavior dependent upon the reception of sound. We can, however, draw inferences concerning the changes that occurred during the evolution of sound receptors, even though we know little concerning the evolution of mechanisms for sound production. Zoölogical texts occasionally mention the evolution of sound receptors (Simpson, Pittendrigh and Tiffany, 1957, for example), but discussions of mechanisms of sound production are largely restricted to texts dealing with individual groups of animals. Hearing in animals is underestimated and therefore neglected in many studies of behavior, as Pumphrey (1950) observes. The effects of sound on animals are mentioned only as details incidental to discussions of other topics in a recent survey of behavior and evolution (Roe and Simpson, 1958). For obvious reasons this work does not attempt to trace the evolution of behavior, nor does it offer much encouragement to those who hope to find simple sequential levels of behavior corresponding to the morphological levels systematists employ to define the higher categories of animals. Comparisons of the behavior of animals in related family or generic groups rarely reveal phylogenetic sequences in their patterns.

SCOPE AND OBJECTIVES

This chapter is primarily concerned with the vocalizations and other sounds living representatives of the Amphibia produce. One Order, the Apoda (or Gymnophiona) is comprised of limbless, secretive, silent creatures, the subterrestrial or aquatic caecilians, none of which is known to be capable of detecting airborne sounds. Salamanders are placed in a second Order, the Urodela (or Caudata), which includes species that may be aquatic, partly aquatic, or entirely terrestrial. Most but not all salamanders are mute, with relatively primitive sound receptors. The frogs or tailless amphibians comprising the third Order, Anura, are conspicuously vociferous at seasonal intervals and far more widely distributed; they occur in many parts of the world uninhabited by caecilians or salamanders.

Much of the ensuing discussion, therefore, is devoted to the Anura. In order to provide perspective in assessing the role of sound in vertebrate evolution and to point out the divergent trends in sound production and sound detection among the ectothermic or "cold-blooded" vertebrates, the subject is reviewed briefly, with emphasis on the reptiles, which are not dealt with elsewhere in this survey.

Efforts to explain the biological significance of anuran vocalizations on a scientific basis scarcely antedate the turn of the century. Many early speculations or field observations reported are suggestive, but numerous statements remain unsupported by conclusive evidence. Such statements, often quoted by later workers to explain equally inconclusive data, are responsible for much disagreement and confusion concerning the adaptive nature of anuran calls. Portions of the literature have been neglected (not without reason in some instances) or reviewed haphazardly and uncritically. In view of recent and rapid advances in the study of frog calls it seems worth while to re-evaluate the evidence upon which various interpretations currently rest.

Renewed interest in animal acoustics, stimulated no doubt by improvements in electronic devices for recording, reproducing and analyzing sound, has widened the horizon of behavior studies. Most recent investigators realize that behavior is not an isolated field of study, but one that interdigitates with systematic, anatomical and zoögeographical studies, all of which are unified to some extent by our efforts to understand the mechanics of evolutionary processes, and of speciational phenomena in particular. This can scarcely be an exhaustive survey, even of the literature dealing with anurans. But before reporting the results of experiments carried out in Florida, and discussing the results obtained by other investigators, I shall try to summarize our knowledge of the mechanisms of sound production and sound perception in the Anura, as well as the nature of the various sounds produced, and the stimuli that evoke them.

Much remains to be learned concerning the combination of physiological and environmental conditions that evoke the migrations and breeding activities of frogs, even though the call plays an important part in much of their breeding behavior. Within recent years several attempts have been made to demonstrate the importance of the mating call as an isolation mechanism, and as will be seen, for some species there is now evidence to substantiate the belief. The utility of anuran voice recordings in working out relationships remains to be established, however, and some pitfalls have been uncovered, as will be explained in the section dealing with voice as a taxonomic character.

SOUND PRODUCTION IN THE ECTOTHERMIC VERTEBRATES

If sound has been a determinant in the evolution of behavior and morphology, its production and use have also depended upon other aspects of the external environment. While such specializations as echolocation entail an integrated evolution of mechanisms of sound production and sound reception, the evolution of one is not always dependent upon the evolution of the other. Sound production is not confined to animals with well developed sound receptors, nor do all animals in which sound perception is well developed produce noises themselves. It is not only teleological but an over-simplification of the situation to say that "one exists for the sake of the other," as von Buddenbrock (1958) puts it. Nevertheless, with a few notable exceptions among the snakes, which appear unable to detect airborne sounds, but respond to vibrations transmitted through the substratum, specialized apparatus for sound production is of wider occurrence among groups of animals in which sound perception is most advanced.

Phonoreception has been studied in relatively few animals. Jahn and Wulff (1950) provide an excellent summary, listing the animals or groups of animals studied or tested in this respect. As these authors note, refinements in techniques disclose the existence of sound perception in fishes and recent work strongly suggests that sound production is of widespread occurrence in the group (Fish, 1956). Even though fishes have evolved divers ways of producing sound, it is extremely doubtful whether the vocalizations of living Amphibia had their antecedents in sounds produced by the ancestral fish that invaded the land.

Salamanders were once believed to be deaf (Noble, 1931; Warden, Jenkins, and Warner, 1936), but the training experiments of Ferhat-Akat (1939) indicate that an ambystomid can distinguish between frequencies differing in pitch as little as a musical interval of a fourth or a fifth. *Ambystoma* responds to frequencies as high as 194 to 244 cycles; the lower limit was not ascertained. Other experiments indicate that larvae of the European *Salamandra salamandra* respond to frequencies as high as 1,035 cycles. Ferhat-Akat concludes that mechanoreceptors in the skin are as important as the labyrinth. Schmalhausen (1957) questions the idea (Noble, 1931; Tumarkin, 1955) that salamanders receive vibrations through the lower jaw or forelimbs. He suggests that phonoreception in aquatic salamanders depends on the transmission of sound through the network of superficial veins in the head, enhanced in many adults by the cutaneous network of blood vessels more directly associated with respiration. Vibrations are transmitted along these liquid channels either directly to the membrane of the fenestra ovalis or through the stapes.

Whether something comparable is present in aquatic species of the limbless caecilians remains to be investigated, but Schmalhausen points out that the complete ossification of the quadratum and stapes in terrestrial forms makes them ideally suited to receive vibrations through the substratum. It may be inferred that terrestrial caecilians, like snakes, are incapable of hearing airborne sounds. None of the caecilians possesses vocal apparatus or any other mode of sound production as far as known.

The majority of salamanders are silent, but a few emit faint squeaks. Whistling sounds have been attributed to *Amphiuma* and *Siren*, and one relatively large Californian ambystomid, *Dicamptodon ensatus*, makes a sound described as a bark. A sound spectrogram (Fig. 1) of one recorded by Dr. R. C. Stebbins discloses the bark to be roughly 0.3 seconds in duration and to consist of about twelve pulsations at a mean frequency approximating 3100 cps. Maslin (1950) describes the vocal cords of the species, indicating that it is part of a defense mechanism. The pulsations in the spectrogram apparently reflect the existence of a bonafide vocal apparatus in the species. In contrast the spectrogram (Fig. 1) of a squeak produced by a lungless California plethodontid,

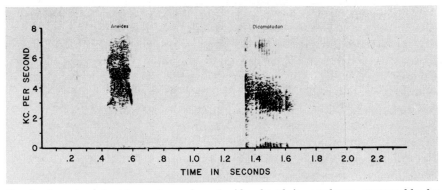

FIG. 1. Squeak a lungless salamander, *Aneides lugubris,* produces, presumably by expelling air from the buccal cavity (left). Sound uttered by a salamander, *Dicamptodon ensatus,* (right), the only species known to possess vocal cords. Both recorded in California by R. C. Stebbins.

Aneides, also recorded by Stebbins, reveals the sound to be lacking in pulsations and scarcely 0.18 seconds in duration, with a mean at a frequency approximating 5000 cycles.

Liu (1950) quotes the unverified statement of Koo Po, who reported (ca. 300 A.D.) that the Chinese giant salamander, *Megalobatrachus,* emits cries "similar to those of a small infant." Geyer (1927), Noble (1931), Myers (1951) and Neill (1952) review the evidence of sound production by salamanders. Prior to Maslin's discovery of vocal cords in an ambystomid, Noble dismisses the subject with the comment that sound is probably accidental and associated with the sudden emptying of the lungs, or of the buccal cavity of the plethodontids, which are lungless. Geyer suggests that the sound of some salamanders have sexual significance; Maslin believes this probable. But no evidence that voice plays any part in the breeding activities of salamanders has been forthcoming, although the experiments of Ferhat-Akat and Schmalhausen's statements indicate that sound may have some bearing on the activities of salamanders. To judge by recent studies of fishes, some aquatic salamanders conceivably produce sounds underwater that have gone undetected. Harris (1959) believes *Necturus* is mute. Dye (1921) reports evidence of its response to vibrations, with lateral line organs as receptors.

Phonoreceptors are far more advanced in the Anura, most of which possess a tympano-stapedial system adapted for the transmission of airborne vibrations. Vocalization is a conspicuous feature of the breeding activities of the majority of species, and serves other functions as well. The adaptive significance of the vocalizations of frogs will be discussed in greater detail in a subsequent section. It will suffice here to point out that while tailless amphibians were probably the first vertebrates to incorporate vocalizations into their reproductive behavior, frogs are far removed from the line of descent that led to the reptiles. The replacement of the moist, glandular skin of the amphibian by the relatively impervious skin of reptiles is a significant feature of the transition, for it enabled reptiles to function at higher and more precisely controlled body temperatures. As Adrian, Craik and Sturdy (1938) point out, nerve response varies with the temperature, and consequently frequency discrimination is dependent upon more exacting thermoregulatory capacities than amphibians possess.

Despite the fact that many reptiles exercise an astonishingly precise control over their body temperature (Bogert, 1959), sound perception is subordinate in importance to vision or chemoreception in the activities of most reptiles. Sound producing mechanisms are absent in the majority of species, but occur in some or all members of the four surviving Orders.

Darwin (1839) was the first to describe the hoarse roar or bellow uttered by Galapagos tortoises during the breeding season. Among other reptiles vocalizations are confined to species with nocturnal propensities. The tuatara, *Sphenodon,* the only surviving rhynchocephalian, sporadically croaks during its nocturnal foraging (Bogert, 1953), and utters a grunting sound when seized in the human hand. Some, if not all, crocodilians bellow. Berger (1924) reports sounds to affect the respiratory rate in the African crocodile, *Osteolaemus tetraspis,* and the grunting of young alligators is said to attract the female (McIlhenny, 1935). Wever and Vernon (1957) review the meager literature dealing with phonoreception in crocodilians and report evidence of auditory response to tones over a range of 20 to 6000 cycles in a South American species, *Caiman sclerops.* Beach (1944) reports that a fundamental note of 57 cps evoked bellowing and an aggressive response in an American alligator, *Alligator mississippiensis,* suggesting that vocalizations play some part in the maintenance of territories. No effort has been made to ascertain whether this is true of the croaking sounds produced by the tuatara, or the varied sounds made by lizards, the vocal abilities of which are largely restricted to members of a single large family, the Gekkonidae.

Like crocodilians and the tuatara, nearly all geckos are nocturnal in most of their activities, which at least suggests that sounds may be of more adaptive significance when full use cannot be made of photoreceptors or vision. An African gecko, *Ptenopus garrulus,* produces a clicking sound described as "almost deafening" in some parts of southwest Africa (Loveridge, 1950), but the vocalizations occur only during a

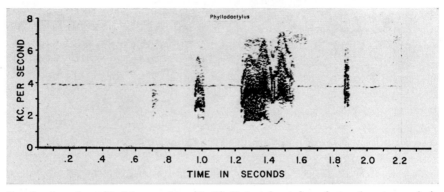

FIG. 2. Squeak emitted by a gekkonid, *Phyllodactylus tuberculosus*, (insect sounds in background). Recorded at Alamos, Sonora, Mexico.

brief interval at twilight, and cease at the onset of darkness. Lizards in other families reputedly emit sounds more often described as squeaks. Probably these are produced fortuitously, unlike the relatively loud squawk emitted by some of the large geckos, *Gekko gecko* and its congeners, as they lunge toward an intruder with the mouth widely opened—a gesture to which few vertebrates fail to react. The feeble squeaking sounds of such geckos as *Phyllodactylus* (Fig. 2) have no obvious behavioral significance.

Crocodilians, a few turtles, and several of the larger lizards, notably the Gila monster, produce a loud hiss by forcibly expelling air from the lungs. Hissing is particularly characteristic of snakes, some of which (*Pituophis*) possess a special membrane at the aperture of the glottis. The membrane is set in vibration by the expulsion of air, to produce a sort of staccato sibilance, probably the nearest approach to vocalization among the serpents. Other snakes inflate the neck with a distensible tracheal lung, as an "aggressive warning attitude," according to Noble (1921), but the distended lung may also serve as a resonator for the hiss. The African puff adder, *Bitis arietans,* lacks a tracheal lung, but hisses so vigorously that the sound emitted has been described as "resembling more the noises horses make when forcing air through their lips." However, it is surely to be doubted that this is a breeding call, as stated in the account, quoted by Pitman (1938). No specialized structures for sound production have been described for this viper.

The Sonoran coral snake, *Micruroides,* expels air from the vent, producing a moderately loud sound that can be repeated as often as the snake is touched. Air, apparently drawn into the cloaca through the vent, is expelled through the same opening. Presumably this entails

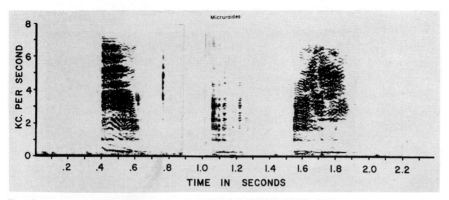

FIG. 3. Sounds elicited by a tactile stimulus in the Sonoran coral snake, *Micruroides euryxanthus*. Air drawn into the cloaca is expelled through the vent, the lips of which are apparently set in vibration to produce the sound. It can be repeated at intervals not greatly exceeding a second. Recorded at Portal, Arizona.

some specialization of the muscles surrounding the lower end of the cloaca that enables the snake to distend the tubular structure to draw air into it and to contract it when air is expelled, setting up vibrations in the lips of the vent to produce the sound (Fig. 3). In somewhat similar fashion the hooknosed snake, *Ficimia cana*, of the American Southwest produces what has been described as a "popping noise" (Taylor, 1931). The saw-scaled vipers, *Echis*, of Africa and Asia, as well as the African egg-eating snakes, *Dasypeltis*, and possibly other serpents, possess scales equipped with serrated keels that serve as stridulatory mechanisms when the lungs are inflated and the sides of the body are rubbed together by characteristic writhing movements (Gans and Richmond, 1957). Gadow (1901) mentions a gecko, *Teratoscincus*, that allegedly rubs together specialized plates to produce a cricket-like noise.

In many respects, however, the most specialized apparatus for sound production is the rattle, a unique structure found only in snakes of the closely related genera *Sistrurus* and *Crotalus*. Klauber (1956) discusses the structure and function of the rattle in great detail, concluding that it is a warning device, often, but not always, effective in discouraging the attacks of predators. It is perhaps noteworthy that one group of rattlesnakes (*Crotalus*) is more widely distributed in the Americas than any other genus of reptiles.

The more specialized mechanisms for sound production appear to have evolved quite independently in various groups of reptiles. Whereas vocalizations among terrestrial vertebrates may date from the Amphibia of the Mesozoic, it is uncertain whether vocal apparatus was restricted to the primitive forerunner of the frogs, or lost secondarily in most salamanders. Eaton (1959) believes that there are a sufficient number of resemblances to indicate that the Urodela and Anura descended from a common stock. Romer (1945), however, places frogs and salamanders in separate subclasses. Because of the general prevalence of vocalizations accompanying the breeding activities of the Anura, more attention has been devoted to their mating calls than to those of other cold-blooded vertebrates, as noted in the introduction.

SOUND PRODUCTION IN ANURAN AMPHIBIANS

Summary of Previous Interpretations

Literary references to the vocalizations of frogs antedate any comprehension of their biological importance by at least two thousand years. Aristophanes, 405 B.C., may not have been the first author who struggled with phonetic symbols to convey some idea of the quality of a frog's voice, but his "brekekex-koäx," is doubtless the best known attempt. Boulenger (1897) considers this an admirable rendition of the voice of *Rana esculenta,* but adds that other species are far more difficult to imitate. Regardless of the author's skill, the difficulties entailed in describing or imitating many sounds produced by frogs make it almost impossible for workers to discuss frog voices or compare those of different species in meaningful or precise terms. If the descriptions of several writers dealing with the voice of a single species are compared (see examples in Wright and Wright, 1949) they usually prove to be completely different. It is evident that many descriptions convey little or no information concerning qualities of the sound, even though the duration of calls and the intervals separating them can, as Stebbins (1951) shows, be reduced to quantitative terms with equipment no more extensive than a stop-watch.

Until recently, however, naturalists were severely hampered in their efforts to investigate the adaptive importance of frog vocalizations by the lack of quantitative data, or precise descriptions of anuran voices. Where the Wrights (1949) credit "a coarse monosyllable wank, wank," to the eastern spadefoot, *Scaphiopus holbrooki,* an earlier author, Abbott (1884) refers to the "shrill, ear-piercing groans" of a breeding aggregation of the species in New Jersey. To judge by his choice of words, Abbott realized that the calls in some manner were associated with reproductive activities, despite his contradictory observation that "the purpose of their deafening epithalamium was somewhat hard to determine." If his suggestion that the sounds were "expressions of delight at meeting" after these amphibians had spent the winter underground seems naïve, it was little more so than those of other naturalists of the period. Darwin expressed the view that a male beetle "stridulates to encourage the female in her work and from distress when she is removed," and believed that birds sing in order "to charm the female."

Relatively few scientific investigations of the biological attributes of frogs were carried out until a fair number of species had been named and described, with foundations laid for some semblance of order in their classification. Modern systematic work with the Anura stems largely from the classification of Boulenger (1882) and Cope (1889), whose studies were largely devoted to describing the external and internal morphology.

Boulenger (1897) a few years later set the stage for the next phase of investigation when he summarized information dealing with the life histories, reproduction, secondary sex characters, and breeding behavior of frogs. Though he dealt exclusively with European species, many of his generalizations apply to some extent to the frogs of other continents. His discussions of the anuran voice include descriptions of the vocal apparatus and the vocalizations of virtually all European species. Boulenger was aware of the restriction of vocalizations to males in most of the forms studied and the association of the voice with mating activities. He mentions the shrill cry that some frogs produce under duress, noting also that some can be induced to emit sounds by rubbing their backs. But he overlooked the fact that such sounds, or the movements accompanying their production, are the principle means employed by males to distinguish the sex of frogs in breeding aggregations.

Boulenger does not commit himself concerning the adaptive significance of the mating call beyond noting that the female responds to the male by a mere grunt. Dickerson's (1906) account of North American frogs is equally noncommittal on this score. She mentions loud croaking during the breeding season, and the conspicuous differences between voices, but any intimation that voice is associated with reproduction is assiduously avoided. Frogs, she says, "feel physical joy and express it in song." Miss Dickerson observes that frogs calling in chorus "respond with instant silence" when the presence of an intruder is detected visually, and she interprets this by assuming that the cessation of vocalization alerts those in the aggregation to potential danger (an idea recently expressed by Martof and Thompson, 1958, first proposed by Yerkes, 1903). She also mentions distress signals or what Yerkes (1903) called the "pain scream," observing that these are produced with the mouth open, in contrast to mating calls, which are made with the mouth closed, in some instances while the frog is submerged, as Yerkes noted earlier.

Meanwhile experiments carried out by Yerkes (1903 and 1905) established the existence of hearing in frogs and stimulated renewed interest in their vocalizations. Wright (1914) offers no explanation for the function of the voice, but provides extensive notes on the life histories of eight anurans at Ithaca, New York, describing the voice of each, and listing air temperatures of the first day that each species was heard over a six year period. Courtis (1907), Miller (1909), Wellman (1917), and Noble and Noble (1923) report field observations interpreted as evidence that the male's vocalizations attract the female. Storer (1925) states that the voice of *Hyla regilla* "serves to bring scattered individuals to the breeding site." Unfortunately none of these authors grasped the significance of Yerkes' (1905) comment that statements concerning hearing in frogs (and hence its importance in their mating behavior) bore little weight unless they were accompanied by satisfactory proof that visual stimuli had been excluded.

Later authors for the most part share a tendency to omit mentioning such investigations as those of Cummins (1920) and Savage (1935), both of whom found evidence in the species studied to contradict the belief that the voices of male frogs attract females to the breeding site. Similarly few authors mention Maynard's (1934) report that a migration of *Bufo terrestris americanus* entailed the toads' utilization of a stream to carry them 2 miles to a point of emergence near a breeding site, which they continued to use after all males calling in the area were removed on one occasion. Pope (1944) provides a summary of the information concerning the species, noting that explanations thus far offered fail to explain how amphibians reach suitable breeding sites.

Noble (1923) briefly reviews the literature, mentioning doubts entertained by earlier authors concerning the role of the voice in the mating activities of frogs, apparently on the basis of data presented later the same year by Noble and Noble (1923.). The evidence presented mentions no attempt to exclude visual cues, and could as readily be interpreted to support alternate explanations for the behavior described. Eight years later Noble (1931) reviews additional literature, but cites nothing actually substantiating his unequivocal statement that "the chief function of the voice in frogs and toads is to attract mates." Oliver (1955) notes exceptions, and states that other cues are employed by males in selecting breeding sites. Von Buddenbrock (1956) says "as is well known, females react to the love croaking of the males by swimming toward them." Herter (1941), oblivious of the criticisms pointed out by Savage (1935), prefers to believe that amphibians are guided in their migrations to the breeding site by visual and olfactory cues as well as by their sensitivity to humidity gradients. Angel (1947) believes that anuran females are attracted by the voices of males of their own species. Bogert (1954) also believes that mating calls of some species attract females, but he indicates that other cues are utilized by the female in her acceptance or rejection of males, thus implying that species discrimination is not wholly dependent upon mating calls.   Jameson (1955) provides a more extensive review, concluding that calls attract females to spawning sites, and play important roles in other aspects of anuran reproductive behavior.

The first experiments designed to ascertain whether voice played a significant role in the complex of isolating mechanisms preventing sympatric species of *Bufo* from interbreeding are those of A. P. Blair (1942), who reports inconclusive results.   Later (A. P. Blair, 1947) he used similar procedures in tests of two species of spadefoots, *Scaphiopus*, pointedly observing that "it has not been experimentally demonstrated that anurans respond preferentially to the calls of their own species." Lowe (1954) believes it would be of greater interest to demonstrate that anurans do not respond preferentially to the calls of their own species, but it is difficult to see what might be gained from such negative evidence. Volpe (1957) comments on the lack of satisfactory proof that mating calls have "attracting power," but W. F. Blair (1958f) says the "function of the call is limited to the attraction of a mate." Blair, nevertheless, admits that evidence for the specificity of the female's response is yet to be obtained.

Despite the lack of evidence from controlled experiments, several authors have little hesitancy in referring to mating calls as "important isolation mechanisms." Cagle (1956), a notable exception, states flatly that the function of the anuran voice is not clear.   Bogert (1958) reviews evidence from various sources, noting the conflicting conclusions drawn from studies of unrelated species and the lack of conclusive proof that voice is of importance as an isolation mechanism.   He adds, however, that field observations strongly suggest that voice differences sometimes play a significant role in discouraging one species from breeding with another, despite the occurrence of hybrids between sympatric species with differences in their mating calls.

Bogert also summarizes the results of experiments designed to ascertain whether males as well as females are attracted by the mating call of the species.   Using the southern toad, *Bufo t. terrestris,* marked individuals of which were liberated at specified distances from a loudspeaker, he broadcast taped recording of a chorus, thereby eliminating visual as well as olfactory cues, or the possibility of responses dependent upon geotaxis or hydrotaxis.   The results showed that both males and females were attracted by the sound, but *only when they were in suitable physiological condition.*

Later the same year Martof and Thompson (1958) discuss the problems pertaining to the function of the voice and report that female chorus frogs, *Pseudacris triseriata,* are attracted by the vocalizations of the male. Martof and Thompson state that even when the male was hidden or when taped recordings were substituted as a means of eliminating olfactory and visual cues, females were attracted by the sound and actively sought the source of the calls. It will be noted that neither Martof and Thompson nor Bogert offer proof of the specificity of the response, even though each report provides evidence that under suitable conditions some anurans exhibit a positive response to the voice of males of their own species.

The majority of investigators reporting field observations or the results of laboratory tests have been unaware of differences in the behavior of individual species, or the apparent absence of vocalizations among others. Cagle (1956), who endeavors to provide a succinct summary of the interrelations of vocalizations and breeding behavior, solves the difficulties encountered by simply stating: "The specific functions of the call differ in various anurans." He is equally correct in qualifying his statement concerning the significance of anuran voices as isolation mechanisms. Nevertheless, unqualified generalizations and categorical statements of several authors mentioned earlier led to confusion as well as to the acceptance of ideas unsupported by scientific evidence.

Investigators less familiar with the literature dealing with amphibians have been less than critical in reporting field observations, and prone to summarize conclusions in terms implying that the behavior described for one species is characteristic of all anurans. Equally unfortunate, the literature is cluttered with statements stemming from assumptions rather than from scientific testing, or from casual observations made under conditions where no controls were employed to eliminate alternate sources of stimuli not mentioned in descriptions of the situation.

Recent Improvements in Technique

Recordings of animals were employed in experimental studies of animal behavior as long ago as 1892 (Garner), even though subsequent experimenters made little use of the phonograph for such purposes. More extensive biological use of recording devices awaited the advent of electronics. There followed numerous other technical improvements, many of which facilitated the studies of zoölogists, and disclosed the shortcomings of conclusions reached by earlier investigators forced to rely upon simple mechanical recorders.   Perhaps because of the recency of electronic improvements and the expense of much of the equipment required, few comprehensive studies of any group of animals have been carried out.   With such notable exceptions as the earlier work done on crickets by Lutz (summarized in popular form in 1941) and the far more extensive studies of bats carried out by Griffin (described in a recent book, Griffin, 1958) the biological significance of sound production in other animals was not investigated scientifically in other groups of animals until recently.

Many animals, including some anurans, are not easily induced to utter their mating calls under the artificial conditions of the laboratory.   Consequently investigations of their vocalizations awaited the availability of battery operated equipment designed to be carried into the field. Portable tape recorders devised within the last decade and vastly improved in some European models greatly facilitate such work, with corresponding advances in our understanding of sound production among animals.   Several investigators are now trying to determine the biological significance of the various sounds produced by anurans, and documenting the differences that exist in the calls of these animals at various taxonomic levels.   The major emphasis has been on mating calls, and their role in the complex interplay of behavioral traits that discourage sympatric species from interbreeding.

Considerable headway has been made in this field by W. F. Blair (1955 *et seq.*) and his students, as well as by Main, Lee, and Littlejohn (1958) in Australia. Dr. Konrad Klemmer reports that similar work is under way in Europe.   Recordings have revealed differences between species (Bogert, 1954; W. F. Blair, 1955, 1958f) or populations overlooked by previous investigators who depended upon descriptions or their recollection of calls.   Geographic variation within the species has also been partially documented for the vocalizations of some species by Blair (1958f).

There has been wider use of sound spectrograms such as those employed by Collias and Joos (1953), in their discussion of sound signals in domestic fowl or those made on a sound spectrograph, the Kay Sona-Graph employed by Blair and Pettus (1954) and Blair (1955 *et seq.*) Sound spectrograms not only provide visual documentation of the quality of calls, and the relative intensities of components, but permit the use of precise quantitative terms describing the pitch, duration, and rates of repetition in mating calls.   Also the fast trills present in the vocalizations of some species can be discussed or compared in quantitative terms since individual pulsations can be counted on sound spectrograms, enabling the investigator to calculate trill rates.

A simpler and less expensive method for determining quantitative features of the call by dusting suitable compounds directly on the tape is described by Frings and Frings (1956). This can be used for such purposes as the analysis of trill rates only when pulsations are widely separated on the tape, but it is a simple matter to copy tapes at various speeds to obviate this difficulty. A more cumbersome method requires a stop-watch, with the pulsations comprising trills made discernible to the human ear by reproducing the sound at known fractions of the normal speed. This procedure has also been used to reveal qualities in the sound not otherwise aurally apparent. W. N. Kellogg's recordings of the ultrasonic sounds of porpoises are brought within the range of human hearing by reducing the playback speed of the tape as reproduced on a record released by Folkways Records and Service Corporation. Bogert (1958) employs this method to demonstrate the rough negative correlation of dominant frequencies and trill rates with body size in toads. Frings and Frings (1957) discuss similar procedures employed in studies of Orthoptera.

Similarities or differences in voice structure revealed by sound spectrograms provide helpful clues to anuran relationships. Blair (1957a, b) employs sound spectrograms of the mating calls of toads to demonstrate the probable affinities of species whose status was not satisfactorily ascertained by students limiting their studies to morphological characters.

Anuran vocalizations are influenced by changes in temperature, as several investigations have shown. Zweifel (1959) reviews the problems arising from this variable. An earlier account by Birkenmeier (1952), that could not be obtained, may provide additional information. Variations occur in the calls of individual anurans, and conspicuous differences between the calls of individuals in geographically isolated populations appear to be the rule rather than the exception. Variations of the sort must be investigated more extensively before the significance of differences or similarities disclosed by sound spectrograms can be assessed with assurance. Recordings of mating calls have already revealed the existence of undescribed species. The use of taped recordings and spectrographic analysis will not solve all taxonomic problems, but their use will introduce some necessary refinements in the procedures now employed in systematic studies of the Anura.

MECHANISMS OF SOUND PRODUCTION IN THE ANURA

The Vocal Apparatus

Fishes lack a true larynx, and its presence in the Amphibia marks the beginning of vertebrate vocalization. Boulenger (1898) succinctly describes the vocal apparatus of anurans with his statement that the larynx is provided with vocal cords set in vibration by the rapid shift of air from the lungs to the buccal cavity. He points out that the sound is intensified in many species by resonance in a single vocal sac situated in the gular region or in paired sacs located behind the commissures of the jaws. Boulenger distinguishes between internal vocal sacs covered by unmodified gular integument, and external vocal sacs that distend when inflated as thinned sheets of muscle and skin. He also describes some modifications, noting that air penetrates the sacs through openings that may be round or slit-like, and paired or unpaired, in the floor of the mouth. Boulenger lists representatives of five European genera that lack vocal sacs.

Gadow (1909) briefly discusses the voice and the mechanisms of its production, and supplies additional information concerning modifications in the vocal sac. His accounts of species in various parts of the world include descriptions of the vocal sac and the voice. Noble (1931) depicts the vocal cords of the American bullfrog, *Rana catesbeiana*, describes the mechanism of sound production in greater detail, and discusses the function of the voice. Liu (1935) also describes the mechanism, and points out that when vocal sacs are present, there is always an internal vocal sac, regardless of whether the external skin remains unmodified or is visibly distensible as a balloon-like pouch. However, he retains the more convenient terminology of "internal" and "external" to designate these alternate conditions. (Fig. 4), despite intermediate conditions.

Modifications in the Vocal Apparatus

Liu (1935) summarizes his investigation of the vocal sacs in 559 species considered to represent 13 families. Among the modifications in the vocal sac, he recognizes three principal groups, 1) the median single subgular sac beneath the throat, 2) the paired subgular sac, with a median partition separating two lobes beneath the throat, and 3) paired lateral vocal sacs situated behind and below the commissures of the jaws. Each of the three categories includes anurans with sacs either internal or external, and intermediate conditions exist, with quite different modifications in closely related species. However, 78% of the species Liu examined had a median vocal sac, and in 46% the sac was internal. Liu concludes that the median gular sac, whether single or paired, is more primitive. What Liu calls the most primitive vocal sac among the species he examined, however, is that of the European fire-bellied toad, *Bombina bombina*, which has the lining of the mouth loose

and folded on each side to form an open pocket as a distension of the whole muscle layer on each side of the tongue. In view of the absence of any vocal sac in other species of *Bombina,* Liu suggests that it evolved independently in *B. bombina.* The complete absence of the vocal sac in *Ascaphus* and the tongueless forms, *Pipa* and *Xenopus,* is interpreted as the primitive condition. However, Liu believes the vocal sac to have been lost secondarily in approximately 15% of the 544 species he lists in the "higher groups."

Differences in the structure of the vocal sac and its presence or absence in closely related species offer strong evidence that the various modifications result from natural selection. Liu makes no effort to explain the adaptive significance of the modifications observed. The Surinam toad, *Pipa pipa,* utters "metallic ticking callnotes" (Bartlett, 1896), and Myers (1951) mentions the underwater call of *Pipa carvalhoi.* The African clawed toad, *Xenopus laevis,* also calls under water (Bles, 1905; Bushnell, 1957). These species, so thoroughly aquatic that they rarely venture on land unless forced to do so, come to the surface at infrequent intervals, and as far as known carry on their mating activities while submerged. Such frogs conceivably would find vocal sacs disadvantageous if not wholly incompatible with their mode of existence.

Absence of a vocal sac in the tailed frog, *Ascaphus,* may reflect its primitive condition or the nature of its habitat. It also lacks a voice, and Noble (1931) suggests that males would have difficulty making themselves heard in the rapidly flowing mountain streams inhabited by the species. However, the Stephensons (1957) report that the New Zealand frog, *Leiopelma,* also believed to be primitive and supposedly related to *Ascaphus,* has no voice "in the true sense," but produces shrill chirping sounds, presumably distress signals, when touched. They add that the absence of middle ear structures in *Ascaphus* and *Leiopelma,* as in urodeles, represents a primitive feature rather than a secondary loss. Hence the absence of a voice may be correlated with their limited ability to detect sounds.

It is conceivable that anuran vocalizations served other functions before they became associated with breeding behavior, although Noble (1931) believes that the original use was probably that of attracting mates. If so the presence of a voice in the primitive tongueless toads indicates that vocal sacs arose from the selective advantage of amplifying the voice through progressive modifications leading to the addition of

FIG. 4. *Bufo compactilis* with "external" vocal sac inflated while calling (upper). Photographed at Chapala, Jalisco, Mexico. *Bufo punctatus* with "internal" vocal sac inflated while calling (lower). Photographed at Portal, Arizona.

such resonating chambers.   The secondary loss of vocal sacs presumably accompanied specializations in habits that either preclude the need for added resonance or, as suggested above, makes it disadvantageous to inflate the sac in order for it to be effective.   However, the voice is commonly retained in species that have lost the vocal sac.   Boulenger (1897) describes the voices of four of the European species among he lists as having no sac.   Calls have been attributed to some of the species in which Liu (1935) found no sac, although information for many is lacking.

Populations with or without vocal sacs may occur within the same species.   Inger (1954) describes the variations in *Rhacophorus leucomystyx;* vocal sacs are present in some populations, absent in others. Liu reports a sac present in the red-legged frog, *Rana aurora draytoni,* but absent in *R. a. aurora.*   Similarly he indicates its presence in *Bufo b. boreas,* whereas it is supposedly lacking in *B. boreas halophilus.*   Wright and Wright (1949) report vocalizations in both, as well as in *B. boreas nelsoni,* whereas the voice of *B. boreas exsul* is not mentioned beyond the comment that the "chuckle (of *nelsoni*) resembles" that of *exsul.*

It is not clear from descriptions whether some authors refer to the mating call or to the "warning chirp" or male release call, readily evoked when *B. b. halophilus* is handled or when seized by another male.   Storer (1925) observes that the call is uttered for a second or two and repeated at intervals, but "to human ears it lacks carrying power and can scarcely be thought of as attracting toads at any great distance."   In contrast the Wrights quote Clifford Carl's description of the voice of *B. b. boreas* in British Columbia as "a high pitched tremulous note," amplified by the distended vocal sac.   It is noteworthy that another member of the *boreas* group, the Yosemite toad, *Bufo canorus,* has a relatively loud voice, as proved by recordings obtained by Dr. Ernest L. Karlstrom (Bogert, 1958) .

B. b. halophilus is the common toad throughout most of southern California, but several individuals who have worked with this amphibian cannot recall having heard its mating call even though all are familiar with its release call.   It seems probable, therefore, that voice has lost its function as a mating call even though *B. b. halophilus* retains the male release call, as suggested elsewhere (Bogert, 1958) .   Negative evidence is inconclusive, although Dr. Richard G. Zweifel informs me that males of another species inhabiting southern California, *Rana muscosa,* apparently have no mating call but emit the release call.   The Tarahumara frog of Arizona and Mexico appears to be mute, and Rose (1950) states that a South African toad, *Bufo rosei,* lacks a voice.   He infers that this is correlated with the absence of a tympanum, implying some degeneration in the ear. The tympanum is also lacking in *Ascaphus*, along with the voice, but it is uncertain whether an obscure or vestigial tympanum is necessarily indicative of voice loss.

Even though there is insufficient information to explain the loss or degeneration of vocal sacs, it is evident that species without such resonating chambers often utter sounds that accompany breeding activity. Among species normally aquatic during the period of reproductive activity males often call while submerged or partly submerged. Under such conditions the relatively feeble mating call characteristic of European discoglossids (Boulenger, 1897) may nevertheless provide an adequate stimulus to submerged females. Even burrowers, such as *Pelobates* that have lost the outer and middle ear, may be well adapted for perception of sounds transmitted through the water, as Schmalhausen (1957) indicates. Inger (1956) mentions the "loud breeding call" of a Philippine frog, *Rhacophorus leucomystax,* lacking vocal sacs, but it is doubtful whether the sound is comparable to that produced by anurans with well-developed sacs.

Interpretations such as those of Blair and Pettus (1954), who conclude that the call of the large Colorado River toad, *Bufo alvarius,* is "evolving out of existence," are based on the assumption that the mating call serves only to attract the female to the breeding site. There is evidence that this is a function of the loud calls emitted by some species (Bogert, 1958), but other anurans assemble at breeding sites prior to calling (Cummins, 1920; Savage, 1935). When individuals of more than one species assemble in breeding aggregations, even a relatively feeble voice may serve as an isolation mechanism if females attracted to breeding pools by cues other than phonation manifest a preferential response to the mating calls of their own species. It is also possible, though not demonstrated, that the vocalizations of some species provide the stimulus necessary for the female's release of her eggs, in somewhat the same manner that the courtship of some ambystomid salamanders provides the stimulus necessary for the female to pick up the spermatophore deposited by the male (Noble, 1931).

Whether the voice merely aids the female in selecting males of her own species after individuals of both sexes reach the breeding site, or whether vocalizations are restricted to male release calls, it is improbable that *Bufo alvarius* is losing its voice. However, the species may be in the process of losing its vocal sac, as Inger (1958) suggests, after examining a series of adult males, in some of which the sac was in a state of arrested development. As in all truly large anurans, the vocal sac of *B. alvarius* is internal, and Blair and Pettus appear to have been misled by making their comparisons with the external vocal sac of *Bufo woodhousei.* W.

F. Blair (1956a) suggests that the large size of *alvarius* might be an effective barrier to cross-mating with other species, which is true of those inhabiting the American deserts, but *alvarius* is sympatric with an equally large toad, *Bufo marinus,* at the southern extremity of its range in Mexico (Bogert and Oliver, 1945). Hence *alvarius* is not restricted to the Sonoran Desert, whereas *Bufo retiformis,* not mentioned in the discussion of Blair and Pettus, produces a fairly long trill, and is the only toad known to be restricted to the Sonoran Desert. There is little to support their suggestion that loss of the mating call is correlated with conditions in the desert habitat, for the species in which the loss has occurred are not adapted for arid conditions, even though such forms as *Bufo boreas exsul* are relicts perhaps restricted to the vicinity of desert pools.

The Mechanics of Anuran Vocalization

Aside from the presence or absence of vocal sacs, and the extensive variations in the morphology of sacs that Liu (1935), Inger (1956), and others describe, there are various modes of sound production in anurans. Boulenger (1897) and others cited earlier in this discussion, as well as Inger (1956) and Bogert (1958), provide generalized accounts applicable mainly to mating calls, rather than to distress signals or release vibrations, which few authors mention. Boulenger selects the European treefrog, *Hyla arborea,* to illustrate the manner in which sound is produced, as air forcibly expelled from the lungs through the mouth to the vocal sac, passes over the elastic rims of the vocal organs, causing them to vibrate. The mating calls of several North American treefrogs consist of short bursts of sound, such as those of the barking treefrog, *Hyla gratiosa* (see spectrogram, Fig. 29). Prior to calling these anurans fill the lungs beyond the capacity required for ordinary inspiration. When ready to call the trunk muscles contract, and it is plain to the observer that a "bark" issues simultaneously with the inflation of the vocal sac, and the deflation of the body. After the burst of sound the gular muscles contract to force the air from the sac back to the lungs. The spacing of the individual calls depends only in part upon the time required to shunt the air back to the lungs before the vocal organs can be reactivated with the next expulsion. The mouth and nostrils remain closed, but it is uncertain whether the entrapped air is used repeatedly or partially replaced each time it is shunted back to the lungs. Negus (1949) believes anuran vocal cords represent a non-return valve.

In contrast the majority of toads, *Bufo,* in the United States emit trills that vary in duration from a fraction of a second to almost a full

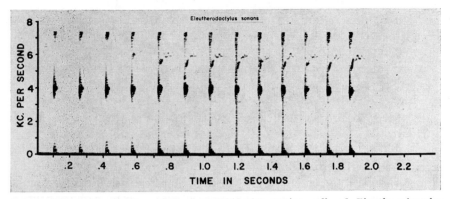

FIG. 5. "Motor boating" sound, presumably the mating call, of *Eleutherodactylus sonans*, recorded by Albert Schwartz at La Esperancita, Gran Piedra, Cuba. Air temperature 19.0°C.

minute; W. F. Blair (1956a) reports a trill in *Bufo cognatus* that continued for 53.8 seconds. Throughout such prolonged calls the vocal sac of this toad remains inflated, seemingly vibrating with the pulsations that comprise the trill. As the toad terminates the trill the vocal sac deflates to some extent, but remains in evidence unless the toad is disturbed, whereupon the sac collapses completely as the toad crouches. The nostrils and mouth remain closed for the duration of the trill, and it seems probable that small amounts of air are rapidly shunted back and forth through the laryngeal chamber to produce the pulsations in the trill. The "motor-boating" sounds emitted by some species, such as *Leptodactylus melanonotus* in Mexico, or *Eleutherodactylus sonans* in Cuba result from a comparable mechanism but the separate impulses are not so closely spaced (Fig. 5).

McAlister (1959) has devised ingenious methods for investigating the mechanics of the vocal apparatus, and summarizes conclusions derived from his study of the American spadefoots, *Scaphiopus*. Some species produce mating calls of moderate duration, with separate pulsations discernible to the human ear as a series of popping sounds. This trill is produced, as McAlister notes, with the continual, smooth contraction of the body wall, and the simultaneous and continuous expansion of the vocal sac. The separate pulsations result from the vibrations of the vocal cords that, in effect, break up the stream of air into a series of separate parcels. In McAlister's words, "a single trill note is produced, then, by one vibration of the cords as a whole, and a series of damped oscillations of the vocal cord edges. The latter creates a sound source; the former chops this sound into a series of sound pulses." He adds that upon terminating the call, the spadefoot shunts most of the air in the vocal sac back to the lungs, but some interchange of air may occur between calls.

McAlister suggests that differences between two of the species "rest largely in the nervous and muscular control of the vocal structures and not in the morphological differences." However, spectrograms of the calls of hybrid anurans (discussed in a following section of this review), including *Scaphiopus,* disclose characteristics in call structure intermediate between those of the parental species that are as readily interpreted as resulting from structural peculiarities of the hybrid's vocal apparatus as from the effects of parental genes on nervous or muscular control. Nerves and muscles in the hybrid may be intermediate between those of the parental species, but call structure may be determined in part by laryngeal and vocal sac characteristics. Physical changes in the larynx may account for seasonal vocalizations according to Aronson and Noble (1945).

The trilled calls of several North American hylids may be produced in somewhat the same fashion as those McAlister describes for *Scaphiopus.* But the vocal apparatus is far from being stereotyed in its mode of operation. Zweifel (1959) describes the vocalizations of the European discoglossid, *Bombina variegata,* maintained under laboratory conditions where its movements could be observed closely. He is convinced that this species, which lacks even the primitive vocal sac of *B. bombina,* produces its mating call as the air from the inflated buccal cavity is forced backward through the pharyngeal chamber to the lungs. Unlike the majority of amphibians, therefore, *B. variegata* utters its soft, untrilled note as the gular muscles contract, and the lungs are inflated. The male of this species habitually calls while almost completely submerged, with only the upper surface of the head protruding from the water. Hence the mode of sound production Zweifel describes may be associated with such aquatic habits. It would be of interest to know whether *Xenopus, Pipa,* and other anurans lacking vocal sacs employ the gular muscles instead of expelling air from the lungs to utter their mating calls while beneath the surface.

McAlister has opened a fertile field of investigation, and his work may reveal additional modifications in the function and morphology of the vocal apparatus. Inger (1956) describes the rather specialized vocal pouches of sporadic occurrence among anurans, principally ranids, and the mechanisms whereby they are inflated along with the vocal sacs. Whether such vocal pouches have any special adaptive significance or are associated with other specializations in the mechanism of sound production remains to be ascertained.

While Boulenger (1897) mentions the shrill cry of "most frogs when seized by a snake or other enemy," Yerkes (1903) was the first to observe that the "prolonged scream, like that of a child, [is] made by opening the mouth widely." It is not known whether the open mouth, permitting the air to be expelled from the lungs more rapidly, results in a scream much higher in pitch than other sounds emitted by *Rana clamitans,* but the "pain-scream," as Yerkes called it, is not so ubiquitous among anurans as Boulenger's statement would imply. The hoarse call uttered by the pig frog, *Rana grylio,* could not be aptly described as a scream, although it appears to be a "distress signal," and pig frogs of both sexes emit the sound with the mouth widely opened.

The so-called "warning vibration" elicited when some anurans are seized has been shown by Aronson (1944) to be produced in toads, *Bufo,* even when the vocal cords are extirpated. He suggests that accentuated respiratory movements cause the entire arytenoid cartilage to vibrate. Recordings of *Bufo t. terrestris* obtained with the microphone close to males uttering their prolonged trills include audible sounds closely resembling those more easily heard when the vibration accompanies the "warning chirp." The arytenoid cartilage may vibrate whenever the vocal cords are activated, even though not involved in the production of sound.

HEARING IN FROGS

The frog is a diligent songster, having a good voice but no ear.—Ambrose Bierce, *The Devil's Dictionary,* 1911.

In parts of Florida as many as 14 species of frogs, each with its own distinctive voice, may breed simultaneously in a single pond. Any female anuran attracted to this mixed chorus is confronted by oncoming sound waves of the utmost complexity, with many more than 14 dominant frequencies and intensities, an incredible number of harmonics, and a gallimaufry of qualities. If the female depends solely upon the vocalizations of males of her own species in selecting a mate, it might be inferred either that she is stimulated only by the sound waves within a fairly narrow spectrum of frequencies and qualities or that she distinguishes one frequency from another, one intensity from another, and can, moreover, distinguish the quality and determine the direction from which one particular sound is coming.

When anurans participate in such choruses as those encountered in Florida, it is not unusual to see a female approach a male of her own species, nudging him or even jumping on his back as though to disclose her presence. Such tactile stimulation is not always required to elicit the clasping response, for the males of some species apparently see the female as she approaches, and advance to seize her (males are as readily seized as females). Hydrotaxis, geotaxis, as well as visual and olfactory cues have been eliminated as factors influencing the orientation and movements of the female in recent investigations mentioned earlier in this survey. Vision, olfaction, or other senses may influence migrations to the breeding site and the female's selection of a mate in some species, but obviously the breeding activities of anurans lacking a voice cannot depend upon vocalizations. Nevertheless the chorusing of males accompanies the breeding of the majority of the Anura. It remains questionable whether females necessarily possess the discriminatory abilities seemingly required to locate a sexually excited male uttering one particular call in chorus, but there is sufficient evidence to support the belief that auditory cues are of major importance in explaining the behavior of several species. It is pertinent, therefore, to inquire whether hearing in anurans is sufficiently acute to account for the behavior observed.

Prior to Yerkes' (1903) experiments with the green frog, *Rana clamitans,* it was assumed rather than proved that frogs could hear. The assumption was based on field observations and such inferences as might be drawn from the structure of the ear. Merzbacher (1900) tested an unidentified species of frog and reached conclusions to the contrary, but subsequent investigations, though not always conclusive, support the belief that frogs can hear. Yerkes (1905) reviews his earlier conclusions, modifying previous statements, and offering additional evidence based partly on tests made with the American bullfrog, *Rana catesbeiana,* and the leopard frog, *Rana pipiens.* Comparatively few species, mostly in the genera *Rana* and *Bufo,* have been tested. Investigators in Europe (Misdorf, 1928; Diebschlag, 1935; Adrian, Craik and Sturdy, 1938, for examples) have tested *Rana temporaria* or *R. esculenta.* Bruyn and Van Nifterik (1920) and Buytendijk (1917, 1918) deal with *Bufo calamita* and *Bufo bufo,* respectively. Strother (1959) tested the responses of *Rana catesbeiana* to pure tones. Not all laboratory investigations are sufficiently pertinent to this discussion to warrant reviewing them in detail, and it is uncertain whether conclusions derived from the few species of *Rana* and *Bufo* tested are broadly applicable to anurans. Summaries of our relatively meager knowledge of hearing in amphibians will be found in the accounts provided by Noble (1931), Warden, Jenkins and Warner (1936), and Jahn and Wulff (1950). Kleerekoper and Sibabin (1959) summarize earlier work dealing with anurans, and report the results of their own investigation of hearing in *Rana pipiens* and *Rana clamitans.*

According to Noble, "there is no doubt that some sounds have considerable significance in the life of frogs." Reflecting the limitations of the studies reviewed and their meager knowledge of anuran breeding habits, Warden, Jenkins and Warner cautiously conclude: "—it appears that in the air-living stage the Anura respond to sound." Jahn and Wulff observe that "frogs are relatively unresponsive to sound, but they may have an acute sense of hearing." The statement made by Yerkes in 1905 that *Rana clamitans* is influenced by sounds ranging from 50 to 10,000 cps, is frequently quoted, though Yerkes himself qualified this conclusion, noting that neither the upper nor the lower limit of audition had been accurately determined. Strother (1959) questions the report of Sato (1939) that the range of hearing in frogs extends to 24,800 cycles, observing pointedly that the audiometer Sato used does not produce sound stimuli exceeding 8,192 cps. Kleerekoper and Sibabin provide a threshold curve of hearing in *Rana clamitans* and *Rana pipiens* based on relative sound intensities. While the curve is "limited to the range of 30 to 15,000 cps," they point out that it "may not represent the whole range of frequencies for the species."

Where Kleerekoper and Sibabin employed an audio-generator, Yerkes, like many early investigators, used Galton and Appunn whistles. Such whistles, of course, do not produce pure sound. The impurities may be effective at short distances, although Yerkes does not state how close experimental animals were to the sound source. Yerkes notes that females react more uniformly than males (Kleerekoper and Sibabin report threshold curves similar for both sexes), and with greater vigor when tested in April and May than during the winter. This may reflect the physiological condition of frogs normally inactive during the winter rather than of temperature influences although few investigators mention the heat levels of experimental animals.

Adrian, Craik and Sturdy (1938) note that the upper limit of frequencies producing measurable changes in electrical potentials in the acoustic nerve varies with the body temperature, supposedly limiting if not precluding frequency discrimination. The acuity of temperature discrimination in amphibians has not been extensively investigated. Toads are more responsive than salamanders to changes in the thermal level of their environment (Bogert, 1952), but anuran activities are not restricted to narrow zones of temperature within the extremes tolerated. Goin and Goin (1957) found *Hyla squirella* active at temperatures ranging from approximately 4° to 22° C. Pearson (1955) records *Scaphiopus holbrooki* to be active between 12° and 29° C. with the peak of activity near the mean of 20.6° C. Strübing (1954) ascertained the "preferential temperatures" of anurans representing seven families, but the mean temperatures reported on the basis of laboratory tests are closer to the maximum voluntarily tolerated under field conditions. Consequently, the methods employed are open to considerable doubt.

The species inhabiting any one locality in the northern portion of the United States follow a rather definite temporal sequence in the initiation of their breeding activities (Wright, 1914; Babcock, 1926; Babcock and Hoopes, 1940). The sequence may reflect differences in the minimum temperature thresholds for activity in the species, or represent a response to more complex stimuli. It is improbable that the body temperature of the female greatly influences her response to the mating call of the male, even though breeding activities of individual species rarely extend over a range as great as 10° C. Frequencies as well as rates of repetition in the mating call vary with the body temperature. Consequently, higher frequencies are produced by the male at the same time the upper limit of response is increased in the female.

Strother (1959) assumes that loudness discrimination is lacking in *Rana catesbeiana* for all but the weakest sounds. The frog's ear, he says, is fairly sensitive to weak tones up to approximately 1,800 cycles, but sensitivity falls off rapidly at higher levels. On the basis of his study of electrical potentials in response to pure tones, Strother concludes "the range of hearing for the frog seems to extend from a few cycles to 3,000 or 4,000 cycles." Frequency discrimination in the Anura remains to be demonstrated. If salamanders, which lack the tympanic membrane and cavity, distinguish frequencies, as the training experiments of Ferhat-Akat (1939) indicate, frequency discrimination in anurans may not be so dependent upon precision in their thermoregulatory abilities as Adrian, Craik and Sturdy infer. Kleerekoper and Sibabin observed a croaking sound in *Rana clamitans* in response to similar sounds emitted by other frogs. The response was also evoked in one male tested repeatedly with a sound at 300 cps from an audio-generator. This closely approximates the dominant frequency of the short croak or grunt uttered at intervals by the northern green frog, *R. clamitans melanota* (a similar sound, Fig. 7, emitted by the southern form, *Rana clamitans clamitans*, is higher in pitch), and believed by Martof (1953) to be associated with territoriality. Kleerekoper and Sibabin, like their predecessors, obtained no positive results in their efforts to condition frogs at various frequencies.

A wide variety of sound stimuli ranging from pistol shots to whistles arouse no overt response in frogs, but may affect respiratory rates and simultaneously reinforce or inhibit responses to other stimuli. As Yerkes (1905) observes, frogs, like many other animals, habitually escape predators by remaining motionless. Such sounds as the grunt or chirp occasionally emitted as a frog takes off from the bank, the sound of the splash accompanying its plunge, or the "pain-screams" or distress signals emitted by individuals of some species, evoke no immediate reaction but may serve to reinforce or modify thresholds of tactile or visual stimuli. Other frogs in the vicinity may escape detection by remaining motionless and yet be on the *qui vive* as an enemy approaches. According to Bajandurov and Pegel (1933) and Diebschlag (1935), sounds of short duration induce a state of increased awareness.

Yerkes considers it noteworthy that when one frog in a pond begins to croak others soon join it or "when one member of a chorus is frightened and stops the others become silent." He considers this conclusive evidence that the animals hear one another. Having commented that none of the older popular accounts "furnishes satisfactory proof of the exclusion of visual stimuli" he is somewhat less critical of his own observation, for he admits that when he approached a pond he could never be certain that none of the frogs had seen him.

Visual stimuli and possibly tactile stimulation from disturbances of the water or movements of the substratum accompanying the approach of an observer occasionally inhibit the vocalizations of frogs. If calling is not resumed when the observer remains motionless, it can be evoked in many species, as Boulenger (1897) observes, by crudely imitating their calls with the human voice. The response of an Australian frog, *Crinia rosea,* to clicking sounds may depend upon the repetition rate, according to Main (1957). In Florida noises from airplane motors induce *Hyla cinerea* to utter its "rain-call." Frogs in a roadside pond call when stimulated by the noise from passing motor vehicles. Loveridge (1953) tells of African toads, *Bufo regularis,* croaking in response to the crackling of a bush fire.

If such varied sounds induce a vocal response, it can scarcely depend upon frequency discrimination. Whether the sounds produced by a gasoline motor have enough in common with the mating calls of anurans to account for the response elicited is a matter of conjecture. It may, nevertheless, be significant that anuran mating calls consist of a 1) series of separate impulses resulting in a trill, 2) a single call uttered at fairly regular intervals, or 3) of a combination of the two, with a short trill produced at intervals.

To be effective in attracting other frogs or orienting their movements, perhaps the auditory stimulus must possess the one characteristic common to all mating calls, namely successive interruptions or pulsations. Adrian, Craik and Sturdy (1938) employed sounds of various frequencies and intensities in their investigation of ranids, measuring electrical potentials arising in the acoustic nerve to determine responses. Interrupted sounds proved to be more effective than continuous sounds. The

results obtained by Strother (1959), who measured electrical potentials
in the inner ear of *Rana catesbeiana,* may have been influenced by his
use of continuous pure tones, even though he varied frequencies and
intensities.

Strother reports evidence of contralateral stimulation of the inner ear
via the Eustachian tubes and the pharyngo-oral cavity. He suggests that
this might play some part in the frog's localization of sounds. His inference is not invalidated by his use of pure tones in his tests, although
it has been realized for some time, according to Fraenkel and Gunn
(1940), that animals locate noises more readily than pure tones. Localization, and hence orientation, depend largely upon relative intensities
and differentials in arrival of sound waves at each of the two ears. At
low frequencies the waves are roughly comparable to ripples in
water, with successive waves of compression reaching one receptor an
instant before they reach the other until the animal orients the body to
compensate for the temporal difference. Pure tones (at frequencies
above 1,800, which according to Strother is the approximate upper limit
of frequencies in the sensitivity of the bullfrog to weak tones) apparently
result in such a rapid succession of waves that differentials in their arrival are not detectable in the neural mechanism.

Because measurements of electrical potentials in the acoustic nerve or
the inner ear give an indication of peripheral auditory functioning
rather than of auditory perception per se, the preceding explanation is
hypothetical. The observations of Adrian, Craik, and Sturdy are at least
suggestive when the peculiarities of mating calls are considered. Low
frequencies in pure tones may be more effective than higher frequencies,
as Strother reports, for the same reason that interrupted sounds are more
effective than continuous sounds.

Regardless of uncertainties concerning the limitations of phonoreception in the Anura, it is evident that frogs orient their movements in response to mating calls, localizing their source under conditions that leave
no doubt concerning the importance of auditory cues. Prolonged repetition of the same sound from the same site, a prerequisite for distant
orientation, is characteristic of frogs. The adaptive significance of
choruses at spawning sites becomes apparent if we consider the implications of this group behavior. An appreciable loss of time and energy
would be entailed were several females at various distances attracted almost simultaneously by a voice that ceased as soon as one of their number
reached the male. Where a chorus exists no such interruption of the
sound occurs. Males may come and go, but the sound emanating from
the site commonly continues for hours. Once a female is aroused by
the sound and sets out to reach its source (assuming that she does so at

a reasonably early hour in the evening), the behavior pattern of the males makes it virtually certain that a mate will be found.

Trill rates or the intervals between calls may be important in species discrimination. The specificity of the female's response apparently depends more on such characteristics of the sound than upon dominant frequencies, which are influenced by temperature and depend upon the size of the individual producing the call. Repetition rates as well as pulse rates in species uttering trills also vary with the temperature. Sympatric species of the same genus may produce mating calls similar in structure, but differing in trill rates. A recent investigation of two species of *Pseudacris* by Crenshaw and Blair (1959) discloses similarities as well as differences in their mating calls, with some overlap in dominant frequencies and the duration of the call. However, the pulse rate in one is approximately four times that of the other species. It follows that if the specificity of the female's response depends upon characteristics of the mating call, there would be much less chance of error in her selection of a mate if it depended more upon trill rate than upon the frequency or duration of the call, even though all three variables are affected by temperature. Alexander (1957) suggests that the rhythm and rate of pulsation or intensity modulation are the structural variants of sound of greatest behavioral significance in insects, in which sound production is, of course, also influenced by temperature.

Adrain, Craik and Sturdy report that only sounds of great intensity produce any response detectable in the eighth nerve of *Rana temporaria*. Use of this particular species in experiments testing phonoreception is perhaps unfortunate. Savage (1935) found frogs of the species assembling silently at breeding sites. Many were in amplexus before males uttered their relatively weak calls. Thus sound may be losing significance in the reproductive behavior of *R. temporaria*. Degeneration of the ear perhaps accompanies adaptive changes in behavior, and chemical, visual or tactile stimuli may be dominant in the mating pattern of the species. Adrian, Craik and Sturdy find *R. esculenta* to be more sensitive to sound than *R. temporaria*.

Other modifications in the ear of anurans, such as the loss of the outer and middle ear in *Pelobates,* and the degeneration of the Eustachian tube in this species and in *Bombina,* are perhaps associated with specializations in the sound transmitting apparatus. It is Schmalhausen's (1957) belief that sound vibrations are transmitted from the body surface through cutaneous blood vessels, reaching the papilla amphiborum via the endolymphatic route, the only channel available in *Bombina* and *Pelobates*. This method of sound transmission may not be restricted to frogs wholly aquatic in their habits for Yerkes (1905) finds sounds continuing to modify tactile reactions in the green frog when both tympanum and columella are severed. However, the response is abolished when the eighth nerve is severed, thus indicating the ear to be the receptor. Yerkes detects a response to sound whether the tympanum is in air or submerged, but apparently the response to auditory stimuli is "most marked when the drum is half submerged in water."

Most anurans have the tympanum exposed, but in a few it is covered with unmodified integument separable from the tympanum. In *Rana clamitans* the eardrum is conspicuous in both sexes but proportionately much greater in diameter in the male. Sexual dimorphism in tympanum size occurs in several species of *Rana* and frogs of other families, but the significance of this difference between the sexes is obscure. Boulenger (1920) reports a curious modification in a Bornean frog, *Rana cavitympanum,* in which the tympanum lies well below the surface at the end of an external ear opening.

Detailed investigations of individual species may reveal the adaptive significance of such structural modifications. More extensive use of anuran mating calls reproduced from taped recordings in laboratory and field studies eventually should enable us to determine not only which species depend on the male's vocalizations to attract the female to the breeding site, but which characteristics of the voice are most effective in stimulating the female to seek males of her own species. Our meager knowledge of the physiological determinants of the female's response and the nature of the combination of external and internal stimuli inducing frogs of both sexes to engage in breeding activities at appropriate seasons is a handicap to be borne in mind, especially when planning laboratory experiments where frogs are subjected to abnormal environments. This will be discussed in connection with other topics.

It might be added here, however, that Kleerekoper and Sibabin report sounds of the same frequency and intensity to be either inhibitory or stimulating, with the nature of the response dependent upon the physiological condition of the frog, rather than upon characteristics of the sound.

Aside from such complexities, including the effects of temperature, results obtained from laboratory experiments particularly pertinent to the problem of explaining the behavior of frogs in mixed choruses appear to be 1) the demonstration by Kleerekoper and Sibabin that at least two species of frogs perceive sounds ranging in frequency from 30 to 15,000 cps, and 2) the discovery of Adrian, Craik and Sturdy that interrupted sounds are more effective stimuli than continuous sounds.

Sound unquestionably influences the activities of most anurans and plays a significant role in the reproductive behavior of many, but not all, species. Differences between them, or even between geographically isolated populations assigned to the same species, may well account for discrepancies in the literature. At best, few statements are applicable to all species of Anura. Information thus far derived from field and laboratory investigations may, nevertheless, be summarized, although where conclusions are based on inferences rather than substantiated demonstrations they are, of course, highly tentative:

1. The nature, or perhaps the level, of the response depends upon a) the sex and physiological state of the frog, and b) any of several characteristics of sound stimuli. Where sounds of a wide variety affect respiratory rates or influence other responses in frogs of both sexes, a vocal response (impossible for females of many species) , whether a simple croak or the male's mating call, is usually less easily elicited by a sound stimulus, especially under laboratory conditions. A series of pulsations or interruptions in the sound may be required to induce males to call, and such stimuli may be effective only during limited portions of the sex cycle. Under natural conditions stimuli inducing a motor response, that is, movement of the female toward the male, or of males to the breeding sites when other males are calling, are far more restricted in character. To be effective the sound serving as the stimulus probably must be within relatively narrow limits of variation in one or more characteristics peculiar to the voice of individual species.

2. The vocalizations of closely related anuran species, or even local populations of those with disjunct distributions, are known to differ in dominant frequencies, timbre (or the relative intensities of the harmonics) , duration of individual calls, their rates of repetition, and trill or pulsation rates. A positive motor response seemingly depends more on pulse rates, or utterance rates rather than upon dominant frequencies or timbre, although the intensity of the sound may determine the maximum distance at which the sound is an effective stimulus.

CONDITIONS UNDER WHICH FROGS PRODUCE SOUNDS

Many species of frogs emit sounds in addition to mating calls. Carr (1934) observes that anurans may have a varied repertoire, and Aronson (1944) reports "three distinct vocalizations" in toads. Occasional ambiguities or discrepancies in the literature, however, are traceable to the author's failure to distinguish one sound from another. Had such terms as "mating call" or "breeding song" been in general use over half a century ago it is questionable whether Yerkes (1905) would have limited his tests of hearing in *Rana clamitans* to sounds that failed to elicit reactions other than changes in respiratory rates.

Perdeck comments (1957) that sounds produced by animals, while having divers functions, are mainly connected with reproductive behavior. Also, he notes that, as a rule, those used by animals during their courtship are more specific than other sounds produced. Perdeck's statement is based on his work with grasshoppers, but he cites recent ornithological investigations bearing out the general conclusion. It is perhaps a matter of definition whether anuran mating calls are to be construed as courtship, but there is no doubt concerning their close association with breeding activities. Unfortunately, the role of sound in breeding behavior has been carefully investigated in relatively few species, and numerous exceptions to nearly any general statement are likely to be necessary as information accumulates or more is learned of breeding cycles in tropical anurans. Sounds other than those believed to be mating calls may have functional significance in the male's discrimination of sex during the breeding season, whereas other sounds have no obvious connection with reproductive activity, but may be of adaptive value in eluding predators. It is far from certain that all anuran vocalizations are beneficial to the species producing them. With our present knowledge it would be equally gratuitous to assume them to be either adaptive or unadaptive.

While sound is an element in the behavior patterns of animals as distantly related as grasshoppers, frogs, and birds, members of each group employ it in quite different ways. Where Perdeck recognizes the normal song, the rival song, the courtship song, and the attraction song in grasshoppers, Collias and Joos (1953) distinguish several categories in the sound signals of domestic fowl, ranging from distress calls, pleasure notes, fear trills, food calls and roosting calls, to warning signals. The various sounds emitted by frogs, previously discussed briefly and assigned to six categories (Bogert, 1958) include both vocalizations and other sounds. None of these is of universal occurrence among anurans. Others occur sporadically in various groups, sometimes restricted to one sex or present in both, and still other sounds not easily elicited are, nevertheless, known to be uttered under exceptional circumstances. I have attempted to improve definitions and extend the classification to include categories not mentioned in the earlier review. At best the classification must be considered tentative, for additional categories may be required as refinements are introduced or ways are found to determine the significance of sounds rarely if ever elicited under laboratory conditions.

Tentative Classification of Anuran Sounds

When sounds are classified with reference to the biological situations under which they are produced by one or more (usually several or many) species, several categories can be defined. These will be taken up more or less in the order of their importance, although some aspects of the adaptive significance of mating calls will be reserved for more detailed discussion to follow this list:

1. *The Mating Call.* The vocalizations of adult anurans most commonly heard, usually but not necessarily in choruses of breeding aggregations, are mating calls. The intensity of the sound varies from species to species, depending in part on the presence or absence of vocal sacs and probably upon requirements dictated by the adaptive nature of behavioral patterns, which along with the call may be modified in response to environmental conditions. Mating calls are, therefore, not necessarily identical throughout the range of each species, and may be absent or at least undetected in some species. More often only the male calls, but in a few species adults of both sexes are vocal during the breeding season, with the voice of the male similar to that of the female, but differing in pitch, or intensity, and perhaps other qualities not easily discernible without spectrographic analysis. The ability to utter a mating call ordinarily is indicative of sexual maturity. Juveniles are invariably mute as far as known.

As a corollary of the wide variation in habitats and modes of anuran breeding behavior, frogs of one species or another utter mating calls while perched at various elevations above the ground, in trees, shrubs, cliffs, walls, or in some of the stouter grasses. Frogs of some species habitually call from exposed positions, others seek sheltered places, beneath shrubs or overhanging foliage, or even call from underground burrows. Calling sites may be some distance from water, or in shallow water at the edge of pools, where frogs sometimes vocalize with only their heads above the surface. In deeper water near the middle of pools, the frogs emit their calls as they float on the surface (Fig. 6). Those of species almost entirely aquatic in habits habitually produce their mating calls while fully submerged.

The term "mating call" may antedate Courtis (1907), but Holmes (1906) refers to the sex call, and subsequent authors have spoken of the male sex call (Noble and Aronson, 1942), breeding calls, sex trills, or male sex trills (Aronson, 1944). The latter term, though applicable to the prolonged calls of some toads, is unsuitable as a general term for the sounds lacking pulsations. In most instances a call characteristic of the species or the local population is repeated at intervals, but the vocalizations of such frogs as *Rana pipiens* are far more complex. Some treefrogs, such as *Hyla smithi* (see spectrogram in Fig. 7), intersperse an occasional distinctive call in a sequence of normal calls, or in the case of *Hyla*

FIG. 6. Normal calling sites of species that often breed concurrently at the same spawning pond in Florida. Shown, clockwise, from upper right: *Hyla femoralis*, on low bush; *Hyla squirella*, near pond's edge, usually clinging to low vegetation; *Hyla cinerea*, on limb below overhanging foliage; *Bufo quercicus*, at base of grass tuft (but usually in more obscure position); *Microhyla carolinensis*, in shallow water near edge of pool (but usually with little more than the head extended above the water); *Acris gryllus*, at edge of pool; *Bufo terrestris*, in shallow water near edge of pool; *Rana pipiens*, floating in deeper water; *Hyla gratiosa*, on stalk a meter or so above the water level.

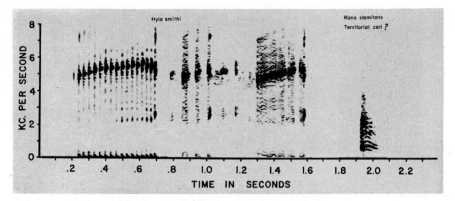

FIG. 7. Mating call of *Hyla smithi* (left), and the raucous sound, possibly a territorial call, inserted at intervals in a sequence of mating calls (middle). Recorded near Tepic, Nayarit, Mexico. Air temperature 21.5°C. Sound uttered by *Rana clamitans* at feeding site, possibly a territorial call (right). Recorded at Orange Springs, Florida.

cinerea, a series of normal calls is terminated sporadically by an accelerated sequence more raucous than the preceding calls, as can be shown in a spectrogram (Fig. 8). When hybrids occur under natural conditions males usually produce mating calls, occasionally imperfect, but usually intermediate in character between those of the parental species, to judge by W. F. Blair's report (1956b) of hybrid toads and the few we have recorded for representatives of *Bufo, Hyla,* and *Scaphiopus* (Figs. 23 and 29).

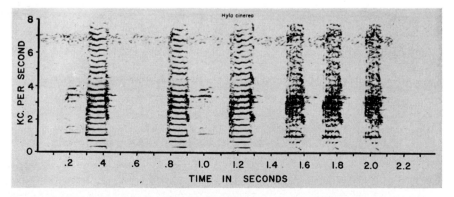

FIG. 8. Mating call of *Hyla cinerea,* showing the transition from the normal call to more raucous sounds uttered at shorter intervals as the vocal sac is partly deflated. The terminal calls may be territorial. Recorded at Orange Springs, Florida.

2. *The Male Release Call.* Among many anurans the male at the breeding site does not discriminate one sex from the other until he manages to clasp an individual. He clasps male or females indiscriminately, but differential behavior in the sexes determines whether he retains his grip. If the individual seized is a male, its struggles, accompanied by sounds variously described as chirps, croaks, grunts, or clucks, usually elicit its release.   In contrast, a female seized by a male of her own species emits no sound, remains passive, and the male retains his grasp.   The female with the male clinging to her back leaps or swims to the place where she expels her eggs.

The sounds accompanying the struggles of the male are uttered spasmodically, apparently produced by accentuated respiratory movements. The vibrations of the body flanks may be more important than the chirps or croaks in eliciting the release of the clasped individual. The sounds may be largely ineffective, even though they invariably accompany the release behavior of some species. Such sounds have been called warning chirps or warning vocalizations, but *male release call,* as suggested by Martof and Thompson (1958), seems more appropriate. The grunt or chirp some frogs emit at the onset of their leap may influence the behavior of other frogs in the vicinity. It may possibly be construed as a "warning signal."

Characteristically the male release call is a short, explosive sound repeated at irregular intervals (Fig. 9). Sounds approximating male release

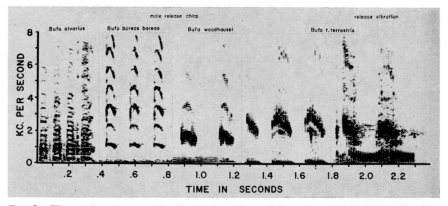

FIG. 9. The male release calls of representative species of toads. Release vibrations are represented in lower frequency bands, but appear to be carried to higher frequencies in the "chirp" of *Bufo terrestris.* In a second recording from the same individual (far right) the frequencies of the release vibration appear at   levels approximating 1,000 cps at the upper limit, with the chirp at a higher level. Recorded at East Lake, Putnam County, Florida.

calls can often be elicited if the male is seized with a thumb and finger applied to each side of the body.   The sounds issuing from males under these conditions occasionally resemble accelerated or imperfect mating calls, interspersed by sounds of short duration in some instances. Bragg (1940b) is perhaps unaware of similar sounds occurring under natural conditions when he speaks of the " 'protesting' " note and the "low, semi-trilled 'fussing' " sounds uttered by *Bufo woodhousei* held in the hand.

Both Boulenger (1897) and Holmes (1906) note that a croak can be elicited by a tactile stimulus, but they attach no significance to the observation. While Courtis (1907) noted male toads (probably *Bufo terrestris americanus*) clasping other males and "squealing like mice," and the prompt release of males clasped by other males, it remained for Miller (1909) to recognize the chirp to be a "warning signal" accompanying the release.   Cummins (1920) criticizes an earlier study of sex discrimination in the wood frog, *Rana sylvatica,* by Banta (1914), after observing males clasping frogs of both sexes.   Cummins notes that females offer brief and weak resistance, whereas clasped males "inflate the vocal sac and croak and are always released."   Noble and Farris (1929) report additional tests with the same species, and speak of the "warning croak of an embraced male" as shortening the period of the embrace.

Noble (1931) reviews the literature dealing with sex discrimination in amphibians, stating that "male toads do not croak but chirp when seized," and little doubt exists "that the warning croak or chirp is one of the factors in sex recognition in some frogs and toads." In various species of *Rana* a short croak commonly accompanies the movements inducing one male to release another. Liu (1931) considers the croak of *Rana nigromaculata* to be important, but in *R. pipiens* Noble and Aronson (1942) find that "small girth plus the warning croak cause the clasping male to release," as reported earlier for *R. temporaria* by Savage (1934). Aronson (1943a, 1943b) finds sex recognition in *R. clamitans* and *R. septentrionalis* dependent upon behavior similar to that reported for *R. pipiens,* with the warning croak comprising an element of the pattern in each species.

Aronson's (1943) investigation of the release mechanism in *Hyla andersoni* discloses differences between hylids and ranids, but he believes the basic patterns are similar, "involving chiefly the warning croak and small girth." Each time Aronson placed one male on the back of another, "the latter sounded a croak almost like the sex call but lower and faster." Aronson reports "warning croaks" in three additional species of *Hyla,* in each case restricted to the male. Release calls are emitted by males in nearly every bufonid, hylid, pelobatid, and ranid thus far tested in North America. Both sexes are mute in *Ascaphus.* North American leptodactylids and microhylids produce mating calls, but Jameson (1954) does not mention release calls in *Syrrhophus* or *Eleutherodactylus latrans*, and they appear to be absent in Mexican leptodactylids, including *Tomodactylus*. No release call could be elicited in the microhylid, *Hypopachus oxyrrhinus*, even though individuals from populations in the Mexican states of Jalisco and Nayarit were tested during the breeding period. Anderson (1954) can detect a faint vibration when male *Microhyla carolinensis* are handled, but no sound is emitted, and there is nothing to indicate that sex discrimination depends on the vibration. Males were never observed attempting to clasp other males under natural conditions, in contrast to toads, *Bufo*, where males virtually always outnumber females, and consequently are seized more frequently. If *Microhyla* is nearly infallible in distinguishing the sexes, errors occur, nevertheless, in species recognition. Volpe (1956) found three males in one pool clasping females of *Hyla squirella*.

Two distinctive male release calls are recognizable in the European discoglossid, *Bombina v. variegata*, according to Savage (1932). He calls one the "cluck," and another, less frequently emitted, the "plaintive hoo." The latter bears some resemblance to the mating call, but seems to be employed as an alternative to the normal male release call or "cluck." From his observations of the response to various stimuli eliciting the male release call, Savage makes the pertinent suggestion that such calls could easily evolve through modification of the mating call. "The latter," as he correctly notes, "is in itself an advertisement of maleness, but it has a disadvantage as a sex warning, because it attracts females just at a time when another male is close by. By the simple addition of a different method of breathing a profound modification of the sound is produced which is distinctive."

Spectrograms of recordings of male release calls uttered by American spadefoots, *Scaphiopus*, in which sounds closely approximating mating calls are interspersed with release calls, offer additional evidence in support of Savage's hypothesis. The parallel is even more remarkable in view of Savage's observation that both release and mating calls in *Bombina variegata* are produced as air passes from the buccal cavity to the lungs and not *vice versa*. Zweifel (1959) comes to similar conclusions concerning the mode of production of mating calls in the species, as mentioned above in the discussion of the anuran vocal apparatus. Savage's hypothesis is not invalidated by the more recent observation (discussed below) indicating that respiratory movements rather than the release call elicit the release of a male toad clasped by another. In fact, loss of the release call with retention of the respiratory movements might easily be considered the next stage in the evolutionary trend hypothesized by Savage.

The release call emitted by most American toads is commonly described as a chirp, but in the larger species, *Bufo marinus* and *B. alvarius,* it is more aptly described as a clucking sound. The release call of *Bufo alvarius* is distinguishable at irregular intervals in a mixed chorus, including two species of *Scaphiopus* and *Bufo cognatus,* recorded near Tucson, Arizona on July 18, 1953, and released on a commercial disk the following year (Bogert, 1954). Under crowded conditions tactile stimuli elicit release calls more often. A chorus of *Bufo alvarius* near Scottsdale, Arizona on July 20, 1953 is described by Blair and Pettus (1954) as consisting of approximately 200 individuals where the predominant sound was "the almost incessant warning 'cluck' coming from all parts of the tank." Evidently toads were in a dense aggregation near Scottsdale, whereas near Tucson perhaps 20 to 25 males were calling from a pond roughly 40 feet in diameter but irregular in shape. No females were seen, but the short trills described by Blair and Pettus were issuing from individual males at rates varying from fourteen to twenty per minute with air temperatures at 27 °C and water 22 °C at the surface. Individuals ceased calling at sporadic intervals when they shifted position, but sequences of calls over periods exceeding a minute were frequent. The clucking sounds, discernible at infrequent intervals, were greatly overshadowed in volume by the mating calls. Under these conditions, therefore, there was nothing to suggest that release calls would serve as a substitute for mating calls, though Blair and Pettus considered this a remote possibility when interpreting their observations.

Warning chirps may have been mistaken for the mating call in *Bufo boreas halophilus,* as mentioned earlier in the discussion of the vocal sac, which is absent in *halophilus* but present in the nominate subspecies. Both races produce relatively loud release calls. Chapman and Chapman (1958) believe mating calls attributed to females of the African toad, *Bufo regularis,* were actually the release calls of males mounted in error.

Few studies of toads have failed to reveal release calls, but Hinsche (1926) expresses the opinion that voice plays no part in sex discrimination in *Bufo bufo bufo.* He noted release calls, but believed the vibration of the female's flanks and the roughness of the skin to be of greater significance. Savage (1934) studied the same species in Britain, noting the "trial and error" behavior of the males, and concludes that sex discrimination depends on the voice of the male, augmented by his "dodging and repulsive action." Asiatic *Bufo bufo* studied by Liu (1932) apparently behave in much the same fashion as British members of the species. The behavior preceding amplexus with the female in North

American toads similar in size and general appearance closely resembles that of *Bufo bufo.*

Savage believes Hinsche's observations reflect the abnormal behavior of toads kept under unnatural conditions in the laboratory. Aronson (1944) doubts that pulsations of the flanks of the female, or the structural and behavioral differences between the sexes Hinsche describes were adequately demonstrated. If Hinsche's interpretation rests on his observation of a male attempting amplexus with an unreceptive female, it would account for the rapid movements of the body, but still fail to explain why this was unobserved when males were clasped. Savage states that seizure of the female following deposition of her eggs elicited the same vibratory movements of the flanks observed in males while uttering the release call even though no sound issued from the female. Aronson does not mention such vibrations in female toads (two species of *Bufo*), but found such vibrations retained in males when the chirp was eliminated by severance of the vocal cords. The vibration alone effectively induced the release response when males were clasped. Aronson concludes that tactile stimuli rather than the chirp account for the reactions of other males. Hence male release calls, though normal elements of behavior associated with sex discrimination in anurans, actually have no functional significance, unless the sound reinforces the tactile stimulus, as discussed below.

3. *The Female Release Call.* Unreceptive females of some species utter sounds similar to the release call of the male. As noted in the preceding discussion, in various species of toads the vibrations of the body flanks accompanying the male release call, rather than the sound itself, induce the release response in the clasping male. Noble and Aronson (1942) report "warning croaks" in leopard frogs, *Rana pipiens,* of both sexes. If clasped by a male, the female utters the croak during the breeding season, except during the ovulatory period, when she becomes receptive as well as silent. She is mute during amplexus and the male's clasp does not elicit the call or croak until several hours after oviposition is completed.

If the conclusions revealed by Aronson's (1944) work with *Bufo* are applicable to other genera, it seems probable that vibrations accompanying the female's "warning croak" in *Rana pipiens* provide a tactile stimulus of more significance than auditory cues in eliciting her release. The anuran female is commonly though not invariably mute, but the vibration of her body flanks, with or without vocalizations, is effective in discouraging the efforts of males to retain her in amplexus during the breeding season, when she is not necessarily ready to deposit her eggs.

Rejection of the male under such conditions has obvious selective advantages accounting for the evolution of such "release mechanisms."

The Mexican toad, *Bufo compactilis,* was tested at Chapala, in the state of Jalisco, Mexico, during the summer of 1959. There were breeding choruses in open sandy or grass-covered areas near the shores of Lake Chapala at frequent intervals throughout the months of July and August. Females found at breeding sites were virtually always accepted when placed in contact with males even though they ceased calling when approached by the observer. Females found outside the breeding area ordinarily were not ready to ovulate and apparently not attracted by the mating calls. Almost invariably the seizure of such females elicited vibratory movements similar to those of the male, but slower and less vigorous. If the "protesting" female was seized she was promptly rejected when clasped by sexually activated males.

Further tests were made by a student, Mr. Allen Brown, who used small rubber balloons filled with water to approximate the girth of female toads. These balloons were clasped promptly when held in front of male *B. compactilis* in the breeding area. The male would retain its grip for prolonged periods if left undisturbed. But if one end of the balloon was manipulated to simulate the vibratory movements of the male or the unreceptive female, the male promptly released its grip.

In view of these observations and Aronson's earlier work with male toads, the female release call can scarcely be of great functional significance, even though it may accompany the production of a croak as it does in *Rana pipiens.* Probably it has been overlooked in many species. A soft clucking sound commonly heard in breeding aggregations of *Agalychnis dacnicolor* in western Mexico is easily found to be emanating from males seized by other males, usually hidden beneath shrubs along pools. These frogs are more sloth-like in their movements than many other hylids, and one male usually clasps the other for several minutes despite the vibratory movements accompanying the latter's release call. In the laboratory a female unprepared for ovulation was clasped sporadically by one of five males for several weeks, even though she invariably emitted sounds, along with the vibrations resembling those of the male under similar conditions.

Noble and Aronson (1942) find the female release call of *Rana pipiens* similar to that of the male, but not so loud. They attribute her inability to utter the warning croak during the period of ovulation to the intra-abdominal pressure resulting from the increased volume of the eggs following their descent into the uteri. Croaking could be resumed approximately twelve hours following completion of oviposition, and after a few days, spent females croaked vigorously. When their girth was increased by injecting saline solution intraperitoneally, the release call was reduced or inhibited and they were retained in amplexus by males as readily as when eggs were present in the uteri.

Noble and Aronson mention a "male warning croak" as well as a "male sex-warning croak" but judging by the description of the circumstances under which it is uttered, the latter is better identified as a variant of the mating call. When choruses of *Rana pipiens* are heard under natural conditions they invariably include a variety of complex mating calls, trills, or grating sounds, interspersed with grunts or miscellaneous noises not easily described.

Savage (1932) describes two calls in *Bombina variegata*. One, the release call of the female, is described as much lower in tone, much slower and more throaty than the male release call, but Savage does not mention its use by unreceptive females, which showed some tendency to avoid males uttering the mating call. In this species the female release call is uttered when a receptive female is seized in the pectoral region. The call induces the male to release his grip, not to permit the female to obtain her release, but to make it possible for the male to shift to the pelvic position normal for amplexus in *Bombina*.

4. *Post-oviposition Male Release Call.* Lutz (1947) describes a call heard only as amplexus nears completion in the Brazilian hylid, *Phyllomedusa guttata*. After spawning was completed, according to Lutz, "the male began to cluck softly (the mating call is a sharp double cluck) and left the female, who remained in the same position for another 30 minutes." Whether this sound regularly accompanies the termination of amplexus in the species, representing a normal element of the release mechanism following oviposition, or whether it is widespread or of any functional significance in other hylids remains to be determined. Aronson (1943) does not mention it in the release mechanism described for *Hyla andersoni*.

5. *Ambisexual Release Vibrations.* As noted in previous discussions, sounds termed "warning vibrations" by Aronson (1944) provide a tactile stimulus more effective than the male release call in eliciting the release of one male clasped by another. Such vibrations do not fall within the definition of vocalizations, for they persist after the vocal cords are severed. Aronson believes that sounds audible to human ears are perhaps attributable to accentuated respiratory movements that cause the entire arytenoid cartilage to vibrate, with the vibrations transmitted to the body musculature. The inflated lungs may serve as resonating chambers when the vibration rate is high enough to be audible to man. Tests with *Bufo compactilis,* described under the discussion of the male release call,

confirm Aronson's belief that release depends almost entirely upon the vibration rather than upon the vocal accompaniment.

As Aronson points out, in *Bufo woodhousei* and *B. terrestris,* the same stimuli eliciting the male release call also elicit the release vibration. Vibratory movements invariably accompany the chirp, but the vocalization is less easily elicited than the vibration; after the breeding season the mating call, the release call, and the vibration disappear in the order listed. Hormone levels appear to be implicated. Greenberg (1942) mentions an unpublished study in which immature male green treefrogs, *Hyla cinerea,* were induced to call following the administration of testosterone propionate.

When Greenberg implanted pellets of the same hormone under the skin of mature males of another hylid, the cricket frog from Iowa (now *Acris crepitans;* see Conant, 1958), no vocality was induced in those collected in October and tested in January. Males taken on May 10 and treated two days later, however, called occasionally while the controls remained silent. When one male seizes another, according to Greenberg, the latter "usually vibrates his sides and throat and this effects his release almost at once." But if silent the male is held until he utters the male release call. This is accompanied by the release vibration in *Acris,* as it is in other hylids. Appearance of the mating call may depend upon higher thresholds for testosterone or upon a complex combination of hormones, as Greenberg suggests. The male release call and vibration probably depend upon the same hormones.

A. P. Blair (1946a), states that release vibrations in American toads can be elicited in juvenile males treated with mammalian gonadotrophins or in juveniles of either sex by administering testosterone propionate. Later Blair (1947) reports the results of a comparative study of vibration rates in six species of *Bufo,* including two races of *woodhousei.* His investigation reveals similar rates of vibration in two races of *B. woodhousei,* averaging 93 per second, with a lower rate of 51 given as the mean for *terrestris.* Spectrograms (Fig. 8) show release vibration rates and pulsation rates of mating calls to be indentical in a male of the species from Putnam County, Florida. Vibration rates may differ from one population to another, for the rate is seventy per second in the individual from Putnam County. The release vibration in these species is described by Aronson (1944) as a "dull, vibratory, barely audible sound, which can be heard only if the toad is held within a few inches of one's ear." Vibration rates in four other species, *marinus, alvarius, cognatus,* and *valliceps,* tested by A. P. Blair are considerably lower, varying from five to sixteen per second. Such frequencies fall below the normal threshold of hearing in man, and possibly in toads.

Aronson mentions release vibrations in male toads, but not in unreceptive females, where vibration rates may be lower, inaudible, or not of universal occurrence, even during periods of breeding activity. A. P. Blair (1947), who mentions his earlier report of release vibrations induced in toads of either sex following the administration of hormones, nevertheless restricted his comparative study to males. Any mechanism insuring quick release of clasped males may, as he says, conserve the reproductive potential of the species. From this standpoint it would be equally desirable for the male to recognize and reject unreceptive females. The mechanism exists in female *Rana pipiens* (Noble and Aronson, 1942), where the vibration rather than the accompanying croak may provide the stimulus for release, as discussed above. Consequently it is not astonishing that release vibrations have since been reported in both sexes of *Bufo* and in several genera belonging to other families.

Release vibrations, *la vibración sexual preventiva* of Argentine authors, are reported in both sexes in *Telmatobius schreiteri, Bufo paracnemis, Bufo granulosus* and *Hyla raddiana* by Rengel (1949), in various Chilean populations of *Pleurodema bibroni* by Cei and Espina Aguilera (1957a), and by the same authors (1957b) in several Chilean populations of *Bufo spinulosus*. In every species tested vibration rates in males exceed those of females from the same locality. This can probably be attributed to size differences, for the female is usually larger, and both sexes may vary from one local population to another, along with vibration rates. The vibration was elicited in all individuals of *Bufo spinulosus* from four localities, but in a fifth it was induced in only one toad of each sex when 15 males and 10 females were tested. Release vibrations could be elicited only during the breeding season in most species, but feeble vibrations were observed in *Bufo paracnemis* and *Bufo granulosus* at other times of the year. Vibrations were also observed in male *Bufo arenarum* by Rengel (1948), and in a male hylid, *Phyllomedusa sauvagi,* in which the vibration rate was similar to that of *Hyla raddiana* (Rengel, 1949). None of the vibrations reported in South American species is audible to man, the maximum frequency reported by Cei and Espina Aguilera (1957a) being 26 cps in one population of *Pleurodema bibroni*.

In view of the tactile nature of the stimulus, and the frequent occurrence of slower vibration rates in females, it is not astonishing that A. P. Blair (1947) finds no clear-cut evidence of specificity in the response. Males obtain their release somewhat more readily when their vibration rates approximate those of the species clasping them, but there are notable exceptions. Blair finds the slow vibrations of the larger species less effective than the rapid vibrations characteristic of the smaller species in eliciting their release. His tabulation reveals a moderately good negative correlation of size and vibration rates, similar to the correlation reported for dominant frequencies and trill rates in mating calls by W. F. Blair (1956a).

Where there is a marked discrepancy in the average adult size, as often happens in sympatric species of toads, size alone discourages males of one species from clasping with individuals of either sex belonging to other species (Lowe, 1954). Where two species similar in size occur together, which also happens, it would be disadvantageous to both if the release vibrations of one did not elicit their release from males of the other. Mechanisms enabling a receptive female to obtain her release when clasped by a male of another species have not been described. When ovulation prevents the female from issuing the release vibration or, if sex discrimination in one species is not dependent upon such vibrations, the female has no way of inducing males of species similar in size to release her. Volpe (1956) found males retaining their grip for prolonged periods in reciprocal mismatings of *Hyla squirella* and *Microhyla carolinensis,* species belonging to different families and incapable of producing hybrids. Anderson (1954) doubts that sex recognition in *Microhyla* depends on the release vibration, and hence the male may not respond. In the instance observed by Volpe, however, ovulated females may have been incapable of producing the vibration. Species discrimination depends on other cues, probably including mating calls, and the majority of pairs Volpe found in amplexus were of the same species.

A. P. Blair does not indicate whether the male release call accompanies release vibrations in the species he tested, but it commonly does in male toads. Yerkes (1905) demonstrates that sound stimuli frequently modify tactile stimuli in frogs. Citing this earlier discovery, Aronson (1944) notes the possibility that release calls may reinforce the tactile stimulus of the release vibration. The absence of vocalizations in many anuran females in which vibratory movements occur does not eliminate the possibility. Release calls in females of such species as *Rana pipiens,* where mating calls are restricted to males, may be an adaptive phenomenon explicable in the terms Aronson suggests. The "warning croak" can scarcely be produced in frogs without accompanying vibrations transmitted to the body flanks.

Whether vibration frequencies are indicative of relationship, as A. P. Blair implies, or whether frequencies more often reflect size rather than affinities, are matters perhaps warranting additional investigation. Rengel (1948) and Cei and Espina Aguilera (1957b) report vibration rates in South American *Bufo paracnemis, B. arenarum* and *B. spinulosus* closely resembling those listed by Blair for North American *B. marinus* and *B. alvarius.* The widely distributed *Bufo marinus* is sympatric with

B. alvarius in the Mexican state of Sonora, and its range extends southward through Central America, and much of South America east of the Andes. *B. marinus,* therefore, could have descended from the common stock that gave rise to large species along the periphery of its range in Sonora and Arizona as well as in Argentina and the adjacent regions. But similarities in the vibration rates of the males are perhaps more readily attributed to similarities in average adult body size than to the descent of these large toads from a common ancestor.

The release vibration, as an ambisexual characteristic of anurans, is unquestionably of wider occurrence than the existing literature would indicate. To summarize, vibration rates may differ when comparisons are made between males and females, or of individuals of either sex representing local populations of the same species. Such differences are associated with those of body size. When species are compared there is usually a negative correlation of body size and vibration rates. During the breeding season release vibrations provide tactile stimuli, (possibly reinforced by sound stimuli, namely, release calls, in some species), that are equally effective in eliciting the release of males and unreceptive females. Whether release vibrations are audible to man or to the Anura depends largely upon hearing thresholds and the size of the individual frogs producing release vibrations, which in many species are inaudible to the human observer.

6. *Territorial Calls.* Calls, emitted sporadically by frogs regardless of whether they are engaged in breeding activities, may be of functional significance in the maintenance of territories or the regulation of population densities. Concepts of territorial behavior date from the seventeenth century, but modern investigations of territoriality in birds, mammals and other vertebrates stem largely from the summary of such behavior in birds prepared by Howard in 1920. The existence of such behavior among the Amphibia remained unnoticed until Martof (1953) and Test (1954) published their accounts. Each of these authors includes a review of the literature dealing with the subject. Allee et al. (1949), Bates (1950), Dice (1952), and Andrewartha and Birch (1954) also review the concepts; Carpenter (1958) provides an excellent summary of current views.

Martof reports a detailed study of the green frog, *Rana clamitans melanota.* The locations of individual frogs in a study area comprising two small ponds near Ann Arbor, Michigan, were recorded and mapped over a period of several months. When closely grouped, the frogs in the area were spaced at astonishingly uniform distances, usually two to three meters, rarely closer. Frogs in a breeding assemblage tended to remain in it for prolonged periods. Of even greater significance, those in the group made approximately the same movements at the same time, retaining much the same spatial configuration even though they made overland movements of more than 110 meters. Despite some shifts in relative position of individuals, the published data reveal some sort of organization within the breeding aggregation. Martof interprets this as evidence for the green frog's maintenance of a primitive sort of territory.

Reviewing the criteria, namely advertisement, isolation, intolerance and fixation, believed by Nice (1941) to be manifestations of territorial behavior, Martof points out that mating calls of *Rana clamitans* could be heard at distances exceeding half a mile. Thus individual males effectively advertised their presence, with an efficiency equalling that of birds whose territorial songs have been interpreted as "proclaiming ownership." Moreover, when issuing its call, each frog was floating at the surface with its body inflated "in open view" where visual cues might have been employed by other frogs.

The isolation of individual males, in itself a manifestation of intolerance, is evident from Martof's data, even though the behavior of the frogs could not be interpreted as aggressive. Fixation, Martof observes, is a matter of defining the conditions under which each species maintains its territory. In birds it may be limited to a mating, nesting, and feeding ground, but the concept of the territory in both birds and mammals has been extended to include the restrictions of individuals to one flock or band (Bates, 1950). The relatively constant position of the green frog within the configuration of an aggregation, even though it moves as an organized unit, constitutes a kind of fixation.

It could not be conclusively shown by Martof that spatial relationships were maintained exclusively by visual or auditory cues. But if territorial behavior is "based primarily on a positive reaction to a particular place [a position relative to others in a breeding aggregation of green frogs] and a negative reaction to other individuals" as stated by Nice (1941), circumstantial evidence would favor vocalization as the stimulus evoking the negative reaction, but visual stimuli cannot be ruled out of consideration. One frog might easily detect the presence of another at a distance of two meters by means of visual stimuli, especially when movements of the vocal sac accompany production of its mating call.

Greenberg (1942) suggests that the yellow and black throat characteristic of the male cricket frog, *Acris crepitans*, during the breeding season has the function of making him more conspicuous, especially when the vocal sac vibrates. Observation of the behavior of receptive females, Greenberg is frank to admit, did not reveal any reaction dependent upon the color of the male's throat. Greenberg did not consider the possibility of negative reactions in males, in which territorial behavior may not have been apparent under laboratory conditions. Differences between the sexes in the pigmentation of the throat, commonly darker in males than in females during the breeding season, is of wide occurrence in the Anura. Any territorial function of the pigmented throat, would, of course, depend upon a negative response mediated by visual cues. Though eliminated in some species as playing any part in sex discrimination (Noble and Farris, 1929), visual cues may prove to be of significance in the territorial behavior of frogs. A negative reaction to frogs of the same sex and species could easily be overlooked unless tests were designed to reveal it.

In view of the inferences drawn from Greenberg's suggestion, Test's (1954) account of aggressive territorial behavior in a Venezuelan forest frog, *Phyllobates trinitatis,* seems particularly significant. In this species the female defends the feeding grounds and home site; her first aggressive act as the resident "is usually a hopping approach to the intruder and a challenge, in which the bright yellow throat is exhibited and slowly pulsated." Is the pulsating throat of the cricket frog also a challenge? The vibration of the black and yellow throat accompanying the vocalizations of *Acris* males could serve as a visual stimulus, perhaps reinforced by the sound. If it can be shown that this combination of stimuli elicits a negative response (retreat) in other males of the species, there should be no question concerning its territorial significance.

In *Phyllobates* the significance of the challenge inherent in the display accompanying the approach becomes apparent. "If the intruder does not retreat," Test continues, "the resident female makes a quick jump over the intervening few inches and alights directly on the other animal, usually on its back or head. In most instances this is sufficient stimulus to cause the attacked frog to jump away, but sometimes the intruder will stand her ground, even to the point of defending herself. Then ensues an actual wrestling bout of several seconds, until one of the pair retreats or is pushed off the rock on which encounters often take place."

Test describes the female as being larger than the male and more brightly colored, but does not mention calls, which may, nevertheless, be of greater importance in maintenance of territories by frogs than past investigators have realized. Jameson (1955b), for example, notes in his account of *Syrrhophus marnocki,* the Texan cliff frog, that selection of a breeding site depends mostly on the activity of the male, which has two distinct calls. One is "the typical cricket-like call" heard throughout the year, and audible to the observer at distances up to 100 feet. The other "rather striking call" is heard only during the breeding season. To judge from the additional information Jameson supplies, it seems probable that the call heard throughout the year serves as an "advertisement of ownership" and qualifies as a territorial call.

This interpretation is in accord with the reactions of individuals when population densities were modified by the investigator. First, we have Jameson's significant observation that cliff frogs quickly move into an area when sites are vacated by removal of the occupants. The maximum concentration of cliff frogs under undisturbed conditions is estimated by Jameson to be 8.9 per acre. Nevertheless within a period of thirty days he removed eighty-seven frogs from an eight-acre plot. The discrepancy is readily explained by the prompt influx of frogs whenever the resident population was reduced. Seventeen of the thirty-seven cliff frogs previously marked for identification in the surrounding fourteen and a half acres were included among the eighty-seven Jameson caught in the eight-acre central plot. He estimates that 46% of the population inhabiting contiguous areas moved into the depopulated transect. To do so they abandoned their original sites and shifted to others 150 to 200 feet away. The distances travelled greatly exceeded those detectable in their normal movements under undisturbed conditions. Some frogs moved well beyond the areas visited under normal circumstances, suggesting that few of the frogs had previously entered the central plot.

Second, when 25 cliff frogs were released in a densely populated area, none of them established residence. Some were later recovered outside the area of release at distances ranging up to 416 yards. Jameson does not attempt to explain why such movements occurred. He doubts that calls heard throughout the year are "entirely breeding phenomena," but he overlooks the possibility of their being territorial calls. If the voice intimidates intruders of the same species or elicits a negative response, it not only accounts for the distinctive vocalizations heard throughout the year, but provides a reasonable explanation for the movements of frogs, and the shift to a different call, presumably one that attracts the female, during the height of the breeding season.

According to Jameson, the dispersal movements of juveniles occasionally exceed 300 yards. After reaching sexual maturity, however, the cliff frog ordinarily establishes residence in an area where its home range is a small fraction of an acre, and it remains there for the rest of its life. Individuals call for prolonged periods from one site, but visit others at unspecified distances during the breeding season. If these frogs move at other times "in response to local areas of low population density," the shift must depend, first, upon an awareness of individual frogs in neighboring areas, and, second, upon an awareness of their absence when they are removed. Auditory cues most readily account for such behavior. They also furnish an explanation for the failure of cliff frogs to establish residence in a densely populated area where all available sites presumably are occupied by frogs vociferously proclaiming ownership.

A Mexican leptodactylid, *Tomodactylus nitidus,* is probably related to *Syrrhophus* and similar in habits, but according to Dixon (1957) males seldom call prior to the rainy season, and infrequently thereafter. It is uncertain whether mating calls are distinguishable from territorial calls in the species. Frogs of both sexes of at least one species in the genus call during the mating season, however, when the voice of the female, which lacks a vocal sac, is higher in pitch and readily distinguished from that of the male.

Among the populations assigned by Dixon to one subspecies, *Tomodactylus n. petersi,* males call "from the ground, rocks, trees or shrubs." Where the calling behavior of members of this subspecies was observed in populations in and around Tepic in the state of Nayarit during the summer of 1958, and near Chapala, in the state of Jalisco during the summer of 1959, the behavior of males in one area differed from those in the other. In the vicinity of Chapala males call from shrubs, usually while resting on branches a meter or less above the ground. Shrubs are invariably calling sites even when rocks or cliffs are available. No more than one male is ever discovered in any one shrub, or in adjacent shrubs if these are within a radius of three or four meters.

In contrast, frogs in the population in and around Tepic are encountered only on walls of brick, rocks or masonry, rocky eminences, declivities or cliffs. They do not occur in trees or shrubs. When a male calls from the ground on level terrain, the site is always adjacent to a steep slope or vertical surface, usually near an erosion channel or where roads have been cut. The site may be little more than a third of a meter above the ground, rarely more than three meters. Frogs invariably emerge from hiding at the foot of the vertical surface, uttering calls as they work their way up the miniature cliff. Relatively flat areas are uninhabited by *Tomodactylus* in the region near Tepic. Males occur only where they can follow the routine of climbing to calling sites. Judging by observations of the few individuals inhabiting the walls of a patio, males begin calling soon after their emergence at dusk, usually around 7:00 p.m., and continue to call until daylight approaches.

One individual calling from the outer wall was observed at least twice a night for nearly every night from July 24, when it was marked, until August 17. Upon its emergence from an undiscovered place of concealment, it began to call as it paused from time to time while climbing the brick wall to reach its calling site, roughly two meters above the ground. The site was on the top of the highest part of the wall, where three additional steps, each a brick in thickness, marked the location of a gate.

The ascent required approximately an hour, and the frog continued to call from this post until at least 4:00 a.m.   There was no evidence of breeding activity; no females were seen.   Voices of three other males inhabiting the patio came from widely separated points, with no shift in their sources detected during the period when the marked individual was under observation.

It cannot be a matter of chance that two *Tomodactylus* never occur in the same shrub, or closer than three or four meters when they occupy the same wall or cliff.   When the air temperature was between 18° and 21° C, males called at fairly regular intervals of eleven to thirteen seconds.   When longer intervals elapsed, frogs on rare occasions were observed devouring an insect.   Calling often ceases if the observer moves, even when more than a meter from the frog.

Toads, *Bufo*, do not call at feeding sites, but it is doubtful whether territorial calls (as tentatively identified) are restricted to ranids, leptodactylids, and hylids.   They are not of universal occurrence in these groups, but seem characteristic of species in which foraging is restricted in some fashion, to streams, pools, cliffs or trees, rather than to the ground.   No other function has been attributed to such calls.   They have no obvious association with breeding habits, whereas the circumstances of their utterance have several features in common with those under which the territorial songs of birds advertise possession.

Hardy (1959) offers dubious evidence that frogs, *Pseudacris nigrita,* call in trios, with louder and more persistent males becoming "lead frogs."   "The lead frog always ceased calling normally when another frog approached and began a rapid, high-pitched 'barking.'"   Moreover, according to Hardy, the "lead frog sometimes charged at an intruder and clasped it," the normal behavior of calling males in many species. The individual was, of course, attempting amplexus, employing the trial-and-error means of sex discrimination, but Hardy interprets this as aggressive combat, for she states that the "lead frog usually retained its dominance and the other frogs disappeared."   The alternate call described as a barking sound, presumably what Martof and Thompson (1958) refer to as "scolding notes," occurs in other hylids (Fig. 7), and may represent a territorial call, as suggested earlier, but Hardy's observations offer little evidence that it is effective in discouraging intruders.

Physical combat, or an overt aggressive response to an intruder, is not a prerequisite for anuran territorial behavior as Kikuchi (1958) assumes in his interpretation of behavioral patterns and home ranges observed in the Asiatic green frog, *Rana nigromaculata*.   On the contrary, the intruder usually responds to a stimulus coming from the resident.   Often there is a selective or discriminatory response of each individual to others

of the same species and sex, particularly of males. Territoriality is a behavioral pattern, essentially adaptive in nature, providing a means of
regulating population densities, and dependent upon the responses of
the individual to sensory cues. In mammals and birds territorial behavior may be far more complex than a simple stimulus-response phenomenon, even though, as Carpenter (1958) observes, "challenge, vocalization, song and other display or signaling activities" are important
aspects of territoriality. Martof and Thompson (1958) mention a "defensive male reaction" in *Pseudacris nigrita* that appears to depend on
the utterance of mating calls.

Circumstantial evidence points to the probability that vocality is of
territorial significance among the Anura. It remains to be demonstrated
experimentally that the vocalizations of *Syrrhophus, Tomodactylus* and
Rana clamitans elicit a negative response, either an avoidance or a withdrawal, in other individuals of the same sex and species. Under many
conditions when spacing is maintained, frogs are too well hidden for
visual cues to be employed. The exception noted by Test (1954) may
be the one that "proves the rule."

In *Phyllobates trinitatis,* it will be recalled, the female aggressively
defends a territory. Considered in the light of the normal anuran pattern, this anomalous behavior is perhaps more readily explicable if it is
assumed that vocality has been largely restricted to males throughout
the evolution of the Anura, as it is in the majority of existing species.
Territorial behavior in *P. trinitatis,* with the female assuming a role
more often found in the other sex, presumably results from adaptive
modifications stemming from peculiar or unusual environmental conditions prevailing at some time in the history of the species. As behavioral patterns changed, with natural selection favoring the female
in the territorial role, her lack of any vocal apparatus precluded modification of her voice. The pattern of aggressive display and physical combat arose, therefore, as a substitute for vocality, with the reponse of
other females (rarely male, usually immature individuals, according to
Test) depending upon visual or tactile rather than auditory cues.

The existence of aggressive territorial behavior in *P. trinitatis* females,
if this hypothesis is valid, reflects the opportunistic nature of evolution.
If environmental pressures placed a premium on territoriality in females,
selection determining this deviation from the ordinary trend of anuran
evolution depended on a sort of Hobson's choice. To use the words of
Simpson (1958), "When a way of life is changing in the course of evolution it is evidently simpler, that is, genetically more likely, to remodel
the existing than to introduce something new." Anuran females of other
species are not always voiceless, but vocal sacs are confined to males

(Inger, 1956a, b) , and no female apparently employs her voice under circumstances suggesting a territorial function. It would be astonishing, nevertheless, if such functions of the female's voice have not evolved in some species.

Where the female utters a mating call, such as Dixon (1957) describes for *Tomodactylus angustidigitorum*, for example, the calls are heard only during the breeding season, when they serve to orient and possibly to attract the male. In contrast, the males of many species utter much the same sort of call before, during, and after the mating season. The breeding season can be delimited accurately only by the observance of freshly deposited eggs, as Jameson (1955a) notes. In the green frog, *Rana clamitans,* breeding extends from the middle of May to the middle of August in Michigan, according to Martof (1953a) , but vocalizations begin as early as April 13 and frogs are occasionally heard until October 18.

The Texan cliff frogs, males of which have two distinctive calls, as discussed above, do not assemble in breeding aggregations. In this species the male attracts the female to a site where the eggs are deposited in moist soil. The majority of tailless amphibians, however, deposit their eggs in water, often with the males assembling at a pond or stream where their vocalizations continue for hours or even days before the females arrive. While seizure of a male toad during the breeding season elicits a release call, or chirp, most species of *Bufo* are silent except during periods of breeding activity.

Despite differences between species in breeding habits, toads ordinarily call only from breeding sites suitable for the species, even though they often forage some distance from pools. The North American pelobatids, *Scaphiopus,* are similar in this respect. In contrast, aquatic frogs of some species, particularly *Rana* in North America, habitually remain in or close to the water, except when rains permit dispersal. While in breeding choruses their calls are repeated as often as they can refill the lungs. Afterward, when the males move to feeding sites, calls are sporadic and, in some species, recognizably different, and not so restricted to the hours of darkness.

In the pig frog, *Rana grylio,* the mating call consists of four or five short grunts. When there is no evidence of breeding activity, a single grunt, rarely two, issues at infrequent intervals from frogs hidden in the vegetation around the edges of ponds or streams. Spectrograms reveal no differences in the structure of the calls, although the longer sequence of grunts appears to be a mating call, and the shorter one a territorial call. When such treefrogs as *Hyla cinerea* or *Hyla smithi* intersperse an occasional series of raucous calls, or a single raucous call, one may attract females, the other repel males.

Bullfrogs, *Rana catesbeiana,* call in choruses during the mating season, and the call heard afterward appears to be identical, even though the male utters it from an established feeding site. Green frogs, *R. clamitans,* call from the water surface during the mating season, when the sound seems to be more resonant, and possibly longer than the call heard after breeding activity ceases. This, however, is merely an impression possibly resulting from the location of males uttering the calls. When not breeding, as Martof (1953a) points out, green frogs call at irregular intervals, from muskrat burrows, under overhanging sods, root entanglements, or from similar situations where sounds would be muffled. Frogs calling from feeding sites may be several yards from water, at least in Florida.

Martof's account implies, perhaps correctly, that spatial relationships are maintained only during the breeding season in *Rana clamitans.* The organization of frogs in a more compact assemblage may be restricted to periods of spawning activity. Similar calls emitted by males at other times could be equally important in regulating population densities. Martof's studies of the green frog (1953a, b) do not indicate whether the mating call of the species attracts the female; proof of this function is lacking for any species of *Rana.* Noble and Aronson (1942) found no evidence from laboratory studies that mating calls in *Rana pipiens* attract frogs of either sex. Vocalizations prior to the mating season in both *R. clamitans, R. grylio,* and perhaps other species, may be territorial, and remain so when males assemble at breeding sites and become more frequently vociferous. Territorial songs of some birds are credited with the dual functions of attracting mates but repelling males of the same species (Huxley, 1942).

Savage (1935), however, finds *Rana temporaria* assembling in silence at the breeding site, with many frogs already in amplexus before mating calls are heard. In this species, therefore, the voice plays no role whatsoever in attracting females to spawning sites. In an earlier account Savage (1934) objects to using the term "call-note" for the mating call of the species. The voice, he believes, could be effective over a short range in guiding females to the spawning site, although "a male does not stay still, even while croaking, but jostles continually in a crowd with his croaking companions."

Clearly no territorial function can be assigned to the voice in the breeding behavior of *Rana temporaria.* Savage's description would apply equally well to the behavior of the western spadefoot, *Scaphiopus hammondi,* the males of which call from temporary pools, milling around in deeper water away from the shore.   In contrast, where ranges overlap, the plains spadefoot, *S. bombifrons,* breeds in the same pool with *hammondi,* but males call from stations distributed at irregular intervals along the edge of the pool.   Another spadefoot, *S. intermontanus,* breeds in permanent pools, and has calling habits similar to those of *bombifrons.*   Commonly, however, the males are even more widely spaced along the bank, rarely within a meter of one another, and usually more widely scattered.   Though visual cues cannot be eliminated from consideration, such spacing suggests a dual function for the mating calls of spadefoots.   At close range they repel other males of their own species, but attract females.   Neither function excludes use of the call in distant orientation or as a stimulus evoking the female's breeding behavior as additional possibilities.   Pearson (1954) reports evidence of territoriality in *Scaphiopus holbrooki,* but it is not dependent upon vocality.

Under exceptional conditions when toads occur in a dense aggregation, such as that described for *Bufo alvarius* by Blair and Pettus (1954), there is little evidence of territorial functions in their mating calls.   In other species of *Bufo,* males may call a yard or so from the water's edge (*B. retiformis* in Sonora, Mexico), but usually closer, often in shallow water.   In small aggregations it is exceptional to find two males calling side by side.   Chapman and Chapman (1958) report calling stations of male African toads, *Bufo regularis,* to be customarily well separated.   One male is never seen calling within approximately a yard of another.   A. P. Blair (1955) speaks of males in *Bufo microscaphus* calling while "strung out along the shore," rather than in aggregations.   But various species of *Bufo,* like those of *Scaphiopus,* differ in behavior.   Nothing that could be construed as territorial behavior is mentioned by Savage (1934), who describes the breeding activity of the male of the weak-voiced European toad, *Bufo bufo bufo.*   Though vociferous, the male "swims rapidly hither and thither," seizing either males or females as he comes across them.   Anderson (1954) reports males of *Microhyla carolinensis* calling when scarcely an inch apart, as Pyburn (1958) notes for *Acris crepitans.*

The behavior of *Bufo b. bufo* differs strikingly from that observed in a loud-voiced species, *Bufo compactilis,* studied at Chapala in the Mexican state of Jalisco during July and August, 1959.   (Parenthetically it is necessary to note the marked differences between the mating call (Fig. 12) of the population in Jalisco and the call W. F. Blair (1956a) describes for a Texan population, Girard's (1854) *B. speciosus,* which may be specifically distinct.)   Other species of *Bufo* recorded from Jalisco were not encountered at Chapala.   Investigation of the movements of marked individuals by Mr. Allen Brown, a student assisting in the work,[3] revealed males frequently to be using the same calling sites on successive nights when rainfall was sufficient for breeding activities. Shortly after nightfall Brown (unpublished) found nine males at calling sites irregularly spaced around a pool, designated as No. 1, in an open grassy area in the golf course. All nine males, previously marked for individual identification, were captured and transferred to a spot approximately 85 feet distant from Pool No. 1. The point of release was some twenty feet away from a smaller pool, No. 2, where three other males of the species were calling. Immediately after the removal of the nine males from Pool No. 1, no toads called from the site. Other toads had been removed earlier in the evening from Pool No. 2.

To reduce interference by the observer to a minimum, Brown entered the area but once every hour to recapture, note the position, identify and again release as many of the nine individuals as he could find. Within two hours he found seven of the toads back at their respective calling sites at Pond No. 1. The other two had moved to Pond No. 2, where they added their voices to the trio calling from this site earlier in the evening.

Brown's data might be intrepreted as evidence supporting an assumption that mating calls play no part in attracting other males to the breeding site. Any conclusion of the sort is belied by further consideration. In view of possible interacting influences of territorial and orientational behavior, it is unfortunate that Brown removed any males at all from Pool No. 2. It is conjectural, but not impossible, that the two toads moving to the site in preference to returning to calling sites at Pool No. 1, did so when vacancies were detected. In familiar terrain the males of *B. compactilis,* like other species of Anura (Pearson, 1955, 1957), evidently have no difficulty in returning to some particular spot. It is equally plain from Jameson's (1955b) work with *Syrrhophus* that anuran amphibians move into vacated areas, but do not establish residence when transferred to areas where all sites are preoccupied. If mating calls of *B. compactilis* attract both males and females to breeding pools, but also function as territorial calls regulating the density or the spacing of males at pools in any breeding area, Brown's data are perhaps better interpreted as representing a demonstration of territorial and orientational behavior in the species.

The interplay of territoriality, orientation, and the reactions of toads to mating calls, would also account for the inconclusive results A. P.

[3] Jointly supported by the National Science Foundation and the American Museum of Natural History as part of an undergraduate research training program.

Blair (1942) obtained in his efforts to ascertain whether toads respond preferentially to the call of their own species. Ten individuals were released midway between two pools; toads of the same species called from one pool, those of another called from the second. Insufficient information is provided concerning the sources of the toads used in the experiment. Hence one can only guess whether territoriality or distant orientation influenced the outcome of the experiment, which may have depended in part on olfaction or other senses (Bogert, 1958). Toads avoid some ponds for no obvious reason.

Jameson (1955b) notes that males of the solitary cliff frog, *Syrrhophus,* sometimes continue to call while clasping females. Under such conditions it is problematical whether calls induce females to move to better oviposition sites, as he suggests. Here too the call could be interpreted as a territorial signal discouraging interference from other males.

The examples reviewed provide evidence of distinctive territorial calls in some species, with mating calls perhaps serving a similar (or a dual) function in those instances when males are distributed around a breeding site. The calls of some species appear to be manifestations of territorial behavior at feeding sites as well as in breeding aggregations, with or without observable differences in the calls. "Rain calls" will be discussed below, but pending further investigation, it should be mentioned that no clear-cut distinction can be made between mating calls and "rain calls." Carr (1940a) observes that they are indistinguishable in *Hyla crucifer*. Rain calls uttered by hylids may be territorial in function, as noted by Bogert (1958).

Territoriality at the breeding site is adaptive in the sense that it facilitates reproduction. Males can effectively detect the presence of females, presumably by visual cues, whereas the spacing may depend upon either auditory or visual stimuli, possibly upon both (Martof, 1953a). When the availability of feeding sites is restricted, as it is in species that forage only in the vicinity of pools or streams, the regulation of densities not only reduces competition among individuals of the same species, but provides for more efficient patrol of the area. Fewer animals, whether prey or predators, could escape detection while approaching the pond or stream.

Benefits the animals of any species derive from having home ranges and defended territories are summarized by Bates (1950). Probably a distinction should be made between territorial behavior at breeding sites and foraging sites among the Anura, but nevertheless, as Bates observes, "An animal on its home territory has a physical as well as psychological advantage. It can know the terrain intimately, where to hide and where to find food. The territory owner, in defending this territory against intruders of his own kind, selfishly insures his own survival and dooms the ejected intruder [perhaps only in *Phyllobates trinitatis* among the frogs mentioned in this review. In other species territorial calls may, in essence, 'eject' other males, as one of Jameson's (1955b) experiments suggests]; but in so doing favors the survival of his species by tending to maintain an optimal density for that species." Mayr (1942) and Dobzhansky (1951) discuss the genetic and evolutionary implications of territorial behavior, but do not mention frogs, in which territoriality remained undetected prior to the respective reports of Martof and Test discussed above.

7. *"Rain Calls."* The sounds uttered by tailless amphibians not engaged in breeding activities, often by males in trees or other locations remote from spawning sites, have no adaptive significance immediately apparent. Some of these calls, as noted in the previous discussion, may be territorial. Noble (1931) speaks of the summer cries of frogs as being "merely a premature awakening of the sex instincts." This explanation could apply to frogs in the American northeast, where a few species that normally breed only during the spring occasionally vocalize, but rarely spawn, in the fall. Noble also mentions the "proverbial treefrog" that calls loudly when the humidity is suddenly raised.

With limited ability to resist desiccation, frogs are far more prone to venture out of hiding when the rate of moisture loss diminishes or approaches zero as the air becomes saturated with moisture and evaporation is curtailed. Consequently we should inquire whether vocality depends primarily upon the frog's activity or whether the change in humidity elicits the calling response. Vocalizations may depend upon a temporal sequence of stimuli. The arrival of moisture laden air brings the frogs out of seclusion, but a sound stimulus triggers their vocalization. In Florida treefrogs call with the rise in humidity prior to thunderstorms, often from sites well above the ground, in trees or on the walls of buildings. Several frogs in an area call simultaneously following thunder or the sound of rain spattering on the foliage. Airplanes overhead also induce treefrogs, especially *Hyla cinerea,* to emit sounds.

The call may be a chirping sound, a feeble rendition of sounds resembling the mating call, or a vigorous but recognizable modification of the mating call. Goin and Goin (1957) point out that the "rain call" of *Hyla squirella* should not be confused with the call given in breeding choruses. In warm humid weather the rain call is "uttered sporadically by resting individuals at any time during the day." W. F. Blair (1958f) refers to the "tree calls" of the species, which are heard at long distances from any breeding pool. He describes them as noise-like, without the harmonic structure of the mating call. Blair provides spectrograms to illustrate these differences. Though he speaks of calls varying "in relation to the sexual excitement of the individual," he concludes his discussion by saying that the function of the tree call is unknown.

The Mexican treefrog, *Hyla eximia* also produces two calls (Fig. 33) with differences resembling those Blair illustrates for *H. squirella*. The rain call was heard on rare occasions in a population near Chapala, Jalisco during July and August of 1959, where *H. eximia* was reproductively active throughout the period. Choruses could be heard near Lake Chapala and neighboring ponds nearly every night. The circumstances under which these hylids emit sounds distinguishable as "rain calls" would not preclude their being territorial in function. The spacing of males at breeding sites points to a dual function of the breeding call in *H. eximia,* and possibly in *squirella* as well. The alternate call, presumably unattractive to females as well as to males of the species, is uttered under conditions where a negative response in both sexes would be advantageous.

Maslin (1957) evidently heard the rain call in population of *Hyla eximia* near Jocotepec, Jalisco, within 25 miles of Chapala. This led to his erroneous conclusion that the mating call of the population differed significantly from mating calls in other populations. The calls Maslin describes were heard during the day after a light rain had fallen the previous evening. The frogs, calling at intervals of four or five seconds, were situated on rocks or in the leaves of plants a foot to over two feet above the ground. As Maslin correctly points out, males of *H. eximia* normally issue their mating calls from positions on the ground, in shallow water, or not far from pools when the terrain is drenched. During the summer of 1959 *H. eximia* was found calling at night in precisely such places at various localities in the neighborhood of Jocotepec. Such characteristics as the pattern and color are subject to change in the individual and extremely variable in many populations of *H. eximia*. Mating calls also differ from region to region, and no character given by Maslin as diagnostic of *H. microeximia* provides evidence of sufficient differentiation in the population at Jocotepec to warrant subspecific recognition, much less specific status for the population.

Pettus (1955) discusses the function of the "tree call" in *Hyla versicolor* in Oklahoma and expresses his amazement at finding several pairs in amplexus in trees some 20 feet from the edge of a pool. This is not unusual among American treefrogs. Barbour (1916), for example, reports *Hyla andersoni* in amplexus "well up in a pine tree" in the New Jersey pine barrens. Wright and Wright (1949) quote A. J. Kirn's account of *Hyla versicolor chrysoscelis*, which mentions five individuals "six feet up" on a limb three inches in diameter. Kirn believed there were two females and three males, "all within ten inches," although none was seen in amplexus. Kirn evidently had difficulty in distinguishing the sexes; if only one male called, as he says, it is very doubtful whether other males were present. Four females may well have been attracted by the single male.

In Florida, when shrubs are present in areas where ponds form, the smaller hylids may be in amplexus while clinging to branches more than a meter above the ground, or above the surface of the water. Treefrogs that normally spawn in pools may resort to trees for amplexus, even though clasping is infrequently observed much above the human eye-level. The rarity of such observations may depend less upon the habits of treefrogs than it does upon the habits of observers. A pair of frogs, silent while in amplexus on the upper surface of a limb, would easily escape detection from below.

If frogs of both sexes react simultaneously to the same stimuli and silently concentrate in groups at spawning sites, as Savage (1935) describes for *Rana temporaria,* pairing of the sexes could depend largely on tactile or visual stimuli. When pairing occurs in a tree even twenty feet from the breeding pond, it is probable that the female orients her movements toward the male in response to his vocalizations.

It scarcely seems advantageous for the female to be encumbered by the clasping male, while moving to the water for oviposition. This minor handicap would, however, be offset under conditions where dense aggregations of treefrogs at spawning sites could be a detriment to survival. When breeding seasons in Oklahoma follow periods of subnormal precipitation, pools are few in number, limited in size, or both. Such predators as raccoons would be quick to take advantage of the situation were most of the adult frogs in a local population concentrated at the water's edge. Mating calls of some species may attract or orient females but still be territorial in function, as previously pointed out. The vocalizations of the male of *Hyla versicolor* at the spawning site may not be the only cues accounting for their scattered locations, but calling sites are rarely close. When the spatial requirements of the species cannot be met at the pool, late arrivals resort to nearby trees as an alternate means of maintaining the distance between calling sites.

Pettus says that spectrographic analyses of the calls of *Hyla versicolor* in Oklahoma reveal that frogs in trees produce essentially the same call as those on the ground. "If the 'tree call' does have a function," Pettus perversely concludes, "it appears that the two types may have been functionally intergrading in the case discussed." If the calls are virtually the same, as indicated by spectrograms, and identical in function, as indicated by pairs in amplexus in both situations, there is no evidence of "two types" of call, and consequently no "intergrading in function." Pettus heard only the mating call, which attracts the female, at the spawning site or elsewhere, as his own observations indicate. The probable territorial function of the mating call offers a simple explanation for the behavior Pettus describes.

Other authors mention distinctive calls in *Hyla versicolor,* aside from the male release call Aronson (1943) describes. Walker (1946) reports two calls, occasionally heard side by side in Ohio. One of these may be a territorial call, the other the mating call (but see below). The two distinctive calls reported for *H. versicolor* in Virginia by Hoffman (1946), however, were heard in separate areas, with a prolonged trill in populations inhabiting the mountains and the Piedmont, and a shorter, harsher call in the populations of the coastal plain. Calls described as being roughly intermediate were also heard by Hoffman, who adds that the males of lowland populations attain sexual maturity at a smaller size. Bogert (1958) employs recordings of *H. versicolor* to exemplify differences, presumably genetic in origin, between populations of the same species. W. F. Blair (1958f) reports pulsation rates varying from 20 to 64 per second in frogs currently assigned to *H. versicolor,* with occasional overlaps in fast-trilling and slow-trilling populations. He suggests that three species may be represented.

Earlier accounts, nevertheless, refer to differences in calls that cannot be attributed to genetic differences. Noble and Noble (1923), who modify the interpretations of previous authors, state that *H. versicolor* has two distinctive calls. One is the characteristic trill the male emits when its vocal sac is fully inflated. Its other call, emitted with the sac only partly inflated, consists of a "series of mournful notes." Detailed observations of *H. versicolor* and other hylids are required before vocalizations of the sort are unequivocally identified either as rain calls or as territorial calls. It is noteworthy, nevertheless, that *Hyla squirella* seems to emit its rain call without fully inflating its vocal sac. The sac is certainly inflated incompletely when the Mexican treefrog, *Hyla eximia,* produces its rain call, a more raucous sound, shorter than the mating call in duration, but repeated at similar intervals. The incomplete inflation of the vocal sac may indicate that some of the air passes out through the nostrils. According to Hinckley (1884), the degree of inflation governs the volume of the sound in *Hyla crucifer.*

Spectrograms of the three calls emitted by *Hyla eximia* reveal similarities in the structure of the rain call and the male release call, which is produced with a very slight inflation of the vocal sac accompanying each utterance. Both the rain call and the male release call lack the dominant band of frequencies and the harmonic structure of the mating call that seemingly result from the resonance provided by the fully inflated vocal sac. The different qualities of the three calls, therefore, depend in part on the amount of air residual in the vocal sac during the intervals between calls, and partly on the amount of air forced into the sac as the call is uttered.

The alternate calls of other species reflect similar changes in the inflation of the vocal sac. In the foothills of the Chiricahua Mountains in Arizona the red spotted toad, *Bufo punctatus,* is heard occasionally at dusk issuing a slowly trilled call, seemingly (but uncertainly) at a lower frequency. Observations of toads retained in an enclosure revealed these calls to come from toads with the vocal sac partly inflated. Before the slowly trilled call could be recorded the toads inflated their vocal sacs and began to issue their shrill, rapidly trilled mating calls. Where pools form from seepages, where stock tanks, or even concrete watering troughs are available in southeastern Arizona, these toads begin to call in May or June, often prior to the first summer rains. They continue to breed during the early part of the rainy season. In the arid portions of California, where summer rains are uncertain or infrequent, *Bufo punctatus* calls as early as February in Death Valley (Turner, 1959), or as late as May in Coachella Valley in the Sonoran Desert to the south, depending largely upon permanent springs for spawning sites. Slowly trilled calls similar to those heard in Arizona are occasionally uttered by toads near pools in such places as Quail Springs in the Little San Bernardino Mountains, or at springs along the periphery of Coachella Valley. Breeding seasons are not dependent upon rainfall, for rains normally cease earlier in the spring.

Though uttered with the vocal sac partly inflated, the slowly trilled vocalization of *Bufo punctatus* can scarcely be identified as "rain calls." The barking frog, *Eleutherodactylus augusti latrans,* in Texas is described by Jameson (1954) as producing a "warm-up call" voiced at twilight, and changing rather abruptly to the normal mating call as darkness falls. Jameson does not indicate whether the "warm-up call" is emitted while the vocal sac is incompletely inflated, but the manner of its utterance parallels that observed in *Bufo punctatus.* The crepuscular calls of both species seem to be little more than premature renditions of their normal mating calls. If the abrupt change from one call to the other with the onset of darkness has any biological significance, it may be attributed to a gradual rather than an immediate response to environmental stimuli.

Judging by the few observations reported for bufonids, hylids and leptodactylids, it is questionable whether rain calls can profitably be defined as vocalizations uttered with the vocal sac partly inflated. Should it be demonstrated that calls of the sort are truly territorial in function among hylids, we should dispense with the term "rain call." The warm-up calls" of *Bufo* and *Leptodactylus,* while conceivably territorial, seem less likely to be of behavioral importance.

8. *Distress Calls.* When seized by snakes, raccoons, or other vertebrate predators, frogs give vent to sounds varying from low-pitched calls to shrill cries, or screams. In some species these are invariably uttered with the mouth open, unlike any other anuran vocalizations. Various terms have been used for these sounds emitted by frogs under conditions of duress; "distress call" is perhaps the most appropriate designation.

Boulenger (1897) describes the cry of the European *Pelobates fuscus* as most startling, adding that when "persistently teased" frogs of the species emit such cries over a period of several minutes. Yerkes (1903) refers to the "pain-scream" of the American green frog, *Rana clamitans,* describing the noise as "a prolonged scream like that of a child," made with the mouth opened widely. The cry, he says, reminds him of the sounds made by many mammals when frightened.

Stephenson and Stephenson (1957) report distress calls in the primitive New Zealand ascaphid, *Liopelma archeyi,* a species with no mating call. When disturbed these small frogs occasionally produce successive, shrill chirping sounds, with the mouth opened widely at each cry. Noble (1931) discusses the sounds various species of Anura emit when "pinched or startled," specifically noting that it is a scream in many ranids, a shrill squeal in the West Indian leptodactylid, *Eleutherodactylus inoptatus,* or a clatter in an American pelobatid, *Scaphiopus holbrooki.* The clattering sound Noble mentions may be a distress call, but when seized by a hooded skunk, *Mephitis macroura,* the Sonoran spadefoot, *Scaphiopus couchi,* emits a short scream.

Distress calls are perhaps of universal occurrence among adult Anura. They are not restricted to males, for Dickerson (1906) refers to cries emitted by both sexes of *Hyla arenicolor,* and similar observations are reported for *Rana.* Jameson (1954) mentions the "blaring screech" of *Eleutherodactylus augusti,* "which he describes as quite startling, even when expected." Anderson (1954) says that when roughly handled, narrow-mouthed toads, *Microhyla carolinensis,* of either sex emit a chirp or squawk. Anderson does not indicate whether this microhylid utters such sounds with the mouth open, but they are probably to be construed as distress calls.

The stimulus required to evoke such sounds varies extensively. Gallardo (1958) observes that females of the Argentine toad, *Bufo arenarum,* are not ordinarily vocal, but one found near a green snake, *Leimadophis,* produced a weak "grruc" when the branches beneath which they both rested were removed. Another female emitted a cry when seized in the water. Aronson (1944) comments on the absence of the "fright cry" in *Bufo terrestris* and *B. woodhousei* during the course of laboratory studies of the two species, but notes that cries have been recorded for *B. terrestris.* Lankes (1928) claims that an Australian treefrog, *Hyla caerulea,* occasionally screams without provocation, but he could have overlooked visual cues that possibly evoke the response, with or without conditioning. Yerkes (1903) found a few repetitions of a weak electrical stimulus induced *Rana clamitans* to scream.

Carr (1940b) tells how he placed a large female American bullfrog, *Rana catesbeiana,* in a box with a small ribbon snake, *Thamnophis sauritus.* "After a brief time the frog set up a screaming that could be heard all over the premises; on investigating I found the snake had fixed its tiny jaws on the enormous calf of the frog, whose first toes the little creature could hardly hope to swallow. The frog continued to cry and shake its leg—until the snake was thrown out of the box." The cry obviously was not responsible for the snake's releasing its grip. It is problematical whether mammalian predators are sufficiently startled by such screams to be induced to release their prey.

Distress calls are more frequently reported in frogs of the genus *Rana* than in other genera of North American Anura. When merely seized after it escaped in the laboratory an adult female pig frog, *Rana grylio,* at the Archbold Biological Station in Highlands County, Florida gave vent to a series of low-pitched screams with a dominant frequency of approximately 2300 cps. Repeated strong tactile stimuli were required to elicit the somewhat higher pitched scream of a southern green frog, *Rana c. clamitans,* taken at Orange Springs, Florida. The slightest tactile stimulus evoked shorter distress calls after the frog was placed in a moist cloth sack.

Leopard frogs, *Rana pipiens,* taken near the Archbold Biological Station occasionally also scream when first seized, and often repeat the sound if pinched. No cry leopard frogs emit in the laboratory, however, is comparable in intensity to the scream heard near midnight on one occasion when a mixed chorus of over a dozen species of frogs called from a single pond. Microphones were being disconnected when a piercing scream came from a smaller pond nearby. A beam of light disclosed a raccoon scarcely twenty feet away carrying a leopard frog in its jaws. The raccoon had seized its prey in shallow water where numerous other frogs continued to call as though oblivious of its presence.

Spectrograms disclose differences in the structure of the screams issued

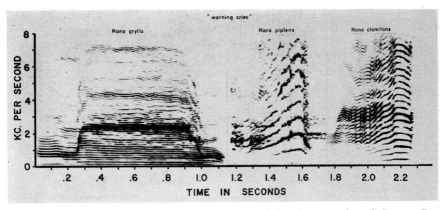

FIG. 10. "Warning cries," or distress calls, uttered by three species of *Rana*. Recorded at Archbold Biological Station, Highlands County, Florida.

by three species of *Rana* (Fig. 10), although distress calls of all three have one feature in common. There is a sudden rise in the frequency near the beginning of the call, and a drop in frequency near the end. Screams emitted at different times by the same individual are seldom identical, but spectrograms of different individuals of the same species reveal similarities. In *Rana clamitans*, no significant difference is apparent in spectrograms when the sound structure of the male's scream is compared with that of the female.

The occurrence of distress calls in such voiceless species as *Liopelma archeyi*, or in females otherwise mute, makes it doubtful whether any special mechanism of sound production is required. The valvular lips of the arytenoids at the entrance to the trachea are perhaps brought together by constrictor muscles simultaneously with the expulsion of air from the lungs as the body muscles contract. Sound is produced in much the same way by pinching the end of a rubber hose through which air is being forcibly expelled.

Though Yerkes (1903) refers to the distress call of the green frog as the "pain-scream," he questions whether it is necessarily indicative of pain. He notes that weak stimuli, even when repeated, do not evoke the scream. Once an electrical stimulus is sufficiently strong to induce the scream, the frog responds almost every time to the same stimulus. Moreover, the frog continues to respond in the same way to weak stimuli. It appears, Yerkes continues, "as if the strong stimulus increases the irritability of the center to such an extent that even weak stimuli are sufficient to cause the reaction. Are we to say that the weak stimulus is painful because of the increased irritability or may it be concluded that the reflex is in this case, like winking or leg-jerk or the head-lowering and puffing, simply a forced movement, which is to be explained as an hereditary protective reaction, but not as necessarily indicative of any sort of feeling.

If we take this stand, says Yerkes, "there is no reason to believe the scream indicative of pain at any time," a conclusion perhaps "nearer the truth than one who hears the scream for the first time is likely to think." Even when gently seized a female *Rana grylio* expelled the air through its open mouth with sufficient force to produce the distress call, as noted above. It is doubtful whether any sensation of pain is entailed, as it might be when a frog is seized by a raccoon. But the shrill cry may not depend upon trauma. A. P. Blair (1947a) describes the reactions of a large toad that emitted no sound when severely wounded by a turtle. Tonic contractions of the body muscles of a frog seized in the jaws of a mammalian predator may result from tactile stimuli, much as described by Wertheimer (1924). Thus even a sudden tactile stimulus might cause the expulsion of air from the lungs, all that is needed to account for the scream.

The absence of any overt response in other leopard frogs, *Rana pipiens*, in the immediate vicinity of one emitting the distress call raises the question of whether other frogs are alerted by the signal. In the instance observed the frogs were extremely vociferous, perhaps indicating a high level of sexual excitement. Under this stress they behaved as though they were oblivious of predators. When not sexually excited frogs may react quite differently to distress signals, even though Yerkes failed to detect motor reactions to such sounds under laboratory conditions. The respiratory changes Yerkes noted leave no doubt that cries are heard by other frogs. Thus the auditory stimulus may reinforce the frog's reactions to other stimuli. The frog may remain motionless in response to screams, but still become alert and watchful. The distress signal could "warn other frogs in the neighborhood," as Noble (1931) suggests, and cause them to react more readily in response to visual or tactile stimuli.

To conclude this discussion, anuran distress calls are the only vocalizations characteristically emitted with the mouth open. They are of wide occurrence in the Anura, where they are neither sex limited nor restricted to species with mating calls or release calls. Judging by recordings of *Rana,* distress calls characteristically change in frequencies, rising at the beginning, with or without a sharp peak preceding the drop in frequencies at the end. There is no evidence that such vociferations discourage the attacks of predators, but distress calls influence the escape reactions of other frogs and thus may be of protective value to the species.

9. *"Warning Signals."* Frogs with riparian feeding habits commonly emit a chirp or a grunt as they dive into the water to escape an enemy. The sound of the splash an instant later may augment the effectiveness of the vocalization as a stimulus alerting other frogs in the neighborhood. Yerkes (1903, 1905) does not mention the chirp, but notes the influence of falling water as an auditory stimulus. His experiments show that sounds simulating those accompanying the frog's plunge produce a marked increase in the respiratory rates of frogs, "precisely what one would expect from a sound which is of special significance in the life of the animal."

The implications of this statement are borne out by Yerkes' field observations. Frogs can be approached within a few yards, as Yerkes says, and they do not leap until they "have evidence of being noticed. Repeatedly" he continues, "I have noted that it is never possible to get near to any frogs in the same region after one has jumped in. In this we thus have additional proof that they hear the splash-sound. To make sure that sight was not responsible for this on-guard condition in which one finds the frogs after one of their number has jumped into the water, I made observations on animals that were hidden from one another. The results were the same. I therefore conclude that the splash of a frog jumping into the water is not only perceived by other frogs in the vicinity, but that it is a peculiarly significant sound for them, since it is indicative of danger, and serves to put them 'on watch.' "

Though Yerkes overlooked the sound emitted prior to the splash, Noble (1931) refers to it as being well known. Martof and Thompson (1958) define the alarm call as "that given when danger threatens," adding that it is "frequently given by *R. clamitans* and *R. catesbeiana* as they dive into a pond to safety when some disturbance occurs nearby." The warning call is not a loud vocalization, but when accompanied by the splash-sound it may have survival value as the statements of Yerkes imply.

Martof and Thompson also refer to the protective function of the mating call: "Anyone who has approached a vigorous chorus of frogs and experienced the suddenness with which they all stopped calling cannot help but be impressed by the effectiveness of this reaction." Over half a century earlier Yerkes (1903) noted that "when one member of such a chorus is frightened and stops the others become silent. This indicates that the cessation of croaking is a sign of danger and is imitated . . ."

The word "imitated" is certainly not to be taken literally, and there is little to substantiate Yerkes' belief that all members of a chorus cease calling when a single individual stops. The statement is evidently premised on the assumption that frogs depend largely upon visual stimuli in their detection of intruders. When frogs in a chorus are stationed at the edge of a pool surrounded by tall grass, they often cease calling when approached, and do so as abruptly as frogs that call from the open water. When frogs call from hidden sites the inhibition of their vocalization must depend largely, if not entirely, upon tactile stimuli resulting from the vibrations of the substratum. Very often the chorus resumes if the human observer remains in his tracks, even though he waves his arms.

Under exceptionally favorable conditions frogs often spawn in vast numbers. Extraordinarily vociferous choruses form after heavy summer rains, whether in the tropics or in such arid regions as the Sonoran Desert. Virtually nothing disturbs choruses of the sort; individual members frequently continue vocalizing until seized. Their timidity appears to be inversely proportional to their level of sexual excitement. Smaller choruses are easily disturbed or inhibited, particularly when they form toward the end of the season when temperatures are barely above the threshold for activity. If all frogs at one pond cease calling, those in an adjacent pond may follow suit. Under such circumstances a sudden drop in the intensity of the sound may, as Yerkes indicates, serve as a danger signal. Collectors or commercial frog hunters make use of sound in locating their quarry, but it is uncertain whether mammalian or avian predators depend to any extent upon sound in seeking out their anuran prey. The silence of a disturbed chorus, regardless of whether it induces a state of increased awareness in the frogs of a breeding assemblage, perhaps facilitates their use of auditory cues in detecting the approach of the larger terrestrial quadrupeds. The advantage inherent in the gliding, relatively noiseless, movements of snakes readily accounts for the abundance of frogs in the diet of many species.

The sound accompanying the frog's plunge, as well as the chirp or croak preceding it, are probably to be construed as warning signals. Like distress calls, they alert other frogs to potential danger. When the majority of frogs in a chorus cease their vocalizations, other frogs may become aware of the reduced intensity in the sound. Without further investigation, however, it remains uncertain whether the cessation of calls evokes a state of awareness. If this could be demonstrated the adaptive significance of chorus structures would be more readily apparent.

Chorus Structure

The several functions of the voice in the diversified patterns of anuran behavior thus far investigated are incompletely revealed in the preceding discussions. Additional evidence supporting the belief that mating calls orient, attract, and possibly stimulate reproductive activities in various species of Anura remains to be evaluated. Enough information has been presented, nevertheless, to indicate that anuran vocalizations facilitate the formation of breeding aggregations, and possibly play significant roles in revealing the receptivity or nonreceptivity of frogs of both sexes. Data for some species indicate that the voice is used to regulate population densities and that it also serves as a warning signal.

The territorial significance of vocalizations within choruses of representative species has already been discussed. The utilization of the voice in the formation of breeding assemblages and the retention of configurations in choruses in *Rana clamitans,* are shown in data supplied by Martof (1953a). However, he provides no information concerning the sequence of calls in choruses, an aspect of anuran behavior neglected by many investigators. Goin (1949) is perhaps the first to mention such phenomena. He points out that choruses of the spring peeper, *Hyla crucifer,* have a characteristic structure, with each chorus arising in the same manner time after time.

"Typically," Goin says, "three frogs sing as a group and a large chorus seems to be nothing more than a number of these trios calling from the same breeding site. Furthermore, each of these trios develops in the same manner. The call is initiated by a single individual sounding the note of A for a varying number of times. After a brief rest, if he does not have an answer, he gives a trill. This trill apparently acts as a stimulus since it usually results in another individual starting to call on the note G#. When this happens the two individuals continue giving their respective notes— A, G#, A, G#; etc.—for an indefinite number of times. If a third individual does not start calling, they stop their alternating calls, rest, and one of them—usually (and perhaps invariably) the one that is calling G#—gives the trill. At the sound of the trill, the third individual of the trio starts giving his call which is B. Thereafter, the three continue to call, each giving its respective note in the order indicated, A, G#, B, for an indefinite number of times."

Once the trio is established the trill is no longer given, Goin adds, and the notes sounded by individual frogs seem to be fairly constant. Variations in the pitch of individual calls in a chorus are apparent in many species. Such variations are attributable to differences in the size of individuals comprising the chorus, as the data provided for *Microhyla* by W. F. Blair (1955a) demonstrate. Duets, (Fig. 11) with the call of one individual immediately followed by a lower-pitched call of another individual, are characteristic of the plains spadefoot, *Scaphiopus bombifrons,* in choruses recorded in Arizona and the Mexican state of Chihuahua. The calling habits of a burrowing hylid, *Pternohyla fodiens,* are

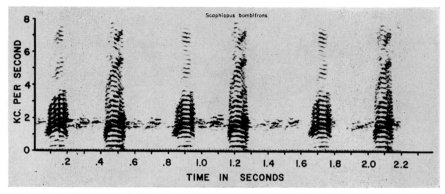

FIG. 11. Mating calls of *Scaphiopus bombifrons*, illustrating the "duets" with the call of one individual (the one farther from the microphone) followed by a lower-pitched call *ca.* 0.25 seconds later. Such "duets" commonly occur in any area within a breeding aggregation. Recorded at Portal, Arizona.

curiously similar. In each of these species duets can be detected in recordings (Bogert, 1958).

Spectrograms of mating calls of representative populations of *Hyla crucifer* in New Jersey, however, provide dubious evidence of the trios Goin describes for the species in Florida. W. F. Blair (1958a) says nothing concerning trios in populations of the species in Ontario, Michigan, or Texas, although he describes four different calls. These include the normal mating call, a geographic variant of it, an "opening call," uttered by an individual as the initial call in a sequence, and the trill to which Goin refers. According to Blair the trilled call is sometimes interposed in a series of normal mating calls, contrary to Goin who says the trill is issued as a stimulus to induce another individual to call, and repeated until the response is obtained. In recordings of *H. crucifer* made in New Jersey, the trilled call is rarely heard. Sequences of calls issuing from three individuals are detectable, but all three call at approximately the same pitch.

In many species issuing short mating calls, one individual commonly alternates with another, leaving the impression that one frog "answers" the other. In small choruses of species with trills of moderate duration, the individuals call in some sort of sequence, not necessarily fixed, but with one frog after another adding his vocalizations to the initial call. Even in a large chorus, frogs seldom start calling simultaneously after an interruption. Almost invariably one frog calls first and the others join in, before the trill is completed if it is of long duration. When the call is short it may be issued once or twice or even several times before

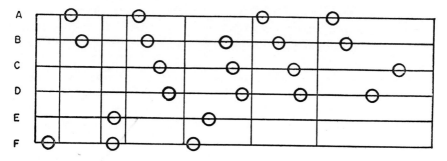

FIG. 12.   Calling patterns of six *Microhyla carolinensis* comprising a small aggregation observed by Paul K. Anderson on July 28, 1950, near New Orleans, Louisiana. Each letter and corresponding line represents a single individual. Vertical lines indicate pauses between sequences in the vocalization of the chorus as a whole.   From Anderson (1955).

other individuals call and the chorus reaches its full intensity.   Jameson (1954) describes the vocalizations of the Texan barking frog, *Eleuthero-dactylus augusti,* as "a very complex pattern involved with the response call of local individuals to that of a leader.   This leader appears to be the frog with the loudest voice in the area."   Hardy (1959) advances a similar interpretation, but her description of trios in *Pseudacris nigrita* is unconvincing.

Anderson (1954), the only investigator to attempt a detailed analysis, reports evidence of a predominant pattern in the sequence of calls issuing from a small chorus of *Microhyla carolinensis* in Florida.   In this instance six males called from a pool less than a meter in diameter.   To record their calls Anderson drew six parallel lines, each designated by a letter representing one of the individuals.   Each time one called a dot was placed on the line representing it.   Small aggregations of this microhylid call at intervals, as demonstrated in recordings (Bogert, 1958) of populations in Florida.   Anderson indicated brief periods of silence intervening between the sequences he recorded by means of vertical lines as shown in Figure 12, which accompanied his original account.

All six individuals in the chorus Anderson describes seldom called in any one sequence, but two or more individuals were represented in thirty-four of the thirty-eight sequences recorded.   As analyzed by Anderson, with six individuals calling, there are thirty possible combinations when one of the six either precedes or follows another.   If it were purely a matter of chance each of these 30 possible combinations would have been expected fewer than three times in the 38 sequences tabulated. Actually 15 rather than 30 combinations occurred in the total of 75; one sequence, AB, occurred 20 times, BC 15 times, and a third, DA, occurred 9 times. If chance determines sequences in the calls of three individuals, there are 120 possible combinations, but only 16 occurred in the total of 35.

Anderson continues, "The chances that any sequence should occur more than once is thus small, yet the pattern ABC occurred nine times, the pattern DAB occurred six times, and the pattern BCD occurred four times. Considering the series of four individuals there are 240 possible combinations; 14 series occurred a total of 20 times, and DABC occurred 4 times, ABCD 3 times, and FABC 2 times. There is thus a definite pattern, revolving around four individuals; A, B, C, and D."

Two individuals, A and B, participated in the majority of the choral sequences, A in 29, B in 25. In contrast both E and F each called fewer than 12 times. They differ, however, in that E called three times without inducing any of the others to follow, whereas F called alone only once, but stimulated others to call on six occasions. But A initiated calling 9 times, and D 8, while B participated in 25 sequences, but initiated only 3. Another individual, C, participated in 16 bursts of vocality, but never called first. Both B and C were primarily "followers" rather than "initiators."

Plainly A was the most active member of the chorus. At least A was the most vociferous frog in the aggregation. But calling was initiated by A in fewer than 25% of the sequences Anderson recorded, and D did nearly as well even though it did not participate quite so often in choruses initiated by others. Thus Anderson's data provide no clear-cut evidence of leadership in the chorus. The vocalizations of male frogs depend upon hormonal levels, probably upon a complex combination of hormones, as Greenberg (1942) suggests. But the arousal, maintenance, and manifestation of sexual excitement in male frogs also depend upon complex neural mechanisms (Aronson, 1945) as well as external influences. The frog Anderson designated as A, therefore, may have displayed more vigor than others for any of several reasons. Its vigor could even have resulted from a fortuitous combination of circumstances that left it harboring fewer parasites. It remained in position and continued to call for a longer period than the others, Anderson notes, but unlike two less vociferous members of the aggregation it failed to attract a mate.

Axtel (1959) interprets observations of *Bufo speciosus* in the field as evidence that the female selects one male in preference to others in a chorus. Noble and Noble (1923) observed females of *Hyla andersoni* pass one or more vocalizing males before reaching a more distant male. Sexual selection conceivably plays a significant role in the evolution of distinctive calls in species, but it is questionable whether the size of the male or the intensity of his vocalizations are of paramount importance. Anderson's observations on *Microhyla* provide no support for the assumption that the most vigorous males are more successful than others in attracting mates.

In such loosely organized aggregations as those described for *Microhyla* by Anderson or the configurations in breeding assemblages of *Rana clamitans* Martof (1953a) describes, vocality is a prominent element in the behavior. Perhaps the voice has greater significance in the social organization of local populations than other investigators anticipated. Most of them ignore other possible functions of the voice or assume that it is used solely to attract the female. Jameson's (1955b) study of the cliff frog, *Syrrhophus,* discloses remarkable precision in the regulation of population densities. This regulation depends on manifestations of territorial behavior, with an interaction of individuals indicative of social patterns. Much of the behavior Jameson describes is attributable to vocalizations of the species that occur throughout the year. His report provides an excellent basis for the additional investigations required to substantiate this conclusion.

The studies of anuran behavior thus far reported show that one individual in a chorus may be more vociferous than others, but there is no convincing evidence of an order in dominance. No frogs manifest behavior comparable to the "pecking order" described for other animals. There is no "social scale," no individual that monopolizes the food supply, nor even evidence that any one male has marked advantages in attracting or retaining his grasp on the more desirable females. The same male may succeed in fertilizing the eggs of more than one female during a single breeding season, and several males may compete in their efforts to clasp one female. But in general the first male to seize a receptive female is the one that fertilizes her eggs.

The loosely organized calling pattern such as Anderson describes for *Microhyla* might be of adaptive significance if other members of the aggregation were placed on the alert by the silence resulting from one individual's awareness of an intruder. Inferences of the sort might be drawn from the statement of Yerkes (1903) quoted in the preceding discussion of warning signals. The irregularity of the calls in the small chorus Anderson recorded would preclude any interpretation of the sort. Yerkes' belief may be substantiated if definite sequences in the calls of individuals occur in other species. Malcolm Smith (1954) mentions European frogs calling while in amplexus, but in North American species males usually cease calling as soon as they clasp. The disadvantages in silence as a warning signal to other frogs are evident. The significance of calling patterns, as Anderson observes, is obscure.

The belief expressed by Jameson (1954) and by Hardy (1959) that the frog with the loudest voice is the leader, or that it is the individual most attractive to females as Axtell (1959) implies, is not in accord with the ideas expressed by Strother (1959). This author concludes that "it is reasonable to suppose that the frog has poor loudness discrimination for all but the weakest sounds." Long ago Gadow (1901) spoke of the precentor that initiates choruses in *Rana esculenta,* noting that country folk in Germany firmly believe that one old frog in each pond serves as choir master.

THE ADAPTIVE SIGNIFICANCE OF MATING CALLS

Conflicting Statements

Even with the application of scientific methods, interpretations of behavior may be difficult or misleading. Despite their use of experimental procedures in their respective investigations of hearing in frogs Merzbacher (1900) and Yerkes (1903, 1905) came to quite different conclusions. Nevertheless, these investigators had some basis for their statements. Much that has been written concerning vocality in the Anura since the turn of the century consists of unsupported assertions. Moreover, relatively few authors make any effort to relate their observations to those of their colleagues or their predecessors. Authors with preconceived notions prefer to ignore rather than explain how previous workers reached conclusions that differ from their own.

Random observations are not completely valueless. The untrained observer occasionally notes something of importance and reports it accurately. His conclusions may be unsupported by his data. If the information he supplies is reliable, however, it can be useful to others better able to design experiments producing results that can be interpreted unequivocally and fitted into conceptual schemes. Progress in our efforts to understand the significance of vocality in anuran behavior depends in part upon our critical reappraisal of previous work.

Much that is said in this review is necessarily speculative owing to the inadequacy of existing data. Many more questions have been raised than it is possible to solve. Hypothetical interpretations have been identified as such and offered with the full realization that they must be tested before they can be accepted. It has been more convenient than rewarding for authors to repeat what others have already said in their efforts to explain why frogs call. But a ready-made explanation is a poor substitute for experimental proof. Our advance is contingent upon concepts arising from experiments and observations that lead to further ex-

periments.   These in turn may or may not require revision of earlier
concepts.   It is immaterial whether the results of an experiment substantiate or disprove exisiting beliefs, but to be adequate results must
demonstrate that the conclusion reached is warranted.

Noting that Yerkes (1903, 1905) had commented on seasonal changes
in the auditory sensitivity of frogs, but had not demonstrated the existence of any motor reaction to sound alone, Courtis (1907) sought to test
the response of toads to their mating call.   He does not state which
species was employed, but probably it was the American toad, *Bufo terrestris americanus,* to judge by Courtis's description of the voice.   To ascertain the reactions of both males and females Courtis separated pairs
found in amplexus, and placed them ten feet apart.   In his first experiment he observed that when the male uttered a shrill, trilling note, "the
female immediately swam towards him and the two were soon mated."
Subsequent tests produced similar results, and Courtis reports that
"males as well as females responded to the call, which they could locate
very accurately."

Courtis cites other circumstantial evidence clearly suggesting but
scarcely proving that auditory cues direct the movements of the female
toad to the vocalizing male.   Courtis mentions a female toad that swam
to a point just beneath the spot where a male was calling.   No provision
was made to exclude visual stimuli, but nevertheless Courtis says, "I feel
sure, though, that this was not because it saw the male."   He also mentions that a female was attracted by the movements rather than the call
of a "couple" of toads, and swam towards them, thus implying that visual
stimuli play at least some part in the mating activities of the species.

Since no serious effort was made to exclude visual cues in the various
experiments carried out, Courtis's observations, while probably accurate,
and valuable at the time, do not offer conclusive proof that "both male
and female toads can hear and locate in space the call of the male," or
that the call elicits a motor response that "serves to bring the sexes together."

Miller (1909) describes the breeding migrations of a Massachusetts
population of a toad identified by the name then in use for *Bufo terrestris americanus.*   Actually Miller observed two species, for he mentions "two waves of spawning," indicating that *Bufo woodhousei fowleri,*
the breeding season of which commonly follows or overlaps that of the
American toad in its mating, spawned in or near the ponds being studied.
At the time Miller wrote the two species, despite their distinctive voices,
were considered to be "varieties" of the same species.   Holmes (1906)
accounts for the differences in voices by attributing the sounds heard
after the breeding season of *americanus* to a change from the shrill call

characteristic of the species to a "shorter, lower-toned note that at night has a peculiar weirdness."

Miller reports no detailed observations on the responses of toads to mating calls; he merely says he repeated the observations of Courtis, "which support the view that the females come to the males." Miller notes that "males reach the water two or three days before the females and begin their trilling.". Males, attracted by the voices of the first males to arrive, he believes, have thus already assembled in large breeding choruses by the time the females arrive. Miller offers no detailed information or quantitative data to substantiate these statements.

Wellman (1917) reports observations on a single pair of American toads, *Bufo terrestris americanus*. The male was calling when first sighted, and a female, only five feet away when first seen, rapidly hopped toward the male. "When the male began to trill—the female would make frantic efforts to reach the male. But when the second trill stopped she was all indifference and often in a few moments would hop off in another direction. But as the trills came every few minutes, she would finally in one of her drives reach the male while he was in the midst of a trill. He would not seem to notice her until she was within an inch of him; then he would scramble on her back and sometimes there finish the trill . . . He would take absolutely no notice of the female if he was not trilling. Thus the interesting feature was that the trill is the apparent stimulus for both sexes."

The earmarks of the casual observer are apparent in Wellman's account. His statement that the female was noticed only when the male was calling is contrary to the observations of others. With the head elevated and the vocal sac inflated while a trill is being produced, few toads detect an approaching female until she actually comes in contact with them. If the male appeared to be unaware of the female when he was not calling, it is probable that the toad crouched and remained quiescent, its normal means of escaping detection when aware of the presence of an intruder. Aside from these and other details indicative of faulty observation or interpretation, the author neglects all consideration of other stimuli to center his attention on the mating call. The female's reaction might easily have depended upon the inflated vocal sac, a conspicuous display when vibrating that might serve as a visual stimulus to receptive females. Greenberg (1942) points out this possibility in a hylid.

It should not be inferred from these comments that Wellman's conclusion is completely erroneous. It may be essentially correct, but his meager observations are inadequate to substantiate either his belief or alternate interpretations. Greenberg could not confirm his assumption on the basis of his laboratory observations of *Acris*. Experiments with *Bufo* do not rule out the possibility that the inflated vocal sac or even the pigmented throat serve as visual stimuli once the female has reached the breeding site where males are calling. Cory and Manion (1955) report that toads in an active chorus would swim toward a disturbance in the water such as that caused by the observer's walking. Tactile, visual, or even auditory cues could account for the response. Experiments summarized by Bogert (1958) show that receptive toads of both sexes were attracted to a loudspeaker broadcasting a taped recording of a chorus. They did not go to the speaker, however, but paused a few feet from it, as though awaiting some additional cue.

Noble (1923) mentions the doubts entertained by earlier authors concerning the role of the voice in anuran mating activities, but offers little to substantiate the thesis he advances. He describes the behavior of three female *Hyla andersoni* that appeared to be attracted by the voices of males. Like Courtis and Wellman, however, Noble provides no proof of the exclusion of visual stimuli. More detailed but no more convincing descriptions of the breeding behavior of the same species are supplied by Noble and Noble (1923). In two instances females were first observed when only three and two feet, respectively, away from males, whose movements while calling might have been visible to the females. A third female is reported to have travelled over one hundred and fifty yards and to have passed no fewer than four males that were calling. This female was intercepted while en route toward a shallow bog where no males called, although four pairs in amplexus were found at the site.

Nothing in this account can accurately be construed as evidence that voice is an important factor in bringing the sexes together. The description of the female that made the long journey, passing four vocalizing males while apparently headed for a breeding site from which no sound issued, could more readily be interpreted as evidence that voice plays no significant part in bringing the sexes together. From the information supplied it would be easier to conclude that other stimuli bring these treefrogs to breeding sites, or that females seek out males only after they are close enough to see them. Nevertheless, Noble and Noble assert that "the female are *attracted to the male by his call* (italics theirs)." They add that the female may exercise some choice in selecting a male, and "the call is not the only factor involved in bringing the sexes together."

Noble and Noble also observe that "when several species are breeding in one marsh, the species are usually separated into colonies because of the *specific* attraction of the different calls." Boulenger (1897) calls attention to the tendency of individual species to assemble in separate areas during the breeding season, but he does not ascribe this to their vocalizations. A. P. Blair (1941a) says that separate aggregations of *Hyla* and *Pseudacris* in the same pond are probably due to their responses to the call. McAlister (1959) maps a mixed chorus comprised of three species of *Scaphiopus* and a few individuals of two species of *Bufo* encountered in New Mexico. The chorus occurred in a flooded grain field with water a foot deep in two extensive areas. *Scaphiopus couchi* was confined to one of these, and the few *S. bombifrons* present were in a single aggregation in shallow water. The most abundant species, *S. hammondi,* was largely concentrated in the other deep area, but several individuals of the species were also present in choruses of each of the other two species. McAlister suggests that the "choice" of the area to which *couchi* was restricted may have depended upon the calls of the first individual to reach the spot. He concludes that "the most obvious stimulus for distance recognition of a conspecific chorus is the mating call."

This explanation is tempting. It could account for phenomena of the sort, but A. P. Blair (1942), it should also be noted, interprets mixed choruses of toads in Oklahoma as evidence that toads "respond to extra-specific calls." The investigations of Maynard (1934), Savage (1935) and Anderson (1954) show that the explanations of both McAlister and Blair may rest on gratitous assumptions. Maynard found toads, *Bufo terrestris americanus,* floating approximately 2½ miles down stream to reach a breeding pond. The majority of the toads left the stream at nearly the same place and crossed a narrow strip of land to reach the pond, from which 257 toads were removed on April 21. Toads continued to migrate by the same route on succeeding nights. On April 30, as the migration neared its peak with a rise in temperature, 190 toads were found floating down stream within a distance of half a mile. How did the toads know where to leave the stream? Maynard could not decide, but he asks, "Do some males arrive first and by their calling attract the females and other males? If so, how do the first males find the pond? After I had removed all the toads from the pond on April 21, what attracted the new arrivals?"

Savage found *Rana temporaria* leaving ponds suitable for hibernation and migrating over land in the pre-spawning season. They did not go directly to the spawning site, but migrated from pond to pond in order to reach it. More significantly, almost the whole migration took place before a single call was uttered. Only one hypothesis can account for the selection of one site in preference to another, Savage concludes, namely that frogs "follow a specific pond-smell." Vocality cannot account for orientation in salamanders, and Twitty (1959) finds neither geotaxis, hydrotaxis, nor vision to be of importance in explaining how the red-bellied newt, *Taricha rivularis,* of California returns to its home site.

When Twitty plugged the nasal passages of newts with vaseline, however, their ability to orient themselves either disappeared or was greatly reduced.

Newts not only detect the presence of females in the water, as Twitty observes, but employ chemoreceptors in locating food as Copeland (1913) reports. Risser's (1914) investigations of anuran amphibians, however, reveal that neither *Rana* nor *Bufo* can detect the presence of food by means of chemoreception. Olfaction is of no importance in sex recognition in *Bufo bufo,* according to Savage (1934). Nevertheless, it may be important in the migratory movements of frogs, as Savage (1935) later suggests, pointing out that the olfactory tissue of the frog's brain is well developed.

Chemoreception may explain other manifestations of anuran orientation. Anderson (1954) reports that large numbers of narrow-mouthed toads, *Microhyla,* bred during the spring in a pond some 60 feet in diameter. Prior to June 20 a field adjacent to the pond was cleared, and the pond was filled in. After a heavy rain on July 28 frogs of the species were calling from puddles and crannies between lumps of earth. Vegetation had been cleared from a 5 acre area, the surface of which was indistinguishable from the site where the pond had been. Despite the pond's absence, the entire chorus was restricted to the area of its former site.

Anderson suggests that narrow-mouthed toads may have "some sort of location sense in regard to traditional breeding sites," but it is not impossible that they responded to odors emanating from the filled in pond. It is far from certain that olfactory cues are as important in orienting the movements of frogs as they are in orienting salamanders, but whatever senses prove to be employed by frogs, there is little reason to believe that their movements are random. Pearson (1957) finds the eastern spadefoot, *Scaphiopus holbrooki,* well oriented within its range. As he reports earlier (1955), techniques for marking and recapturing spadefoots show that individuals migrate distances of at least a quarter of a mile in the direction of breeding ponds. These were probably visited before the frogs returned to home ranges; if so some spadefoots migrate slightly greater distances. Pearson finds spadefoots using the same burrow for prolonged periods, but sometimes they move a few feet or alternate in their use of as many as five burrows. Some are found in the home ranges for periods of nearly five years, presumably making occasional trips to breeding sites over a quarter of a mile away, even though their routine movements while foraging rarely exceed 32 feet.

If the spadefoot can return to a burrow following such forays, why should the selection of a breeding site depend upon the vocalizations of a single individual that finds it by chance? In most areas, ponds form year after year in the same locations whenever there is sufficient rainfall, and in all probability frogs use the same site on successive years.

Several authors question the significance of vocalizations in the mating activities of anuran species. Boulenger (1912) removed toads, *Bufo bufo*, from a pond where they were breeding, and liberated them midway between this pond and another in which frogs, *Rana*, spawned but toads avoided. Individuals, pairs and "groups" were employed in successive trials and the toads, after some hesitation or a few exploratory hops in the wrong direction, all "made their way straight towards the pond whence they had been taken." Boulenger points out that "the toads were not influenced by hygroscopic sensations, since there was water in both directions." He doubts "whether the sounds uttered by their fellows in the pond were a guidance," considering the very feeble voice of *Bufo bufo*. Malcolm Smith (1954) describes the mating call as a "short, plaintive staccato note, something like the bark of a small dog."

Inasmuch as the ponds were "only a short [but unspecified] distance apart," it is difficult to evaluate Boulenger's observations. Results evidently similar to those Boulenger reports were obtained with *Bufo compactilis* in Mexico, where some toads not only returned to their original pool, but to their original calling sites. In the Mexican species familiarity with the areas as well as territorial behavior may have been involved. Boulenger suggests that if the European toads were guided by sound "it would denote a very acute sense of hearing." Nevertheless, Savage (1934) is of the opinion that the voice of the male *Bufo bufo*, can direct the female. Heusser (1958), however, asserts that *Bufo bufo* has no means of social communication, and the sexes come together only because they converge independently on the spawning site.

The Yosemite toad, *Bufo canorus*, a species restricted to higher elevations, from 6,500 ft. to over 10,000 ft. in the Sierra of California according to Stebbins (1954), carries out its breeding activities largely during the hours of daylight. Conspicuous differences between the sexes in the pattern and coloration of this toad may imply that the male of *B. canorus*, unlike other species, makes use of visual cues to distinguish the sexes. This has not been demonstrated, however, and if vision is of importance in its mating behavior, the species has nevertheless retained its relatively strong voice, as well as the male release call and the release vibration. A related species, *Bufo boreas halophilus*, inhabits adjacent areas and possibly occurs sympatrically in portions of the range of *B. canorus* (Stebbins, 1951). *B. b. halophilus* normally breeds at night, but lacks a mating call. Thus the situation in these two species is the reverse of what might be expected if toads depend largely on either vision or hearing in their mating behavior or their migrations to spawning sites.

Herter (1941) states that amphibians are guided during their migrations by visual and olfactory cues as well as by their sensitivity to humidity gradients. He does not mention auditory cues as a possible alternative in the Anura, nor does he offer sufficient data to support his conclusions. Similar assertions or even explanations originally offered as suggestions, have been repeated so often that the tendency to accept them seems to stem more from a religious faith in the printed word than from any critical appraisal of the evidence upon which they are based. Heusser (1958), who comes to conclusions the opposite of Herter's, says that toads, *Bufo bufo,* orient themselves when migrating to spawning sites without using chemical or physical stimuli. But Heusser, in essence, is begging the question when he states that a "sense of direction—without learning" accounts for the principal breeding aggregations observed in *Bufo bufo.* Eibl-Eibesfeldt (1950) believes *B. bufo* uses the same spawning site year after year, and depends on memory to reach it.

The absence of a mating call in such species of *Ascaphus truei, Rana muscosa,* and *Rana tarahumarae,* to cite examples among those in the United States, makes it plain that some anurans locate receptive females or assemble in breeding aggregations by means of sensory cues other than sound. This, of course, does not preclude the effective use of voice by other species, nor prove that the voiceless species depend upon either vision or olfaction. Savage (1935), whose detailed study of the spawning migrations of *Rana temporaria* in the British Isles is mentioned earlier, reports that frogs of this species assemble silently at the breeding site. While there is no direct proof, Savage's data offer strong support for his suggestion that "the smell of the pond is the directing factor." He points out that a chemotropism could direct frogs to ponds, or portions of ponds, with distinctive odors. His data provide strong evidence that the spawning of *R. temporaria* may be more or less tied to growth rates in one or more species of algae. Odors emanating from the essential oils produced by such plants would provide satisfactory olfactory stimuli, presumably at the time most propitious each year for oviposition by the species. Savage's data show rather conclusively that the migrations of *R. temporaria* are carried out independently of hydrotaxis, geotaxis, or voice, even though additional experiments are needed to prove that chemoreception is the decisive factor in migrations. Malcolm Smith (1951) correctly summarizes our knowledge of the manner in which frogs of the species find their way to spawning sites with his statement that we do not know. Inexplicably Smith says later that the sound of the male chorus "undoubtedly helps guide the female to the pond." Unless audition is more acute in the species than the experiments of Adrian,

Craik and Sturdy (1938) indicate, the voice would be of limited use in orienting the female. Savage states that choruses of 1,000 males were sometimes inaudible when he was 50 yards from the pond.

As far as *Rana temporaria* is concerned Savage has ample reason to state: "No theory based on the idea that the first frog to croak attracts others to him, and that this spot becomes the spawn site, will stand for a moment in the light of the facts." Noble and Aronson (1942) mention the supposed function of the mating call in *Bufo* and *Hyla,* but extensive laboratory observations of *Rana pipiens* "gave no indication whatever that either the male or female was attracted by the sex call." Liu (1941) may or may not be correct in his assertion that the male of an Asiatic species, *Rana adenopleura,* builds a nest and calls from it "in order to attract the opposite sex." Malcolm Smith (1954) says that the male of *Rana esculenta* "calls to attract the female to the breeding site, [but] summer croaking presumably has no sexual significance."

Bragg (1940b) asserts that the mating calls of *Bufo cognatus* attract others of their own sex, but he doubts that males of another species, *B. woodhousei,* are attracted by the mating calls of conspecific males. His assumptions prove to be based on circumstantial evidence, larger choruses in *cognatus* than in *woodhousei.* The size of choruses might be attributed to any of several behavioral, populational, or ecological differences between the two species.

Cummins (1920) reports the results of observations made near Ann Arbor, Michigan, where he trapped four species of frogs, *Rana pipiens, Rana sylvatica, Pseudacris nigrita,* and *Hyla crucifer* as they attempted to reach a breeding pond in March, April, and May. Migrations occurred in waves, Cummins states, and they appeared to be more closely correlated with high relative humidities at moderately low temperatures (5° to 11° C) than with periods of vocalization. He intercepted greater numbers of frogs en route to the breeding pond following periods when no mating calls issued from the breeding site. Moreover, vocal activity was not followed or accompanied by any increase in the numbers of individuals migrating. Cummins's conclusions resemble those reached by Savage (1935) for *Rana temporaria,* even though quite different methods were employed.

Efforts should be made to repeat Cummins's work. If his results can be verified, they strongly suggest that many, but not necessarily all, frogs reach breeding sites without benefit of auditory cues, perhaps depending on olfactory cues, as Savage suggests. If so the vocalizations of many species may be construed as something more in the nature of courtship, or behavior necessary for the arousal and maintenance of sexual excitement in the female; equally probable, the call attracts the female only when migrations are completed, after both sexes reach the spawning site. Juszczyk (1951) quotes Herter's (1941) conclusion that migrating amphibians are guided by visual and olfactory cues, as well as by their sensitivity to gradients of humidity, although Juszczyk is of the opinion that hearing too plays an important part in the orientation of frogs, especially on their spawning migrations.

Angel (1947), without presenting evidence or citing authority, states that the sexes come together "guidés, dans chacune des espèces, par un chant particulier sans rapport avec celui des espèces voisines," implying that the voice of the male is not merely attractive to the female, but provides her with the means to distinguish one species from another. Oliver (1955) in his useful summary of the literature for North American amphibians, states that "the calls of the males may serve to bring females, and other males, to the ponds and streams where mating takes place. This has been shown to be true for at least most toads (*Bufo*) and Tree Frogs (*Hyla*), but does not appear to be true in some frogs (*Rana*). The males move to the breeding sites first, being guided by gravity and moisture and possibly by light and 'muscular memory.'" Heusser (1958) believes that when toads, *Bufo bufo*, fail to reach their usual breeding sites before spawning begins they respond geotactically or hydrotactically to any pond they come near.

Savage (1935) points out that geotaxis is readily ruled out by the ability of frogs and toads to cross all sorts of barriers while en route to the breeding site. It is rarely true, he adds, that by following a direction continuously downhill one reaches a pond. As for hydrotaxis, Savage correctly observes that there has never been a scrap of evidence presented to substantiate the belief, nor have the implications been realized. When the entire landscape is wet during or following a rain, as it often is precisely at the time when frogs migrate to the breeding ponds, orientation in terms of humidity gradients is out of the question.

Chapman and Chapman (1958), who studied the breeding and migrations of *Bufo regularis* in southwest Tanganyika, agree with Savage in ruling out geotaxis and hydrotaxis. They report that greater numbers of toads visited a pool during the dry season, but some also reached the pool when the areas surrounding it were flooded. They conclude that toads find their way to pools as a result of their familiarity with the general area, in addition to being "guided by the calls of their fellows already in the water."

Winston (1955) reports mating calls of the species in Nigeria during at least one night of each week in the year, and the Chapmans make essentially the same statement for the population in Tanganyika. Breeding is largely restricted to the wet season from November to January, according to the Chapmans. But on a dry year maximum numbers of toads appeared at the pool during May. It might be suggested, therefore, that toads wander when stimulated by moisture losses during periods of excessive drought, and are oriented by calls from the ponds. The Chapmans note that desiccation may have influenced fluctuations in the number of toads visiting the pool, but do not explain why toads call in the absence of breeding activity. The use of auditory stimuli by toads seeking water in arid or semi-arid regions would have obvious adaptive advantages. Or the crowding at the pool may have been the stimulus eliciting vocalizations territorial in function.

The Chapmans observe that the spawning of *Bufo regularis* is often preceded by an increase in the number of toads and more vocal activity at the pool. They consider it possible that toads are attracted to the breeding site by the mating calls of the first males to arrive, and point out that some individuals remaining near the pool could easily reach it and provide the initial auditory stimulus. Nevertheless, they doubt that vocalizations are important in directing the movements of toads at any distance from the pond, but "when close to the pool, females were attracted by the calls of males."

The implications of these assertions are legitimate and worth while. The bald statement of other authors that "mating calls serve to attract mates" is ambiguous in that it fails to indicate whether the writer considers vocality an element of spawning behavior, or a stimulus inducing or orienting migrations. In a British population of *Rana temporaria* Savage (1935) distinguishes 1) a migration season, 2) a pre-spawning season when the frogs have assembled at the pond but are not mating, and 3) the spawning season, when the males become vocal as the mating gets under way with pairs in amplexus. Heusser (1958) describes the spring cycle of behavior in *Bufo bufo* in Switzerland as consisting of three phases, the migration to pools, the mating, and the return migration. When males call prior to the arrival of females, as Miller (1909) reports for *Bufo terrestris americanus,* a pre-spawning period might be recognized in *Bufo.* From what may be inferred from our limited knowledge of toads and the more precise information obtained for species in other families, by Pearson (1954) for a pelobatid for example, it is probable that toads return to established home ranges after spawning. The return migration is, of course, accomplished in the absence of auditory cues.

Mating calls might nevertheless influence behavior during migrations or attract females only after both sexes, aroused by other stimuli, reach spawning sites. There is no evidence that toads hear better than man, but much would depend on the intensity of mating calls. Under favorable conditions a small chorus of *Bufo cognatus* is audible to human beings at a distance of four miles. H. J. Moore (1954) is perhaps justified, however, in his belief that the voice of *Bufo bufo* in Britain is too weak to be of importance during migrations. He is not on firm ground in rejecting auditory stimuli altogether merely because choruses reach their maximum intensity after the migration is virtually completed. Savage (1934) believes that calls of *B. bufo* may attract the female during the spawning period, although he too doubts their importance during the period of migration. Gallardo (1958) reaches a similiar conclusion concerning the function of the voice in the Argentine toad, *Bufo arenarum*.

Under normal conditions frogs travel rather astonishing distances, but there is little to indicate that such movements are random. The toads observed by Maynard (1934) behaved as though they knew the route to the spawning site when they were over two miles away from it. Nichols (1937) reports a toad that spontaneously travelled 1400 yards. A. P. Blair (1943) found toads, *Bufo terrestris americanus,* moving from one chorus to another, and discovered one individual that travelled 900 yards within ten days. H. J. Moore (1954) marked a toad, *Bufo bufo,* and recovered it a year later at a point over two miles away. Such small frogs as *Microhyla olivacea* travel rather impressive distances; a male Fitch (1956) marked was found for three successive years in the same study area. It turned up four years later at a pond 500 yards from its original site.

The interplay of the territorial and mating behavior may influence movements of the sort, as explained in the discussion of territorial calls. Perhaps population pressures, drought, or other environmental changes induce frogs to shift from one area to another. Several recent studies reveal a tendency for the majority of adult frogs to remain in one limited area. It is uncertain whether they ordinarily leave it except to spawn. This was first shown by Breder, Breder, and Redmond (1927), who tagged individuals of six species, including *Rana clamitans* and *Bufo woodhousei fowleri.* It has since been reported for *Rana esculenta* in Poland by Juszczyk (1951), for *Rana sylvatica* by Bellis (1958), for *Hyla versicolor, Pseudacris nigrita, Microhyla olivacea,* and *Rana catesbeiana* by Fitch (1958), for *Leptodactylus ocellatus* and *Bufo arenarum* in Argentina by Gallardo (1958), for *Acris crepitans* by Pyburn (1958) and confirmed for *Rana clamitans* by Ryan (1953). Raney's (1940) study of the bullfrog, *Rana catesbeiana,* in New York revealed that one individual moved 100 yards, although others moved less than 100 feet during a summer. In contrast, Fitch (1958) detected little if any movement in bullfrogs in Kansas, where each individual confined its activities to "its own small area within the pond."

Fitch found a notable exception in the leopard frog, *Rana pipiens,* which evinced no tendency to remain within a familiar area. No individual was ever recaptured after being marked in the study area. Other species not only forage within familiar areas, but return to them when moved. Breder, Breder and Redmond report homing behavior in *Rana clamitans* and *Bufo w. fowleri.* Jordan (1954) reports that *Bufo regularis* returned when moved ¼ mile away, and Archer (1959) offers circumstantial evidence that a male of the species came back to a fish pond when transported to a quarry pond a half mile away. Heusser (1958) reports that several individual *Bufo bufo* returned to "their own" area when intercepted in their migrations to one spawning site and moved to another 800 meters distant.

These accounts together with those previously cited provide ample evidence of the orientation of anuran movements. Chapman and Chapman may, therefore, be justified in rejecting auditory stimuli in favor of "a knowledge of their home locality" in their efforts to explain the migrations of *Bufo regularis.* Where Heusser considers the "sense of direction" to be innate or unlearned in *B. bufo,* however, the Chapmans define "knowledge" as "learnt visual, olfactory and tactile knowledge of the [home] area." The recent investigations of a newt, *Taricha,* by Twitty (1959) have already been mentioned. Several newts returned to a home site upstream from the point of release even when deprived of their eyes. Other newts appeared to be confused when Twitty plugged their nostrils. If these urodeles depend upon olfaction in orienting their movements and "smell their way home," as Twitty suggests, they must be familiar with the odors within a fairly wide radius of the home site or perceive familiar odors at some distance. It is conjectural, but doubtful, whether visual or tactile stimuli are more important than olfaction in orienting the movements of *Bufo regularis.*

Something other than knowledge of the home area is necessary, however, to explain the results obtained by Bogert (1947) in an investigation of the movements of *Bufo t. terrestris* in Florida. Toads were transported from a partially wooded area inhabited by the species to a contiguous area from which most of the trees had been removed several years previously. Repeated searches had failed to disclose any toads of the species in the cleared area except at the breeding pond adjacent to the area they inhabited. Thus toads were believed to be in unfamiliar territory when released in the cleared area one mile distant from the pond.

Nevertheless, 8 of the 43 toads released were recovered in the area they originally inhabited. Other individuals probably returned, as indicated by sampling techniques employed in similar tests. The results are inconclusive, but show that toads are not necessarily confused when released in unfamiliar terrain. It was suggested that the toads utilized auditory cues and that their orientation and return depended largely upon choruses of the species at the home site. Perhaps distant perception of odors emanating from the pond provides an alternate explanation, but if so, the toads must have detected familiar odors at a distance of a mile before they began to "smell their way home." Goldsmith (1926) claims that several spadefoots, *Scaphiopus hammondi,* were quiet when a mile away from a chorus, but became excited and active when they were transported to within 600 yards. Sound may have been the stimulus, but without more data than Goldsmith provides, it cannot be ascertained whether the activity he describes could have been attributed to other stimuli.

There is no satisfactory evidence that mating calls evoke a response in frogs until they reach the vicinity of spawning sites. At close range auditory stimuli are unquestionably important, but may be supplemented or supplanted by visual, tactile, or olfactory cues, rarely ruled out in the interpretations of casual observers. A notable exception, Mr. Ellis Schwab, sent specimens of *Microhyla carolinensis* to the American Museum with a note telling how five of the females included had been intercepted as they approached a male Schwab had placed in an upright open can where it could not have been seen by the approaching females. When frogs call from burrows, as Orton (1943) reports for *Rhinophrynus dorsalis* in Mexico and Stebbins and Hendrickson (1959) for *Leptodactylus poecilochilus* in Colombia, visual cues would be eliminated if the female is actually attracted to an underground cavity, as assumed. Actual observations appear to be lacking.

Responses to visual and tactile stimuli are revealed in Breder's (1946) account of the stereotyped courtship of *Hyla rosenbergi* in Panama. The male calls from a circular depression in the soft earth. This "nest" is soon filled with water by seepage from adjacent pools. When the female approaches the male, he moves to a position on the opposite side of the nest, with his back toward the female. This allows the female to leap on his back. In exceptional instances the female merely touches the male from the rear, but ordinarily she leaps on him. When Breder placed a male near a nest, the occupant promptly moved to the opposite side of the depression and continued to call while facing the other way, exactly as it did when the female approached. Since the male did not leap, sex recognition apparently depends upon the differential response of the sexes. Females leaping on males has been reported for *Hyla cinerea* by W. F. Blair (1958b), and for *Hyla versicolor* by Noble (1923). Littlejohn (1958a) reports a female of the latter species that followed a circular route to reach a male that could not have been seen until the female was a few inches away. The female circled the male before it actually made contact and was clasped.

Visual cues may, however, have played a more significant part in the behavior Dunn (1941) observed in *Dendrobates auratus* on Tobago Island during the morning hours. Uttering a "low, soft, buzzing sound," only when pausing between leaps, the male was usually followed by several females, one of which occasionally managed to leap on his back. Less aggressive tactile stimuli apparently serve to reveal the female's presence even though amplexus does not invariably follow. Visual stimuli sometimes suffice, as Bragg's (1959) account of *Pseudacris nigrita* indicates. A female was clasped after she merely swam in front of a male as he called.

In the preceding accounts, the female seeks the male, as observations for numerous other species demonstrate. It seems peculiarly significant, therefore, that in species where both sexes are vocal, the male goes to the female. Gadow (1901) reports that several males of the midwife toad, *Alytes obstetricans,* often gather around a single female, whose call is higher pitched than that of the male. In Mexico, Dixon (1957) observed both sexes calling during the courtship of *Tomodactylus angustidigitorum.* The male called from a slightly elevated position on the ground approximately 10 feet from a female emitting a higher-pitched call. Uttering its call at intervals, the male rotated its body between calls until it seemingly detected the direction of the female's call. Thereupon it hopped toward the female, pausing to call sporadically while the female supposedly remained in position. When near the female (as visual cues came into play?) the male's call shifted from chirps to a short trill "of about five notes, repeated three to five times in rapid succession."

Males among other vertebrate groups are commonly more aggressive than females. This may have been true of the Anura before vocality became an adjunct of their mating patterns. Males of *Ascaphus truei,* a supposedly primitive frog in which both sexes are mute, are said by Noble and Putnam (1931) to swim about in search of the female.

Functional Adaptations in Mating Calls

How are we to reconcile these conflicting views concerning the functions of mating calls? Several can be dismissed as undocumented assertions, of little help in explaining how frogs find their way to breeding sites, or in determining the significance of vocalizations prior to or during the spawning activity. The anuran voice may have arisen as an adjunct of territorial behavior, or vocalizations may have been incorporated in the mating behavior of some of the earliest anuran ancestors. Patterns of behavior diverged as the ancestral lines diverged and gave rise to new species.

It follows that when conclusions are well founded, conflicts may be traceable to differences between species, or even to differences between populations. If frogs of a few species spawn in silence, it is possible that vocality also occurs as a vestigial element of no functional significance in the mating behavior of other species. This does not imply that weak voices are necessarily functionless.

Mating calls of frogs assigned to the same species differ from population to population, as shown conclusively by spectrograms. In a few instances spectrograms disclose such marked differences in the calls of disjunct populations (Bogert, 1954) that it seems improbable that the same species is represented in both, despite similarities in the morphology of individuals comprising the two populations. Modifications in mating behavior may also be expected within species, or workers in separate areas may be dealing with frogs erroneously assigned to the same species by taxonomists relying too heavily on morphological characters. Taxonomic implications of differences in mating calls will be discussed later, but here it will suffice to note that disjunct distributions of species are of wide occurrence among the Anura. Individual populations, frequently isolated ecologically as well as spatially, are adapted to local environments in diverse ways. Moore (1942, 1959, 1957) and his students, Ruibal (1955) and Volpe (1952, 1957) conclusively demonstrate this for physiological traits closely associated with reproduction in *Rana pipiens* and *Bufo*. Anuran behavioral traits are assuredly inherited and subject to similar adaptive modifications.

The integration of behavioral, physiological, and morphological traits in tailless amphibians is reflected in recent studies of hybrids between species that breed at the same time or whose spawning seasons overlap. Where *Bufo terrestris americanus* and *B. woodhousei fowleri* hybridize, *B. t. americanus* invariably begins calling two or three weeks in advance of *B. w. fowleri,* as noted by Hinckley in Massachusetts as long ago as 1883, and in Indiana by A. P. Blair (1942). Hybrids, with an intermediate voice, call in some areas during an intermediate period that commonly overlaps the breeding seasons of both parental species. Cory and Manion (1955), who investigated the breeding behavior and morphology of the two species in Michigan and Indiana, report that hybrids call throughout the breeding seasons of both species. The hybrids show a progressive change, however, from "early-breeders" in which morphological characters are predominantly those of *americanus,* to "late-breed-

ers" more closely resembling *fowleri*. The breeding season in individual
hybrids apparently depends largely upon the amount of back-crossing
with one or the other of the parental species. Intermediacy in behavior
was not easily detected in the hybrids, but it is doubtful whether
dichotomous differences in the reproductive behavior of the parental
species ever existed. The species maintained their identity largely because of different habitat preferencs until habitats were disrupted by the
clearing of forested areas.

When sympatric species breed simultaneously, they demonstrate
marked differences in calling behavior where they share the same spawning sites. If hybrids occur, they often join choruses of one or the other of
the parental species. In southeastern Arizona *Scaphiopus bombifrons*
habitually calls from the edge of the pool (contrary to what Jameson,
1955a, reports for populations in Texas), whereas *S. hammondi* calls in
the deeper water, usually near the middle. Presumptive hybrids with a
dorsal pattern closely resembling that of *bombifrons,* but with a mating
call intermediate between those of *bombifrons* and *hammondi,* were
found calling from the middle of a pool with a chorus of *hammondi* in
July, 1955. Similarly, a frog intermediate between *Hyla gratiosa* and
Hyla cinerea, in size as well as in structure of its voice, was found
calling near Hicoria, Florida, with a chorus of *H. gratiosa.* In pattern
and coloration it more closely resembled *H. cinerea,* but it called from a
site that appeared to be identical with those occupied by *H. gratiosa* in
the same chorus.

It is not to be assumed from these meager data that behavior determining the selection of calling sites is genetically dominant in one species or
the other. The representatives of *Hyla* and *Scaphiopus* producing the
hybrids described above breed sporadically during the warmer portion
of the year, especially after heavy rains. During the summer of 1958, Dr.
Richard G. Zweifel found *Scaphiopus* hybrids similar to those found in
the same area in 1955, but this time they called with a chorus of *S. bombifrons.* It is not known whether hybrids respond to the calls of parental
species; their presence in choruses of one species or the other does not
prove that they respond to auditory stimuli. It may still be noteworthy
that in each instance the hybrids joined choruses of one or the other of
their parental species when other species of their respective genera called
from adjacent ponds.

The situation Cory and Manion describe for the two species of *Bufo*
differs in that the breeding activities of both parental species are restricted
to relatively short periods in the early spring months, with *B. t. americanus* normally preceding *B. w. fowleri.* The responses of the hybrids as
well as the parental species to environmental changes, among which the

rise in temperature is outstanding, determine the breeding season. The data obtained by Cory and Manion clearly imply that the temporal sequence in calling activities depends upon environmental influences and their interaction with physiological mechanisms under genetic control. Intermediate calls uttered by the hybrids during the interval between the normal breeding seasons of the parental species indicate that both the vocal apparatus and the behavior with which it is functionally integrated are genetically controlled.

Adaptive modifications in the call will be discussed further in the section dealing with isolating mechanisms. Detailed comparisons of the migrational or breeding behavior can be expected to reveal differences in the breeding behavior of local populations. But unless comparable procedures are employed in separate investigations, the data obtained may disclose differences in technique rather than differences between populations. It is improbable, however, that the behavior of *Bufo bufo bufo* in the British Isles is identical with that of populations on the mainland. It would not be astonishing if the behavior of *Bufo bufo asiaticus* in Japan proved to be radically different, even though some elements of its behavioral pattern could also be nearly identical.

Aside from the confusion that may stem from behavioral differences between local populations, the behavior of frogs inhabiting any one area may be modified by external environmental conditions that vary from year to year. In the San Simon Valley east of Portal, Arizona, *Scaphiopus hammondi* and *Scaphiopus couchi* were in full chorus following the first heavy rain during July of 1953. A third species, *Scaphiopus bombifrons,* did not appear until two weeks later, when it became approximately as abundant as the other two species, even though there was no evidence whatever of breeding activity either at the time it emerged or later in the summer. Two years later all three species were in breeding aggregations following the first heavy rain at approximately the same season. On this occasion, *S. bombifrons* called first, with choruses during the afternoon, at least three hours before the other two species began. W. F. Blair (1958e) reports the breeding pattern of *Bufo valliceps* to vary greatly from year to year in Texas. Einem and Ober (1956) discuss environmental conditions influencing the seasonal activities of frogs in Florida.

Conflicting conclusions concerning the role of mating calls in anuran breeding behavior or distant orientation, therefore, could stem from infraspecific variations, from actual differences between species, faulty experimental techniques, careless observation, or from misleading if not erroneous interpretations of data. Since Noble (1931) stated his belief that frogs call in order to attract mates, many investigators have been

prone to assume that mating calls have no other functions. For some
species there is proof that the male's call attracts females, but it may have
any of several other funtions as well.

Auditory stimuli can influence behavior in a number of ways. As a
corollary, if the vocal abilities of the Anura have been fully exploited
during the course of their evolution, the usages of voice must have shifted
concomitantly with adaptive modifications of ancestral patterns of behavior. The vocalizations of one species often stimulate members of
other species to call, but on the whole mating calls exert little if any influence on the behavior of other species. Various functions of the mating
call have been suggested in the preceding review and discussion of the
literature. There is little if any evidence for some interpretations.
Others obviously would not apply to species whose behavior is sufficiently
well understood to leave no doubt concerning the significance of their
calls. Depending on the nature of the data and what can be learned concerning the behavioral responses of the individual species, the following
alternatives are worth considering.

1. Mating calls provide the female with a means of species discrimination after receptive males and females have converged at spawning sites
in response to other stimuli. Where several species breed concurrently
in the same pond, the female depends largely or entirely on her response
to the male's calls. To be effective as a barrier to interbreeding, such behavior would depend upon the specificity of the female's response to a
distinctive mating call characteristic of males of the same species. When
both sexes call, the specificity of the response in either sex, possibly of
both, may be entailed.

2. Mating calls orient the movements of both sexes only during the
migration, but pairing depends upon other senses after frogs reach
spawning sites. Such functions of the call would depend upon the is-
suance of the initial calls by males residing in or near permanent pools,
or by males that fortuitously discover temporary pools suitable for
spawning.

3. Mating calls orient and attract frogs of both sexes during their
migrations as well as during the formation of pairs after the spawning
site is reached. Here too the initial calls would have to come from males
already at the spawning site.

4. Males assemble at spawning sites independently of auditory stimuli,
but their choruses orient and attract receptive females only when the
chorus reaches an effective threshold of intensity. After reaching the

spawning site pairing would depend upon vision or other senses in the female or in both sexes.

5. Mating calls neither attract nor orient the movements of females, but are territorial in function and provide for the spacing of males in a breeding aggregation. Spacing at a breeding site would enhance the chances for males in the aggregation to become aware of any receptive female that arrived in the area. Pairing could depend on visual, tactile, or olfactory cues.

6. Frogs of both sexes assemble at breeding sites when aroused by an interplay of internal and external environmental stimuli that result in their convergence on breeding sites where mating calls function in the arousal and maintenance of receptivity in the female.

7. Mating calls have no function, but are uttered as an ancestral trait retained in the pattern of behavior as a vestigial, functionless element. This explanation is improbable, and though possible, it would be difficult to prove.

8. When frogs utter mating calls in the absence of spawning activity during periods of drought in regions where rainfall is sporadic or uncertain, the response may be conditioned by moisture loss rather than an arousal of sexual activity by prevailing environmental conditions. Equally probable perhaps, frogs in desiccated condition become vocal upon reaching pools in response to stimuli similar to those eliciting their mating calls during the spawning season.

STIMULI AROUSING BREEDING ACTIVITIES

More questions are raised than settled by the observations of anuran breeding behavior now on record. If we know little concerning the role of mating calls in the migrations of frogs, we know even less concerning the interplay of internal and external conditions that determine the onset of reproductive activities. We know that ovulation cycles are affected by changes in temperature, but we do not know what determines the length of breeding seasons. We know that some species breed at intervals during several months of the year, but we do not know why some females are ready to ovulate well in advance of others in the same local population. We know that one pond may be used as a spawning site while others are avoided, but we do not know why.

Breeding migrations occur under favorable climatic conditions, often but not necessarily including rainfall. Changes in environmental temperatures, and possibly the relative humidity or atmospheric pressure, may be effective in arousing migration behavior in some species, or they may be necessary supplements of rainfall as the primary stimulus in others. We know little concerning thresholds, whether environmental stimuli exert their influences directly or indirectly, or whether some influences are cumulative in their effects. Vocality and the appearance of the clasping reflex in the male, and their concurrence with ovulation and the response of the female to mating calls, may depend entirely on the anterior pituitary. If changes in the weather are directly or indirectly responsible for the release of the hormones governing breeding behavior, we do not know how external stimuli exert their effects on the pituitary. If the arousal and maintenance of sexual activity depend on hormonal levels, we know little concerning the extent of the interdependence of the various components of reproductive behavioral patterns.

Over a dozen species may call and breed simultaneously in one locality. Under slightly different conditions only a few of the species present participate. There are possibly as many different breeding cycles as there are species of frogs. No two of the fifteen species studied by Cei (1949) in the Chaco of Argentina had breeding cycles that were identical. It is improbable that environmental changes influencing one cycle are the same changes that influence others.

The trend toward rising temperatures may be largely responsible for the fixed sequence in which several species initiate breeding activities in some regions. Babcock and Hoopes (1940) report that several species of frogs in New England emerge and begin to call in virtually the same order on consecutive years. It is also noteworthy that when the ranges of New England frogs extend southward to Florida, the same species call much earlier in the year, as Carr (1941) reports. At Ithaca, New York, Wright (1914), however, assembled data over a period of years that reveal little consistency in temperatures on the dates of emergence. Furthermore, the earliest dates when calls are heard vary from year to year. Similar variations in the temperature and dates of emergence were observed in British populations of *Rana temporaria* by Savage (1935), who suggests that the effects of temperature during the months preceding spawning are cumulative, whereas temperatures during the spawning period are much less critical. The time when the breeding migration occurs in March may depend upon the weather during February. The amount of rain that has fallen may also influence the time of the migration, but when the time arrives, frogs move to the ponds and spawn regardless of the presence or absence of rain.

In arid regions, such as the Sonoran and Chihuahuan deserts of North America, where the precipitation permits frogs to breed during the summer, their breeding may depend as much upon the lower tempera-

tures that prevail during or following a storm as it does upon the formation of pools. A drop in the temperature of the water was shown by
Bles (1905) to be important in stimulating breeding activity in the
African clawed frog, *Xenopus.* This may be true of other species inhabiting tropical or semi-tropical regions.

In arid or semi-arid regions heavy rainfall during the warmer months
is a prerequisite for the breeding activity in some species. Where the
rainfall is abundant at nearly all seasons, as it is in such humid regions
as Florida, the advent of moisture may not be so important as casual observations imply. Some species breed almost every night throughout the
summer in permanent pools. It is understandable that species adapted
for breeding in temporary pools restrict their spawning to periods following heavy rains. It is not so easy to account for the emergence of great
numbers of individuals belonging to other species that were already
spawning in permanent pools prior to the rain. The greatest concentrations of frogs in Florida are, in fact, nearly always encountered in newly
formed temporary pools, where temperatures are likely to be lower than
in permanent pools similar in size.

Innumerable differences in the responses of members of the various
species to changes in weather reflect the adaptations of populations to
local environments. Many species are specialized in their breeding
habits or in their tolerances to extreme environmental conditions. Wood
frogs, *Rana temporaria* in Europe, like *Rana sylvatica* in North America,
are adapted to such low temperatures that they occasionally spawn when
ice is still present on the ponds, and commonly do so in water only a
few degrees above freezing. They are less tolerant of higher temperatures. Balcells (1957) reports that males of *Rana temporaria* from the
Pyrenees become sexually inactive when subjected to temperatures ranging from 15° to 18° C for four or five days. Under similar conditions
the females do, however, remain able to spawn. In contrast to *Rana
temporaria,* many frogs in the warmer portions of the United States
habitually breed at temperatures exceeding eighteen degrees. W. F.
Blair (1956a) reports vocal activity (not necessarily indicative of breeding) in toads, when water temperatures are as high as 30° C.

Cei (1944) points out that endocrine-sexual cycles in European wood
frogs, *Rana temporaria* and some related species, are correlated with their
geographical distributions. The seasonal cycles of northern species,
along with those of their relatives in montane habitats in southern
Europe depend upon endocrine changes, but these changes are under
genetic control. In the species that inhabit Mediterranean climates,
spermatogenesis is potentially continuous. Cei found that sex cycles
were not affected by photoperiods, the availability of food, or the amount

consumed, but he believes that sex cycles, whether they are seasonal or continuous, are influenced by environmental temperatures.

A recent study of spermatogenetic cycles in *R. temporaria* by van Oordt (1956) shows that gonadotrophic activity of the adenohypophysis depends upon the environmental temperature. According to van Oordt, the spermatogenetic cycle of this frog is determined by an "inherent mechanism" manifest in the sensitivity of the primary spermatogonia to gonadotrophins during the colder part of the year. Higher temperatures during late spring and summer limit spermatogenesis, chiefly by inhibiting the gonadotrophin secretion of the adenohypophysis.

Breeding seasons vary considerably in duration from species to species. Professor John A. Moore informs me that on occasional years local populations of *Rana sylvatica* complete their spawning within a 24 hour period. Mating seasons of other species extend over weeks or even months in similar latitudes, but it is doubtful whether any one female breeds more than once. Piatt (1941) asserts that in New York a female toad, *Bufo terrestris americanus,* found mating on April 20 was again discovered mating and depositing eggs on May 7. It is questionable whether the same toad produced two clutches of eggs. Perhaps oviposition did not occur on the first mating, but the report can more readily be attributed to an error in the identification of the individual.

A. P. Blair (1943) doubts that *B. t. americanus* breeds every year, and Bragg (1940b) entertains similar notions concerning *Bufo woodhousei.* Assumptions in both instances are based on the observation that males greatly outnumber females at breeding sites. Choruses of toads continuously lose and gain members, as Blair notes for *B. t. americanus.* If males resume calling following oviposition while spent females leave spawning sites, as Savage (1935) reports for *Rana temporaria,* it is virtually inevitable that males outnumber the females on any one night. Spent females soon become unreceptive, and ordinarily leave spawning sites soon after oviposition is completed. It is uncertain whether the spent female no longer responds at all or whether her response becomes negative. When the breeding season is short, and spawning is completed in a day or so, as it is in *Rana sylvatica,* virtually every male in some instances is in amplexus simultaneously. Males and females arrive and depart at approximately the same time.

In regions with long growing seasons females of some species often spawn more than once. In Algeria, Boulenger (1897) reports, the female of *Discoglossus pictus* normally spawns three times between January and October. Bruce and Parks (1946) report five successive spawning of the species in the laboratory at intervals of less than three weeks. In Louisiana populations of *Microhyia carolinensis* there is no hibernation period, according to Anderson (1954), but his study of the species discloses gonadal cycles attributed to seasonal changes in temperature. The changes in the gonads of *Microhyla* are, however, very different from those described for *Rana pipiens* in Vermont. Prolonged or heavy rains initiate breeding in *Microhyla*, although Anderson (1954) did not discover why some females deposit eggs in April, whereas others spawn in September. Examination of females taken in June discloses no appreciable variation in their degree of readiness for spawning.

Sex cycles may differ in species that live side by side, perhaps because they occupy different microhabitats, or respond to different thresholds of temperature, rainfall, or their combination. In Argentina Caruso (1949) finds almost continuous reproductive activity in *Hyla raddiana* in the same areas where *Phyllomedusa sauvagi* breeds only during periods of rain. In the eastern part of the United States several species breed in the absence of rain. Others respond to moderate amounts of precipitation, but an unusually heavy downpour, at least an inch or more within one or two days is required, according to Gosner and Black (1955), before breeding occurs in the eastern spadefoot, *Scaphiopus holbrooki*.

Hansen (1958) attempts to account for the unusual requirements of this species. He suggests that individuals in their burrows are subjected to desiccation. Following heavy rains they become physiologically conditioned for breeding, supposedly because the moisture absorbed induces the pituitary to release gonadotrophins. The burrows inhabited by spadefoots in low areas become flooded, Hansen assumes, the occupants emerge, and initiate choruses that stimulate other individuals to assemble at the pools, which thereupon become breeding sites.

Some mechanism of the sort may explain the appearance of large numbers of spadefoots following abnormally heavy rainfall, but the explanation Hansen suggests could more readily be applied to species inhabiting arid regions, *Scaphiopus hammondi*, *S. bombifrons*, and *S. couchi*. These species west of the Mississippi Valley breed in response to moderate amounts of rain. Where water tables are as close to the surface as they are in many sandy areas where *Scaphiopus holbrooki* occurs in Florida, desiccation must be extremely rare. Furthermore, rainfall heavy enough to form pools may nevertheless fail to arouse breeding activities in *Scaphiopus holbrooki*. Little attention has been paid to the possibility that the sudden lowering of atmospheric pressures stimulates breeding activity in the species. The drop in pressure commonly accompanying periods of abnormally heavy rainfall would, however, offer a more plausible explanation than the absorption of water.

Is the whole intricate pattern of reproductive behavior regulated primarily by pituitary control of gonad cycles, or does the sequence in the pattern depend upon a sequence of responses that the behavior of one sex evokes in the other? Gosner and Rossman (1959) note that females of *Pseudacris nigrita* arrive at breeding sites prior to ovulation and wait in the pool until ovulation occurs, perhaps induced by the auditory stimuli of the calls issuing from the males. Or does ovulation in some species depend upon the stimulus of amplexus, as Bragg (1942a) speculates? Observations of Colombian forest frogs, *Atelopus cruciger*, reported by Sexton (1958) reveal that pairs remain in amplexus for periods perhaps exceeding nineteen days, but it is not known whether ovulation preceded or followed the initial clasping. Gosner and Rossman failed to induce ovulation in females of *Hyla* and *Pseudacris* when males were permitted to clasp them for three or four days.

Females of *Microhyla carolinensis* are receptive prior to ovulation, which may be nearly completed in advance of amplexus or continue after the female is clasped, according to Anderson (1954). In contrast, Noble and Aronson (1942) find estrus, or the period of receptivity, dependent upon recent ovulation in *Rana pipiens*. They suggest that in *Hyla* and *Bufo* the female's response to mating calls may be another manifestation of estrous behavior. Other evidence indicates that a positive response to mating calls may be limited to the period of estrus. Mature *Hyla*, *Bufo*, and *Rana* of either sex are often observed in routine feeding activities while choruses of the same species are breeding a few meters away.

The females of *Pseudacris nigrita* that Gosner and Rossman found entering breeding ponds often arrived several days prior to the onset of ovulation. As in *Rana pipiens*, however, no female was found in amplexus until ovulation had occurred, even though "non-ovulated females were equally accessible." Gosner and Rossman suggest that females in estrus approach males in response to mating calls, as the experiments of Martof and Thompson (1958) indicate. It is significant that ovulation was well advanced or completed in all females Gosner and Rossman found in amplexus. In the absence of other data, however, it is not certain that "females take the initiative" in the formation of pairs. Martof and Thompson mention males that remained in position and called until touched by a female, but under some conditions one male seized another. These authors observe that a clasped male utters a release call, but for obscure reasons they attribute sex discrimination to other stimuli and say nothing concerning differentials in the behavior of the two sexes. The release vibration of the female, though not mentioned, may provide a means for the male to discriminate between receptive and unreceptive females, as it does in other frogs, including hylids. It is improbable that sex discrimination by the male depends wholly upon the response of the estrous female.

Manifestly the appearance of estrous behavior in *Microhyla* prior to rapid ovulation accelerates mating activity. Anderson (1954) observes that it permits the species "to take advantage of sudden rains for breeding purposes." The spawning of *Microhyla* may occur in permanent pools, but receptivity of females prior to or concomitant with their arrival at breeding sites may be largely restricted to species with short spawning seasons, such as *Rana sylvatica,* or to species that breed in temporary pools. Rapid transformation, and the tolerance of the eggs or larvae to high temperatures and water low in oxygen content, are among other adaptive modifications in reproductive patterns occurring in species that habitually breed in temporary ponds. Among species that breed in relatively permanent pools, no serious disadvantage is incurred if the female arrives at the spawning site and remains unreceptive until ovulation is completed. The temporal element is not important when environmental conditions are coupled with such adaptations as those allowing the tadpole to transform the following year.

Where rains are sporadic and uncertain as they are in arid regions, the females of species adapted for breeding in temporary pools are apparently receptive and ready to ovulate almost immediately upon their arrival at spawning sites. In the American Southwest spadefoots, *Scaphiopus,* often deposit eggs within a few hours after the first summer rain. But it is not unusual for pools to disappear before their larvae have transformed. The odds in favor of the tadpoles' transformation are manifestly enhanced if the eggs are deposited immediately after pools form.

Thus receptivity and rapid ovulation may be correlated to some extent with adaptations dictating the use of temporary pools. It is questionable, notwithstanding, whether anything is to be gained by distinguishing "xeric" and "mesic" patterns of breeding behavior. The terms carry erroneous implications. Species utilizing permanent pools are encountered in arid regions; breeding in temporary pools occurs in species restricted to humid regions. In Florida numerous species utilize either permanent or temporary pools, depending on the amount of rainfall at any given time. Anderson (1954) discusses the inadequacy of the concepts, noting that the gonadal cycle of *Microhyla carolinensis* is adaptable to either mesic or xeric patterns, whichever is most suitable to local climatic conditions. At noted above, Cei (1944) distinguishes two breeding patterns in one group of closely related species. In northern or montane frogs seasonal cycles are perhaps under genetic control, whereas in the southern species spermatogenesis is potentially continuous. Breeding cycles in both are influenced by temperature, but the adaptations to climatic conditions depend more upon the length of the growing season than upon the rainfall. Volpe (1957) suggests that a distinction might be made between species with breeding seasons and those with breeding periods.

The numerous patterns of anuran reproductive behavior reveal the complexity of the adaptive phenomena associated with breeding. In temperate climates where comparatively few species inhabit any one locality, diversity in spawning sites, with rare exceptions, is limited to streams, or to pools that are either permanent or temporary. In humid regions in the tropics, where species are far more numerous, eggs are not only deposited in various kinds of pools; they may be deposited in moist places on land, in such plants as bromeliads, or be carried on the back or in pouches by either the male or the female. Diversification in reproductive cycles, and specializations in spawning sites may be regarded as means of avoiding competition between species. Roughly 12 species inhabit the whole of New England, whereas Dunn (1931) estimates that at least 50 species of Anura inhabit tiny Barro Colorado Island in Panama. Park, Barden and Williams (1940) describe the vocal evidence of breeding behavior in the frogs inhabiting rain forests of Panama, where some species restrict their calling to short periods of time each night. Some call at dusk and again at dawn, beginning their vocalizations at almost the same time night after night.

Vocality, therefore, is integrated with anuran habits and behavior in complex ways. Although receptivity precedes vocalization in some species, the utterance of mating calls is usually a manifestation of receptivity in the male. Such utterances of the male precede or accompany the period of estrus in the female. In light of the report by Gosner and Rossman (1959) that females of *Pseudacris nigrita* reach the pond days in advance of ovulation and estrus, it is questionable whether mating calls orient the migrations of females, unless it can be demonstrated that their response to mating calls is temporarily inhibited upon their arrival at spawning sites. Anderson's (1954) disclosure that amplexus occurs immediately prior to or during ovulation in *Microhyla* may explain the pre-spawning period noted by Savage (1935) in *Rana temporaria*. Frogs of both sexes assemble in silence at spawning sites, and some are already in amplexus before any voices are heard. Malcolm Smith (1954) asserts that frogs of this species vocalize while in amplexus. Males of *Rana temporaria* are evidently exceptional in being receptive prior to becoming vocal. If the female is receptive prior to ovulation, it is at least plausible that mating calls help induce ovulation, as they may in *Pseudacris nigrita* before amplexus occurs.

This is conjectural, for we know little concerning the interplay of behavior and endocrine functions in the Anura. Houssay (1954) summarizes some of the results obtained in numerous investigations of the physiological or morphological changes resulting from the administration of hormones.   Noble (1931) defines and discusses secondary sex characters, some of which are seasonal in occurrence under natural conditions, and influenced by hormones.   Release vibrations can be induced in juvenile male toads treated with mammalian gonadotrophins, as shown by A. P. Blair (1946a), or in either sex by administering testosterone propionate. Males of *Acris crepitans* treated with testosterone call somewhat earlier than the controls, according to Greenberg (1942), but the hormone fails to elicit the whole pattern of sex behavior.   Greenberg also mentions a preliminary investigation (unpublished) in which he and L. R. Aronson find that immature male treefrogs, *Hyla cinerea,* can be induced to call by administering testoterone.

It is well known that pituitary implants ordinarily induce ovulation in anuran females, but little attention has been devoted to influences of such implants on vocality in males. Mating calls are seldom issued by males of some species under laboratory conditions. *Rana pipiens* is sometimes vocal, but not every male calls. Aronson and Noble (1945) increased the proportion of vocal males in an experimental series by means of homoplastic pituitary injections. Their efforts to ascertain the nature of the neural mechanisms controlling sexual behavior reveal the complexity of the interdependence of the brain, the endocrine glands and other physiological mechanisms upon which the vocalizations of the species depend.   Aronson and Noble report that males of *Rana pipiens* sometimes utter the mating call following ablation of the forebrain, diencephalon, optic lobes, cerebellum, and anterior tegmentum.   On the basis of these results and inferences drawn from other experiments, they conclude that the neural mechanism mediating the mating call is "probably located in the midbrain" but is somewhat more diffuse than the male release call.   The release call is "integrated in the inferior colliculi and is relatively independent of higher centers."

Heusser (1958), who studied the migrational and reproductive behavior of *Bufo bufo* in Switzerland, concludes that the spawning migration is not merely "appetitive behavior," but must be considered as belonging to a "higher center."   This is merely an inference, however, rather than a conclusion based on experimental investigations of neural mechanisms in *Bufo.*

MATING CALLS AND DISTANT ORIENTATION

Discussions in preceding sections call attention to the shortcomings of interpretations based on casual observation, and the difficulties encountered in devising experiments that leave no doubt concerning the behavioral significance of anuran mating calls. Ambiguities in the statement that the "function of the call is limited to the attraction of a mate" are apparent, quite aside from the probability that mating calls are of territorial significance in some species. If mating calls serve as auditory stimuli, we should endeavor to determine the maximum distances of their effectiveness if we are to decide whether they orient the movements of frogs during breeding migrations, or come into play only when both sexes are assembled at spawning sites. Little attention has been directed to this aspect of the problem.

Several investigators accept or reject evidence favoring the belief that the vocalizations of males attract other frogs without stating whether they refer only to the role of mating calls in orienting movements during the migration. W. F. Blair (1956a) is more explicit, for he states that females are attracted to males vocalizing in the breeding pools where species discrimination rests almost entirely on the response of the female. He adds that calls "serve to accumulate an aggregation of reproductively ripe individuals of both sexes at a breeding site." In support of the latter assertion, he cites the statements of A. P. Blair (1942) and the report of an investigation of homing by Bogert (1947). The tests described in the latter report demonstrate that toads can return to a home site when released a mile away in unfamiliar territory, and it was suggested that they may do so in response to choruses of the species.

Martof and Thompson (1958) doubt that sufficient evidence supports the belief that mating calls are important in the formation of breeding aggregations. As an alternative explanation they suggest that "males and females respond to physical factors, such as slope of terrain and temperature and humidity gradients—factors which aggregate caudate amphibians." Twitty's (1959) recent investigation of California newts throws considerable doubt on the work of earlier investigators who ascribed the movements of salamanders to such responses, whereas Savage (1935) points out the futility of trying to explain anuran migrations in terms of geotaxis or hydrotaxis.

Nevertheless, statements that frogs of both sexes respond to mating calls rest largely on the meager evidence supplied by Goldsmith (1926). To ascertain whether toads (*Bufo terrestris*) of either sex would respond to mating calls at distances exceeding a few meters, tests were carried out in 1954 and 1957 at the Archbold Biological Station in Highlands County, Florida. A brief summary of these experiments is included in a semi-popular summary (Bogert, 1958) that appeared prior to the statement by Martof and Thompson (1958). The experiments will be described in greater detail here, and discussed in the light of the preceding review, and the results of recent work by other investigators.

Recent Investigations of Responses to Mating Calls

Responses in a Bufonid. Experiments with the southern toad, *Bufo terrestris,* were carried out at the Archbold Biological Station near Lake Placid in Highlands County, Florida on two years, during June 1954 and during July in 1957. Miss Alice G. C. Grandison of the British Museum (Natural History) collaborated in the work during the summer of 1957.

PURPOSE. The first experiments were devised to ascertain whether toads of either sex would respond to mating calls at distances sufficiently great to be effective in the orientation of individuals during their migrations to spawning sites. Later experiments included the additional objective of determining the interrelationships of reproductive cycles and the behavior of the female.

PROCEDURES. During 1954 toads to be utilized in the tests were obtained from areas in the immediate vicinity of the Station, with the exception of one lot taken approximately 25 miles to the east on the Seminole Indian Reservation in Glades County. Most of the toads employed in tests were not engaged in breeding activities when captured. Males greatly outnumbered females at feeding sites as well as at spawning sites. During the first week in June, 24 females and 138 males were taken. This total includes 49 males and 5 females taken in a breeding aggregation assembled at a pond in a pasture on the Seminole Indian Reservation.

The investigation was hampered by the relative scarcity of female toads. To be certain that all individuals were in good physical condition, none was retained in the laboratory for more than a week prior to being tested. Unfortunately this made it impossible to use comparable numbers of males and females in the respective trials. By chance 24 females were employed in each of three tests, although in no instance were the same individuals used in more than one trial. Even when retained in the laboratory for short periods of time, many females spawned before they could be tested. It was uncertain whether spent females would respond to an auditory stimulus, but no satisfactory means of delaying oviposition could be devised if samples of any size were to be used. Consequently all females available were tested, regardless of whether they had spawned at any time during the preceding week.

To avoid any possible confusion with other toads in the area, all toads were marked for identification by clipping one toe on each individual.

FIG. 13. The Archbold Biological Station, viewed from the east. Toads were released in the paved plaza in front of the laboratory during the course of experiments with *Bufo terrestris*, to ascertain whether broadcasts of recorded choruses influenced their movements.

The toads used in each trial were released shortly after dusk, between 8:30 and 9:30, depending upon the exigencies in preparing the apparatus.   In each trial the point of release was forty meters from a loudspeaker set up in the paved plaza in front of the laboratory (Fig. 13). The plaza is 13 meters in width and extends over an area roughly 100 meters in length, terminating in an unpaved road at the south, and in a broader paved area north of the laboratory buildings.   Toads were liberated in this paved area in preference to unpaved plots principally because it was desirable to recover every toad possible at the conclusion of each trial.   Toads released in the plaza could move freely either north or south, but the laboratory buildings prevented any movement toward the west, a disadvantage that could not readily be avoided.   Toads moving eastward easily climbed the low curbs to reach lawns or areas planted with shrubs.   The few toads unrecovered at the conclusion of some trials may have succeeded in secreting themselves in such areas.

The sound from the loudspeaker came from a field recording of the chorus of 49 males taken on the Seminole Reservation.   The chorus was taped at $7\frac{1}{2}$ inches per second on a battery-operated Magnemite with a frequency response of 50 to 10,000 cps, and reproduced on a Magnecord with the same frequency rating at the same speed.   The intensity of the sound being broadcast was judged to approximate that of the chorus recorded on the tape employed. It is problematical whether this level was judged with accuracy, but at a distance of 40 meters the sound from the loudspeaker seemed to represent a reasonably faithful duplication of the original sound. On alternate trials the loudspeaker was shifted from the position 40 meters north of the point of release to a position the same distance to the south. The sound of the ersatz chorus was provided at approximately the same moment the toads were released from a sack. With the cooperation of Mr. Richard Archbold and his staff at the laboratory, tests were carried out in the absence of all artificial lighting. After the chorus had been broadcast for half an hour, the lights were again turned on and several members of the staff at the Station assisted in recovering the toads, relatively few of which were not recovered although some had travelled distances exceeding 50 meters during the half-hour the sound was broadcast.

To facilitate the work of capturing the toads and tabulating the numbers and locations of those retrieved, a line was marked on the plaza at the point of release. Any toads found either north or northeast of the line were tabulated as having gone north. Similarly, toads retrieved south of the line were included in the tabulation as such, even though they may have veered more to the east. This may not have been the ideal procedure, but in view of the sporadic and sometimes erratic movements of females at spawning sites, where they may even take a zig-zag route to reach a calling male according to Axtell (1959), it seems questionable whether much could be gained by plotting recoveries with greater precision.

In one trial, conditions as nearly identical as possible with those of preceding trials were maintained except that no sound was provided. The toads in this group served as controls. An approximation of random scattering would be expected if their movements were not influenced by other stimuli in the absence of sound from the loudspeaker.

Similar procedures with the same equipment were followed in 1957, although a recording of a smaller chorus (described below) was used as the sound stimulus. Also females retrieved after each test were labelled to indicate the direction of their movements following their release and preserved for future examination. Meanwhile, it had become apparent that more significant results might be obtained if toads in a breeding aggregation were obtained and tested soon after capture. Owing to the meager rainfall at the Station during July, toads of the species called only sporadically, and no choruses were encountered. On July 25, near Placida, in Charlotte County, Florida a breeding aggregation of *Bufo terrestris* was found following a storm accompanied by over 135 mm of rainfall. With the invaluable assistance of Dr. William Tavolga the chorus of males in the aggregation was recorded on tape at approximately 2:00 a.m. on July 26. The aggregation consisted of 39 males and fourteen females, several of which were in amplexus when captured.

The toads were segregated by sex at approximately 3:00 a.m., placed in cloth sacks, transported 90 miles eastward to the Archbold Biological Station in the afternoon, and liberated in the plaza when preparations for a trial were completed at 9:00 p.m. In this trial the taped recording of the chorus obtained earlier the same day was reproduced as the sound source. Thus all males and females were exposed to virtually the same sound the males of the aggregation were producing when caught 18 hours earlier. An undetermined number of females spawned in the sacks while being transported.

RESULTS. The data obtained are summarized in two tables. Separate tabulations are employed to distinguish the toads collected at random and not tested the same day they were captured (Table 1) from those taken in a breeding aggregation at 3:00 a.m. and tested at 9:00 p.m. the same day (Table 2).

Considering first the data in Table 1, it will be noted that in the absence of sound from the speaker the movements were as nearly random as the situation permitted. The males in Experiment No. 2 were apparently uninfluenced by the sound, and it is doubtful whether the results obtained on the third trial are indicative of auditory influences. The males employed in Experiment No. 4, however, manifest a definite tendency to retreat from the sound. Notes describing the conditions of the individual experiments provide data that may account for the differences. Detailed notes for Experiment No. 4 reveal 1) that a shower occurred immediately preceding the trial, resulting in a higher humidity and a wet pavement, 2) that the sound reproduced was from the recording made at Placida, and 3) that the experiment was carried out later in the summer, on July 29, 1957. In the two preceding trials showers occurred earlier in the afternoon, but the pavement was dry or nearly so when the experiments were conducted after nightfall. In both earlier trials the sound from the speaker reproduced that of the chorus taped on the Seminole Indian Reservation, and the experiments were carried out on June 2 and June 4 in 1954, more than 50 days earlier in the season.

The tape of the chorus on the Seminole Reservation was employed in all three experiments with females (Table 1), but No. 5 and No. 6 were carried out on June 6 and June 10, respectively, in 1954, whereas Experiment No. 7 was later in the season, on July 23, 1957. In each of the three trials more females moved in the general direction of the speaker than away from it. As in the experiments with males, the trial conducted later in the season during 1957 yielded more conclusive results. However, the relative humidity was no higher, and there was no rain or wet pavement that might account for the slightly greater percentage of the toads that moved toward the loudspeaker.

Turning now to Table 2 and the results of the experiment in which toads were removed from a breeding aggregation early on the morning of July 26 and released in the plaza at 9:00 p.m. the next evening, the following conditions prevailed: There was a drizzle, with rain falling in minute drops sufficient to wet the pavement. The relative humidity was 96%, as measured with a sling psychrometer under the roof at the front of the laboratory, roughly two meters above the pavement. The humidity may have reached the saturation point at the spot on the wet pavement where the toads were released.

As indicated in Table 2, more than twice as many toads were recovered from the area in the direction of the speaker than from the area in the opposite direction. Of greater significance, many of the toads that presumably responded to the stimulus provided were found arranged in a semi-circle facing the loudspeaker. None was close to it, however, for they were in positions evidently reached before the sound was curtailed, approximately two to three meters from the loudspeaker.

All seven females recovered in the area toward the loudspeaker on July 26 were spent females. Two of the three recovered in the other area were also spent females, but the third and smallest individual was apparently sexually immature. Although it was taken in or near the breeding aggregation at Placida, it could scarcely have been engaged in reproductive activity. Examination of the 23 females retrieved following the test on July 23 (Experiment No. 7, Table 1) reveals that of the 19 recovered in the area toward the sound source, 17 had ovulated but had not spawned, whereas the oviducts of the other two were empty. Among the four that moved away from the sound source, three were spent females, with vestiges of eggs in the oviducts, and the third had not yet ovulated.

DISCUSSION. It is evident from the results of these experiments that much depends upon the influences of the internal and external environments, neither of which is subject to precise control if the object of the investigation is to determine what happens under natural conditions. It is equally evident that clear-cut results cannot be expected until we have more detailed knowledge of reproductive cycles in the species investigated, and know more than we now do concerning the influences on behavior of weather during various stages in the reproductive cycle.

It is virtually certain that the males found facing the loudspeaker, after having travelled at least 37 meters to reach the position, did so in response to auditory stimuli. The results of the experiment are not conclusive, but they point to the probability that choruses at breeding sites orient and attract other males in the vicinity. The reactions of males at distances exceeding 40 meters would depend upon their receptivity upon the volume of the sound and thresholds in the auditory mechanism. Earlier observation at the Archbold Station revealed that all toads in the vicinity did not participate in choruses, even when breeding aggregations formed at distances of 20 to 30 meters from established feeding sites. Mature toads of both sexes, but principally males, were often encountered in the same areas where they had been found and marked on preceding nights. The apparent retreat of 11 of the male toads from the sound of the same chorus in which they participated earlier the same day, points to the possibility that they were nearing the end of a period of receptivity. They may also have been adversely affected by the handling entailed in capturing, transporting, and marking them.

The results of Experiment No. 4 are indicative of a negative response to mating calls. Because all conditions could not be duplicated in Experiments 2, 3 and 4, however, it is uncertain whether the lack of any pronounced response in the earlier trials can be attributed to the dry pavement, or whether the wet pavement and more humid conditions prevailing during Experiment No. 4 had anything to do with the response. It is doubtful whether the negative response of these males can be attributed to the source of the recording, or to the difference in the season. In view of the definite positive response of the majority of the males in Experiment No. 8, carried out just three days prior to No. 4, the negative response of the toads may be attributable to the combined effects of the more humid conditions and their lack of receptivity.

Judging by the combination of circumstances under which the various tests with males were carried out, it may be inferred that the responses of males, whether positive or negative, depend upon a wet substratum or more humid conditions. Since moisture distribution was fairly uniform, this does not imply that toads were responding to humidity gradients. Hydrotaxis, geotaxis, and olfaction are also ruled out, because the pavement was level, and there was no pool or possible source of odors that could have been effective. All toads used in Experiment No. 8 had been transported from an area ninety miles away. Thus familiarity with the area cannot have played any part in the reactions of the toads.

The toads, mostly males, that moved toward the sound but paused facing the loudspeaker while 2 or 3 meters from it, behaved as though they were waiting for some additional cue. Contrary to what male toads presumably might do upon reaching a chorus at a spawning site, they did not start calling. Does the calling response depend upon a visual stimulus from other males with their vocal sacs inflated, upon the presence of a pool, or upon both? Or was the cessation of movement at a distance from the source of "mating calls" a manifestation of territorial behavior? Such questions can be answered only by further experiment.

Positive responses to mating calls evidently depend upon ovulation, but the high percentage of spent females among those exhibiting a positive response indicates the persistence of estrous behavior for several hours. Some females tested were in amplexus when captured, but oviposition followed the segregation of males and females immediately after their capture. Possibly the estrous period is prolonged when oviposition occurs in the absence of the male, but this seems doubtful. The presence of spent females among those retreating from the sound source may be indicative of abrupt reversals in the response to auditory stimuli.

CONCLUSIONS. Receptive females and sexually aroused males of *Bufo terrestris* manifest a positive response to sounds closely approximating if not duplicating the mating calls voiced by males in breeding aggregations. The elicitation of such responses at distances of forty meters points to the probability that mating calls play a significant part in the distant orientation and attraction of the toads forming breeding assemblages. The reactions of toads upon reaching the proximity of a sound source suggests that behavior at spawning sites is complex and not governed exclusively by auditory stimuli. The selection of calling sites, pairing, and other elements of the behavior pattern may depend in part upon visual cues, but this remains to be demonstrated. The evidence of a negative response to mating calls in unreceptive toads of both sexes is suggestive but inconclusive.

Responses in Hylids. The experiments with *Bufo terrestris* point to the probability that mating calls in the species play a significant role in the formation of breeding aggregations. Females may also be attracted to individual males in response to their calls at close range, but the complexity of the behavior at spawning sites, rather than the nature of the stimuli governing the reactions of toads, was revealed by the experiments at the Archbold Biological Station.

The experiments of Martof and Thompson (1958a, b) deal with *Pseudacris nigrita,* relatively small frogs mainly terrestrial in habits even though they belong to a family (Hylidae) in which many species are largely arboreal. These investigators used taped recordings to test the

responses of frogs to auditory stimuli at relatively close range.   The enclosure in which females were tested was less than three meters in length.
Males used in some experiments were induced to call in response to electronically reproduced calls of the local population.   Preliminary investigations in the laboratory showed that females would approach only the
males uttering mating calls.   When within a few centimeters each female
would pause and then crawl forward until she was in contact with the
male.   Apparently a tactile stimulus was necessary before the male ceased
calling and clasped the female.   Amplexus did not occur when females
were placed in a tank with males that did not call.   Females placed in
the tank with an unspecified number of males that were calling were
observed in amplexus within one to nine minutes.

Martof and Thompson state that "gravid females . . . were easily
recognized because eggs could be seen through the postero-lateral part
of the abdominal wall."   They do not mention that ovulation invariably
precedes the onset of estrous behavior in the species, as Gosner and Rossman (1959) report.   Eggs would not have been visible through the body
wall prior to ovulation, however, and the females tested by Martof and
Thompson apparently were in estrus.   "All females observed in our experiments," they report, "moved directly to specific calling males, even
though noncalling and some calling ones were close by."   The basis for
the choice was not evident "except that the male had to call persistently."
When males were induced to call while hidden in cloth bags supported
by hardware cloth, females moved toward the bags, sometimes jumping
over them, or crawling around the edges.   When the males inside the
bags ceased calling, females often moved to other bags in which males
were vocal.   As many as four females moved to a bag containing a male
described as having a "somewhat louder and more persistent" call.

In other experiments Martof and Thompson used a loop of tape from
which the call of *Pseudacris* was reproduced at intervals of 1.23 seconds,
approximating the call-rate of the frogs in the field.   The sound was
transmitted through a crystal earphone placed on the floor of the enclosure, with the volume adjusted to approximate the natural sound.
Only females were tested.   They reacted in much the same fashion as
they had when released near the males that called inside the bags, except that the behavior of the females appeared to be influenced in part
by the direction from which the sounds issued from the earphone.   One
female "jumped onto the back of the earphone, crawled over and tried
to get under it, made six trips around it, jumped over it, turned, [and]
jumped over it again and again."

Martof and Thompson did not test for discrimination, but doubt that
a female in a mixed chorus risks being clasped by a male of another

species before reaching a male of her own species. "Our observations," they conclude, "indicate that a female responding to the calls of a male moves so adroitly that the risk of being clasped by a frog, other than the one to which she is responding, is very small. We think this isolating mechanism is simple and highly effective."

When reinforced by other isolation mechanisms, mating calls undoubtedly play significant roles in preventing interbreeding between species. Hybridization between hylids nevertheless occurs under natural conditions. A. P. Blair (1941a) reports interbreeding between *Hyla crucifer* and *Pseudacris triseriata*. The latter species is similar in many respects to *Pseudacris nigrita* and was in fact once regarded as being subspecifically related. Blair suggests that the distinctive voices of *Hyla crucifer* and *Pseudacris triseriata* may be responsible for the separate breeding aggregations of the species. Interbreeding is doubtless inhibited by such behavior, but it remains to be shown that isolated aggregations depend upon the vocalizations of *Pseudacris*, whether the calls attract males, or whether females respond at distances greatly exceeding 3 meters.

The experiments described by Martof and Thompson do, however, provide clear-cut evidence that females of the species tested respond to mating calls in the absence of other stimuli. It seems probable that receptive females might be as effectively attracted to males of their own species in a mixed chorus as they are when separated, but experimental proof is required to substantiate this assumption. The greater agility of hylids perhaps accounts for their movement to the immediate vicinity of the sound source, in contrast to the results obtained with toads, *Bufo terrestris*, that paused 2 or 3 meters away. However the majority or perhaps all the toads that behaved in this manner were males. As indicated in the discussion of the results of the experiments in Florida, the response may have been a manifestation of territorial functions in the mating calls, even though calls may be responsible for the breeding aggregations characteristic of these toads. Where hylids depend upon the female's response to mating calls, pairing in toads may occur only in response to visual cues once both sexes assemble in a breeding aggregation.

MATING CALLS AS ISOLATION MECHANISMS

The carriers of some genotypes survive and reproduce more successfully under one set of conditions than do carriers of other genotypes. Because genotypic variations exist in any population, changes in its genetic composition are largely the result of the effects of natural selection.

No two populations are identical in genetic composition principally because no two areas possess the identical environments. Widely distributed species commonly comprise numerous slightly different populations. Genetic divergence depends upon the degree and the duration of isolation in each population, as well as upon genetic drift and sequences in climatic changes. When separate phyletic lines arise within a population, they may converge under some conditions or remain separate under others. Genetic discontinuities ordinarily arise when gene flow is interrupted for prolonged periods, usually if not always, when populations are geographically isolated. Rates of change vary from one population to another, but the maintenance of genetic isolation when geographical barriers cease to exist must depend as much upon the nature as upon the extent of the genetic divergence.

Transient Geographical Discontinuities

The frogs belonging to widely ranging species are not continuously distributed, but under favorable conditions they occur at numerous localities within a broad range that may become fragmented when ecological barriers arise as a result of climatic change. Increasing desiccation, for example, may result in the survival of geographically disjunct populations, each of which is surrounded by inhospitable environments. Reversal of a prolonged climatic trend may, however, eliminate ecological barriers and each of the disjunct populations may extend its distribution. As ranges expand, populations previously isolated may be brought into contact. Whether they interbreed depends largely upon the nature of the adaptive changes that occurred in each population during its spatial isolation. If modifications of the adaptive complex integrating morphology, physiology, and behavior have been slight and similar habitats were occupied during isolation, members of any two populations may interbreed freely. As a result of gene exchange, any small differences between the two gradually disappear.

When one population without appreciable changes in its mating behavior has become adapted for xeric environments while the other has become adapted for mesic environments during the period of isolation, expansion of their respective ranges may be influenced by ecological conditions. This happens, for instance, when derivatives of a parent population extend their respective ranges toward a zone characterized by a sharp reduction in rainfall. The dispersal of a population not so well adapted to arid conditions may bring its range in contact with the expanding range of a population genetically adjusted to the xeric conditions. Further expansion of either population is prohibited following contact because suitable habitats are preoccupied by individuals better adapted for the conditions beyond the zone where the abrupt change from humid to semi-arid conditions occurs. If the two populations interbreed, the hybrids are unlikely to be as well adjusted genetically for either environment as the parental species and may, therefore, be restricted to the relatively narrow zone where the parental populations are in contact. Even though hybrids are completely fertile, there may be little evidence of introgression under such conditions.

The situation can be quite different if there has been a shift in habits because of differences in selective pressure under dissimilar environments while the populations were geographically isolated. Expanding ranges may bring together representatives of populations so unlike each other that they do not compete for food, shelter or breeding sites. One population may be adapted to rocky habitats, the other may be restricted to open terrain. Significant changes in breeding habits during isolation, with members of one population adapted to lower temperatures, may now mean that members of one population breed earlier in the season. Frogs in one population perhaps spawn only in permanent pools while those of the other spawn in temporary pools or in streams. If they spawn in the same pool, calling sites may differ. Among several possibilities (Fig. 6), frogs of one population may call from the edge of the pool, those of the other from deeper water at the center.

Mating calls may be absent in one population but present in the other. If vocality persists as an element in their respective patterns of breeding behavior, the mating calls of one population may differ from those of another in frequencies, trill rates, duration of the calls, or their rates of repetition. The sexes may come together in response to auditory or tactile stimuli in one population, while pairing in the other depends largely upon visual cues. If the adaptive responses during isolation have influenced size, members of one population may be larger than those in the other, with such pronounced discrepancies in size that amplexus is inhibited or prevented. In exceptional instances differences in the secondary sex characters of males, the mode of amplexus (Fig. 14), the manner in which the female approaches the male, or even the male's dependence upon the vocalizations of the female in the formation of pairs, may inhibit or prohibit interbreeding.

Should the male of one population seize the female of another he may nevertheless fail to fertilize her eggs. If no mechanical or physiological barriers prevent the sperm from reaching the nucleus of the egg, embryos may start to develop but die before reaching the adult stage. Should the hybrids reach sexual maturity they may be sterile; they produce few

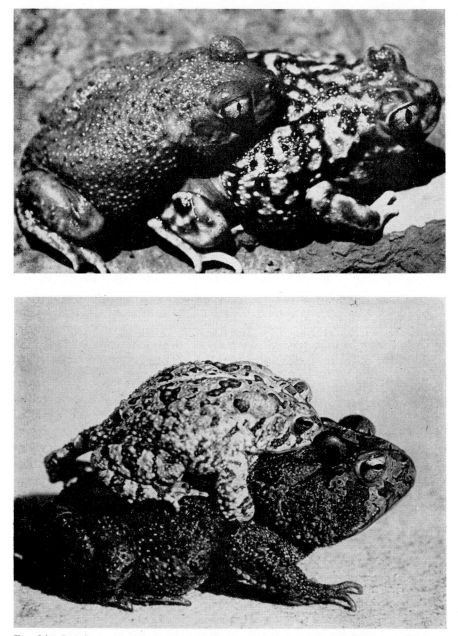

FIG. 14. Inguinal amplexus, characteristic of the Sonoran spadefoot, *Scaphiopus couchi*, with the male gripping the female at the pelvic region (upper). Axillary amplexus of the southern toad, *Bufo terrestris*, with the male gripping the female at the level of the pectoral girdle (lower).

viable gametes or none at all.   This usually happens in the first generation, but sterility may not appear until subsequent generations (J. A. Moore, 1957a).

From what may be inferred from the distributions and morphology of several species and subspecies of the Anura, differences between closely related populations virtually always can be attributed to earlier geographic isolation.   When the populations are sympatric, gene exchange is negligible, but it may not be blocked completely merely because geographical spatial barriers no longer exist.   Interbreeding is averted under natural conditions by several means, as Dobzhansky (1937) suggested when he proposed the term "isolating mechanisms" for any of several conditions or processes that hinder or prevent gene interchange.   The classification of isolation mechanisms accompanying Dobzhansky's proposal has been modified somewhat in recent discussions, by Dobzhansky (1951) and J. A. Moore (1957a), for examples.   Isolation mechanisms among the Anura are briefly discussed by Littlejohn (1959b).

Noble (1931) observed that isolation accompanied by changes in environment is particularly important in the formation of species.   Many biologists were not fully aware of its significance, however, until Mayr (1942) emphasized the importance of geographic isolation in the discussions of speciation in his more widely read book.   Since this work appeared few authors have questioned the belief that geographic isolation is a prerequisite for extensive genetic divergence.   Geographical isolation can, of course, be easily overcome when populations are brought together by accidental transport.   Or stream capture may bring together populations of aquatic animals previously isolated.   Geographic isolation becomes pre-eminently consequential in setting the stage for genetic divergence.

Few authors focus attention on the biological significance of the adaptive phenomena associated with the divergence of populations during periods of isolation.   Differences in morphology, physiology, and behavior, (and also the interactions of these attributes that lead to ecological differences) all aid in maintaining the integrity of populations, but speciation occurs only when gene exchange ceases or diminishes to negligible levels.   This, of course, usually results from isolation complexes rather than from individual mechanisms, many of which originate during periods of allopatry.

Until recently, investigations of isolation mechanisms among the anura were largely concerned with demonstrating the varying degrees of genetic incompatibility.   The implications of such studies are reviewed in recent discussions by J. A. Moore (1955, 1957b, 1958).   Hybrid inviability, hybrid sterility, mechanical or physiological barriers to fertilization—all mechanisms of the sort—are of unquestionable importance in speciation. It is not always realized, however, that there is no simple relationship between the systematic position of two populations and their ability to form hybrids.   Moore (1955) makes this plain, observing that his earlier work reveals the difficulties encountered in hybridizing *Rana pipiens* from populations in Vermont with those of the same species from Florida, despite the fact that normal hybrids result when individuals from either population are crossed with *Rana palustris*.   There is no doubt that populations of *R. pipiens* in Florida and Vermont belong to the same species for the two are connected by a series of annectant, freely interbreeding populations.

Adaptive Changes in Mating Calls.

The experiments with *Pseudacris nigrita* Martof and Thompson (1958b) describe clearly indicate that the female localizes the source of mating calls.   A continuous succession of auditory stimuli undoubtedly facilitates the orientation of a female as she responds by moving toward their source.   Males calling continuously thus appear to be more attractive than males that call sporadically.   A prolonged series of calls effectively induces the behavior that brings the female to the male, but it is uncertain whether the male clasps the female in response to visual cues, or to the tactile stimulus the female provides.   Perhaps visual perception of an approaching object followed by a tactile stimulus is essential.   If auditory stimuli within a narrow range of characteristics are required to elicit the movements and orientation of the receptive female, the majority of females might approach only the males of their own species.   The movements of the females must, however, depend to some extent upon vision if they escape being clasped by other males while responding to the calls of one male more vociferous than the other, as Martof and Thompson assert.   Males of *Pseudacris nigrita* were not tested to determine whether any object of suitable size is clasped solely in response to a tactile stimulus.

Males of other species exercise little discrimination.   When suitably stimulated, toads clasp inanimate objects of suitable diameter (Boulenger, 1897; A. P. Blair, 1957b), or animals as distantly related as the axolotl, *Ambystoma tigrinum*, (Bogert, 1958).   Whether tactile or visual stimula elicit the clasping response in hylids, it is evident from Volpe's (1956) account that males of *Hyla squirella* clasp females of an unrelated species, *Microhyla carolinensis*.   Moreover, they do so under conditions where mating calls might have been effective in attracting only the females of their own species.   It is improbable that females of either species respond to the mating calls of the other. Specificity in the responses of females to mating calls of one species cannot be wholly effective in preventing mismating, therefore, unless the females of other species similar in size also avoid contact with all males except those of their own species.

Plainly such contacts are not invariably averted. When several species breed concurrently at a pond, a sexually aroused male occasionally seizes the female of another species if she is of approximately the same size as conspecific females. The disadvantages of such mismating are manifest from Volpe's account of hylids clasping microhylids and vice versa. There are, therefore, selective advantages in patterns of breeding behavior that tend to minimize mismating. The chances that a female will inadvertently come in contact with males of other species are greatly reduced if each species in any one habitat calls from a characteristic site (Fig. 6). Calling at separate seasons would more effectively isolate one species from another, but this imposes disadvantages on animals with spawning habits dependent upon rainfall or the availability of surface moisture. Hence truly effective seasonal isolation is exceptional among the Anura. Females are less likely to be clasped by males of other species if the male's response depends upon the female's leaping upon his back, as Breder (1946) reports for *Hyla rosenbergi* in Panama, or if the male's call elicits a vocal response in the female that permits him to orient his movements. It is noteworthy that males are oriented by the calls of females only in species (*Alytes obstetricans* and *Tomodactylus angustidigitorum*, for examples) that lay their eggs in moist places on land rather than in communal breeding pools. All specializations of the sort enhance the probability that pairing will be restricted to conspecific individuals.

If mating calls were completely effective in the absence of other isolation mechanisms, it is doubtful whether there would be so much diversity in breeding patterns. Dobzhansky (1937, 1951), A. P. Blair (1942), and W. F. Blair (1956c) emphasize the point that isolation mechanisms are usually effective in combination, with each reinforcing others. The interplay of isolation mechanisms and natural selection may, in fact, augment the extent of isolation complexes. Suppose, for example, that two populations of frogs diverge physiologically but retain essentially similar patterns of mating behavior during their geographical isolation. Should they become sympatric, genetic incompatibility may be completely effective in preventing interbreeding. In the absence of any ethological mechanism to obstruct mating, however, there would be considerable wastage of gametes from reciprocal mismating. As a result of fruitless matings the selection of genotypes leading to divergent mating behavior might be extremely effective. Selection among the Anura inevitably would lead to ethological isolation mechanisms, including differ-ences in mating calls, calling sites, or any of several others mentioned in preceding discussions. It is, therefore, not difficult to account for the rarity of mismatings between genetically incompatible species under natural conditions. Such mismatings as those between hylids and micro-hylids that Volpe (1956) reports probably result from fortuitous com-binations or circumstances rather than from any lack of divergence in mating patterns.

Littlejohn (1959b) correctly points out that premating isolation mechanisms, including ecological, mechanical (principally discrepancies in size among anuran species), or ethological differences between species that inhibit mating, conserve gametes and hence are more efficient than postmating mechanisms. If sympatric species fail to interbreed because of ethological isolation, further genetic divergence may lead to genetic incompatibility. Because of the opportunistic nature of adaptive trends, however, and the lack of evidence that genetic divergence is closely cor-related with genetic incompatibility, it is perhaps a matter of chance whether genetic barriers arise.

The futility of distinguishing between ecospecies and cenospecies seems apparent. Presumably the concept of the cenospecies was once at-tractive because ethological or other premating barriers can more readily be overcome experimentally than hybrid inviability or hybrid sterility, which seem irreversible. Under natural conditions isolation mechanisms, regardless of whether they prevent matings or result in hybrid inviability, may be equally effective in blocking gene exchange. Furthermore, according to Dobzhansky (1951), any form of reproductive isolation is theoretically reversible, "inasmuch as any genotypic exchange compounded of mutational steps may be undone by reverse mutations."

The failure to realize that species may be reproductively isolated with-out being sterile seemingly led Moriya (1951) to believe that he was deal-ing with sympatric subspecies of Japanese frogs. One species, *Rana nigromaculata,* is widely distributed. A smaller frog, previously describ-ed by a taxonomist as *"Rana nigromaculata brevipoda,"* is restricted to a limited area in the swampy plains. The two frogs differ in habitus and pattern, as well as in size and coloration. Where they occur together, *nigromaculata* assembles in dense breeding aggregations in April and May, whereas *brevipoda* is widely scattered in irrigated paddy-fields when it spawns in June and July. The smaller frog differs in being much less active. Its mating call is different, and the larvae differ in morphology as well as temperature tolerances. In the laboratory males of one species briefly clasped females of the other species, but did not induce oviposi-tion.

In view of this extensive array of well-defined isolation mechanisms it is not astonishing that hybrids are unknown in the area where Moriya conducted his investigation. Nevertheless, reciprocal crosses, made in the laboratory, produce hybrids reaching sexual maturity in their third year. Eggs obtained from hybrid females could be fertilized with spermatozoa from both parental species. Backcrosses resulted in smaller percentages of viable offspring, but normal metamorphosis sometimes occurred. It proved difficult to backcross hybrid males with *Rana nigromaculata,* but somewhat less difficult to cross them with *brevipoda.*

Evidence of hybrid breakdown is apparent, nevertheless. Perhaps because of language difficulties Moriya asserts in his summary that hybrids are normal in sex ratios as well as in reproductive capacity. The situation he describes is, of course, typical of those where a combination of isolation mechanisms reinforcing each other under natural conditions effectively blocks all gene exchange between sympatric species. Because he could partially eliminate these normal barriers by experimental means, Moriya apparently assumes that genetic incompatibility has not yet reached an "irreversible stage." Therefore he retains the erroneous sub-specific designation for a population that plainly has reached the species level, and should, in consequence, be known as *Rana brevipoda.*

Ecological or seasonal isolation may be more important than behavior in maintaining the integrity of the sympatric species Moriya describes. Nevertheless it becomes increasingly apparent that behavior plays a major part in preventing the interbreeding of species otherwise capable of hybridizing. Mayr (1955a, 1955b, 1957a, 1958) repeatedly stresses the importance of ethological isolation mechanisms, to which ornithologists devoted more attention than students of other vertebrate groups until recently. Little importance was attached to behavioral isolation mechanisms among the Anura until A. P. Blair (1941b) suggested that mating calls might serve as isolation mechanisms. As a result of later investigations (1942, 1947a) he questioned their importance, but thought they might be of some significance in conjunction with other mechanisms. However, his brother, W. F. Blair (1955a, *et seq.*), renewed the attack on problems associated with mating call differences as isolation mechanisms, and provided the first detailed comparisons of calls in species and populations among the Anura inhabiting the United States.

Much of the evidence for an isolation function of mating calls remained circumstantial, however, until Littlejohn and Michaud (1959) devised the kind of experiment required to demonstrate the specificity of responses in two species of *Pseudacris.* The diversity in the mating calls of frogs inhabiting any one area was emphasized by Carr (1934) and Breder (1946). Carr provides a key to the mating calls of all species inhabiting Florida, and Breder supplies a similar means for identifying the species heard in one area in Panama. Bogert (1958) discusses the significance of anuran vocalizations, and employs recordings to illustrate the diversity of mating calls in a single chorus encountered in Florida. Following his "dissection" of the chorus, he asserts that the voices comprising it are "readily distinguishable to human ears, as they probably are to the frogs."

This statement does not imply that characteristics of sound facilitating discrimination by frogs are the same characteristics that enable man to distinguish one anuran voice from another. Littlejohn (1959b), who made detailed analyses of seven Australian leptodactylids of the genus *Crinia,* suggests that in sympatric situations the female's discrimination in her response to mating calls depends upon the characteristic in which the greatest differentiation occurs. This may be a valid assumption, but it could be proved only by employing special experimental techniques.

Comparisons of the calls of congeneric sympatric species that fail to interbreed under natural conditions do not necessarily reveal which characteristics of the sound are most effective in determining the specificity of the response in the female. As emphasized in preceding discussions, mating calls commonly comprise but one element in an array of isolation mechanisms effective conjointly rather than singly. Physiological divergence leading to genetic incompatibility, as explained earlier, may precede any appreciable divergence in mating calls. There may be relatively little divergence in mating calls if other combinations of isolation mechanisms entail differences in breeding habits that obviate the utilization of auditory stimuli in blocking gene exchange. Conversely, two sympatric species may interbreed despite radical differences in their mating calls when and if other isolation mechanisms cease to be effective.

To illustrate, were there no differences in the mating calls of *Rana nigromaculata* and *Rana brevipoda,* the other isolation mechanisms Moriya (1951) describes for these sympatric species are adequate to account for their failure to interbreed. They differ in size, their spawning seasons do not overlap, and one species breeds in dense aggregations, the other in scattered pairs. There are differences in their mating calls, but in view of the seasonal isolation, vocality can scarcely be important in curtailing gene exchange. In the natural environment isolation is apparently complete, for hybrids are unknown outside the laboratory. In contrast to this situation, hybridization between Fowler's toad, *Bufo woodhousei fowleri,* and the American toad, *Bufo terrestris americanus,* occurs wherever disruption of their habitats brings them together, despite differences in their mating calls. Spectrographic analysis reveals similarities in the emphasized frequencies of the calls (W. F. Blair, 1956a,

1957a), but the pulsation rate is four times faster in the short call of *B. w. fowleri* than it is in the long call of *B. t. americanus* (Figs. 26, 28).

Hybridization under natural conditions occurs far more frequently in *Bufo* than in *Rana, Hyla,* or other genera widely represented in North America. Most authors concur with A. P. Blair (1941b, 1942), who suggests that interbreeding between *B. w. fowleri* and *B. t. americanus* can be attributed to man's disruption of habitats. If this is the correct explanation, differentiation in toads must depend largely upon ecological divergence. There are few ethological barriers preventing hybridization between sympatric species of *Bufo* unless breeding aggregations are isolated either in time or space. Hybrids may be inviable or sterile, as Thornton (1955) reports for crosses between *Bufo valliceps* and *Bufo woodhousei* or between *Bufo valliceps* and *Bufo terrestris,* as Volpe (1959) shows. Gene exchange may be limited in such instances, despite the absence of ethological barriers.

When two species of toads breed at the same time in the same pond, such discrepancies in size as those between *Bufo terrestris* and *Bufo quercicus* in Florida, or between *Bufo cognatus* and *Bufo debilis insidior* in the American Southwest, preclude amplexus between species. Toads similar in size seldom inhabit the same area without forming hybrids unless there are marked differences in their respective spawning seasons, or in spawning sites, usually in both. The segregation of species in separate breeding assemblages may be rather complete in undisturbed habitats. Where one species breeds in pools situated in open meadows or grassland, while the other forms choruses along stream banks in densely wooded areas, for instance, spatial or seasonal isolation of the aggregations may be complete. As a result of deforestation, differences in habitat diminish, along with the effectiveness of any isolation mechanism that depends upon the formation of separate breeding aggregations in response to mating calls.

If mating calls are effective in arousing and orienting the movements of tailless amphibians during their migrations, it may seem doubtful that the same calls are ineffective in orienting the movements of females at close range, when individuals of both sexes have assembled at spawning sites. As explained in earlier discussions, however, calls may provide the stimuli resulting in the formation of choruses, but species discrimination by females upon reaching spawning sites is perhaps dependent largely upon other sensory mechanisms.

The behavioral patterns of toads, particularly their responses to mating calls or choruses, appear to be associated with other specializations. As a group, toads are restricted to terrestrial situations. Though tied to the water by their mode of reproduction, their movements are not so restricted to the vicinity of pools or streams as those of hylids or ranids. In humid as well as arid regions toads apparently forage at some distance from their spawning sites. They are perhaps less dependent upon surface moisture, as suggested by the relative abundance of toads in such arid regions as the Mexican state of Sonora, where there are at least ten species of *Bufo,* but only two ranids and four hylids.

The extent of this differentiation in toads in Sonora also reflects the diversity of habitats represented. Within the boundaries of the state there are elevated plains, moderately high mountains, deserts, and semitropical barrancas and lowlands (Bogert and Oliver, 1945). Isolation mechanisms dependent solely upon the formation of separate breeding aggregations can be more effective under such varied conditions. Disturbances of the habitat resulting from agricultural developments in the state are probably responsible for recent extensions in the ranges of some species. *Bufo cognatus* is now abundant in areas where it was not encountered in 1942. Mr. Roger Conant collected toads in southern Sonora during the summer of 1959 that can with little doubt be identified as hybrids between *Bufo cognatus* and *Bufo mazatlanensis.*

At least five species of *Bufo* occur within a few miles of the city of Hermosillo, where two small toads, *Bufo retiformis* and *Bufo kelloggi,* occur together. *Bufo kelloggi* is restricted to the coastal plain from Sonora southward to Nayarit. Near Hermosillo it is known to occur from the edge of the city westward, in the flat plains recently irrigated, whereas *Bufo retiformis* may or may not have been restricted to the low foothills bordering the coastal plain, but it occurs in such terrain immediately south of Hermosillo. Collections made during the summer of 1955 suggested that the two species occupied distinctive habitats. Separate breeding aggregations of the two were, however, found within 3 or 4 kilometers of each other, and in 1957 Dr. Richard G. Zweifel found both species breeding at the same time in an area sixteen miles west of Hermosillo.

Bufo retiformis is somewhat larger than *Bufo kelloggi,* and there is some indication that individuals comprising the population of *kelloggi* in the zone of overlap are smaller than those of populations to the south. *Bufo kelloggi* calls from shallow water, whereas *B. retiformis* usually calls from sites a meter or so from spawning pools. Trill rates and emphasized frequencies in *B. retiformis* are, respectively, 184 pulsations per second and 3,000 cps. At comparable temperatures the voice of *B. kelloggi* from the overlap area is approximately 1,000 cps higher in pitch, but the trill rate is lower, with approximately 132 pulsations per second. The duration of the trill varies from 2.0 to 3.0 seconds in *retiformis,* from 2.5 to

3.9 in *kelloggi,* with means, respectively, at 2.50 and 2.80 seconds.   In view of these several differences, it is not astonishing that Dr. Richard G. Zweifel found no evidence of either mismatings or of hybridization.

There are differences between the calls of the two species that hybridize, *Bufo cognatus* and *Bufo mazatlanensis,* but data are not yet available for calls in the region of overlap.   Pulsation rates for the trills of *B. cognatus* (Fig. 20) at Tucson, Arizona at air temperatures of 19° C vary from 18 to 20 per second, whereas there are 26 to 28 pulsations per second in calls of *Bufo mazatlanensis* recorded at nearly the same temperature at Hermosillo, Sonora.   It is questionable whether such meager differences in pulsation rates would be effective in inhibiting interbreeding if this characteristic of mating calls determines the responses of females of the two species.   The emphasized frequency in the shorter call of *Bufo mazatlanensis* at Hermosillo is approximately 3,100 cps.   This is somewhat higher than that of the call of *Bufo cognatus* in the population at Tucson, Arizona, but dominant frequencies in the calls of *mazatlanensis* from areas south of Sonora are nearly 1,000 cps lower.   Until the voices of the parental species are recorded in areas where hybridization occurs the extent of the similarity in their mating calls remains uncertain.   Despite the recency of their dispersals into newly irrigated areas, their ranges may now be sympatric in an area extending over 200 miles along the coastal plain.

The situation is quite different in the limited area where *Bufo retiformis* and *Bufo kelloggi* are known to be sympatric.   Circumstances here suggest a much older contact, with greater differentiation in habits and adaptations for somewhat different environments.   Until recently *Bufo mazatlanensis* and *Bufo cognatus* appear to have occupied similar habitats in geographically isolated areas.   They are so different morphologically that few taxonomists would regard them as being closely related. The superficial differences between *Bufo kelloggi* and *Bufo retiformis* are obvious.   Owing to similarities in body proportions and gratuitous assumptions concerning their distributions, taxonomists have placed them as subspecies of a third form, *Bufo debilis.*   Contrary to the sources upon which Stebbins (1954) relied in mapping distributions, the ranges of *Bufo debilis insidior* and *Bufo retiformis* are not contiguous.   The hiatus between their ranges is at least a hundred miles, in an area where innumerable collectors have worked.

It is too early to say with certainty that isolation mechanisms between toads similar in size often prove to be ineffective because speciation in the genus *Bufo* is largely dependent upon the use of the call to assemble breeding aggregations rather than to attract one individual to another.

Loud calls consisting of prolonged trills, ranging from a few seconds to at least 53 seconds in *Bufo cognatus* (W. F. Blair, 1956a), are perhaps specializations for distant orientation. Shorter calls, a fraction of a second in duration in *Bufo quercicus* of Florida and the Gulf Coast, may be characteristic of toads whose vocalizations are largely effective in orienting females after they reach spawning sites. More detailed observations and experiments are required to test this hypothesis.

J. A. Moore provides a summary of the numerous crosses between species and subspecies of *Bufo* produced in the laboratory or reported from the field. The large percentage of the crosses producing hybrids that reach the adult stage, as Moore observes, is correlated with the larger proportion of poorly differentiated populations and the confused taxonomic treatment of toads. Although man's activities have doubtless accelerated changes in habitats, ecological barriers, upon which differentiation in toads appears to be particularly dependent, undoubtedly have been no more stable than climates. No one seriously questions the belief that extensive fluctuations in climate occurred in all parts of the world prior to the advent of man. W. F. Blair (1958d) discusses climatic changes, their influences on the distributional patterns, and their importance in speciation. While there is a tendency to date all speciation from the Pleistocene, Zweifel (1956) comments on the far more ancient lineage of existing species. In many instances speciation among the Anura must stem from innumerable climatic changes that occurred much earlier in the Tertiary.

The behavioral specializations of toads that permit them to wander farther from spawning sites than many other Anura, account to some extent for their wider dispersal. If isolation of breeding assemblages depends largely upon behavioral specializations associated with ecological divergence, climatic changes may be responsible for repeatedly bringing together populations lacking any effective means of maintaining their integrity in the absence of ecological barriers. Do toads interbreed because they are poorly differentiated, or are they poorly differentiated because they have frequently interbred in the past? This is much like asking which came first, the chicken or the egg.

Reinforcement of Differences in Mating Calls.

As noted earlier, divergence of closely related anuran populations during periods of geographical isolation may entail changes in morphology, physiology, or behavior, without necessarily inhibiting interbreeding when their respective ranges expand and converge. If such populations interbreed, the interplay of environmental conditions in the zone of contact and the preadaptations of the species impose limitations on introgression. W. F. Blair (1955a, 1955b) advances the hypothesis that selective forces under such conditions enhance the effectiveness of partially effective isolation mechanisms. Blair bases his views on detailed analyses of size and the mating calls of *Microhyla carolinensis* and *Microhyla olivacea*. As set forth by Blair (1955b). "The existence of the greatest size differences as well as the greatest call differences where the two species are exposed to possible hybridization supports the argument that these potential isolation mechanisms are being reinforced through natural selection."

The implications of this hypothesis are discussed and criticized by J. A. Moore (1957b), who concurs in Blair's belief that isolation mechanisms are the consequences of natural selection. As viewed by Moore, however, there is no selection for isolation mechanisms *per se,* and "no critical evidence that isolation mechanisms develop as *ad hoc* contrivances that prevent hybridization between incipient species." Greater differences between species in the area of overlap, in Moore's opinion, can be attributed to genetic divergence resulting from competition or other influences he discusses. Volpe (1957) voices a similar objection, observing that "A far simpler and more plausible interpretation is that clines demonstrated by W. F. Blair are due to differences in selection in the range of each species, possibly correlated with environmental gradients." Recordings of the mating calls of two populations of *Microhyla olivacea* in Sonora tend to support the latter interpretation.

As described by Blair, the mating calls of *Microhyla carolinensis* and *M. olivacea* in the zone of overlap differ by 1,334 cps, a difference possibly related to size. The duration of their mating calls is, however, unrelated to size, and where the two species occur together the call of *carolinensis* averages 1.14 seconds, in contrast to the mean of 2.15 seconds calculated for *olivacea*. Comparison of populations geographically remote reveals the average duration of mating calls for *carolinensis* in Welaka, Florida to be 1.25 seconds, not appreciably different from those for a population of *olivacea* in Santa Cruz County, Arizona, where calls average 1.45 seconds. The species ranges southward through the desert and the barrancas and coastal plain of the Mexican states of Sonora and northern Sinaloa. The mating calls of a population in the more humid barranca region at Alamos in the southern extremity of Sonora average 1.48 seconds in duration. But the calls of a population near Hermosillo in the more arid coastal plain scarcely one hundred miles to the north, and hence closer to the Arizona population, average 2.27 seconds. Thus the difference between these two populations from separate habitats closely approximates the difference Blair attributes to reinforcement in call divergence of the two species in the zone of overlap. Emphasized frequencies are nearly identical in the two Sonoran populations, the individuals of which are not demonstrably different in size. These data confirm Blair's assertion that pitch and duration of the call vary independently in *Microhyla,* but they also suggest that the duration of the call may be influenced by adaptations not in any way associated with the effectiveness of the call as an isolation mechanism.

In the situation Blair describes for *Microhyla,* limited hybridization occurs within the area of overlap. Differences between the species in size and habitats are probably more effective than differences between mating calls in discouraging gene exchange. Reciprocal crosses of *M. olivacea* and *M. carolinensis* produce normal larvae, and evidence for reduced viability is inconclusive. When interbreeding is blocked by the genetic incompatibility of two species brought into contact the situation can be quite different. Under these conditions differences in mating calls or other premating isolation mechanisms can arise as a result of natural selection. Dichotomies in vocalizations or the responses of females, however, "do not develop as *ad hoc* contrivances that prevent hybridization between incipient species." For in this instance we are dealing with species rather than with the incipient species to which J. A. Moore (1957b) refers. Isolation, already complete as the result of physiological divergence during the antecedent period of allopatry, cannot be further enhanced by natural selection.

As implied in preceding discussions of heterospecific matings among the Anura, premating isolation mechanisms inevitably arise when genetically incompatible populations are sympatric. Under these circumstances, however, there is no selection for isolation mechanisms *per se.* Divergence in the mating calls of sympatric species, for example, is the result of selection for genotypes better suited for survival under environmental conditions where the element of sound assumes unusual importance. Selection favors the retention of gene combinations for calls in males and responses in females that result in higher percentages of productive matings. There can be no selection for mechanisms blocking gene exchange where there is no gene exchange to block. Premating isolation mechanisms, therefore, may arise as a result of natural selection, but as by-products of adaptive responses to an environmental change resulting from sympatry, rather than from any situation that jeopardizes the integrity of the adaptive complexes of the sympatric species. Disharmonious gene recombinations were averted by antecedent genetic incompatibility.

Consideration of the situation J. A. Moore (1955) describes for *Rana pipiens* will clarify interpretations of data indicative of call reinforcement. Frogs from any two adjacent or contiguous areas inhabited by *Rana pipiens* between Vermont and Florida are easily hybridized in the laboratory, and would be expected to interbreed freely in the absence of minor ecological barriers that may, in fact, be incomplete. Nevertheless, the frogs from Vermont would not interbreed with those in Florida for they behave as genetically isolated species. Their calls are not identical, but comparisons of the calls of even more widely separated populations make it doubtful whether the minor differences between the mating calls of the two would inhibit interbreeding.

Suppose now that all annectant populations were eliminated by some highly improbable and only hypothetically feasible climatic cataclysm that desiccated the terrain between Florida and Vermont. Following a brief period of isolation the two populations might conceivably expand their distributions with the resumption of normal climatic conditions. Assuming that no ecological or ethological isolation mechanisms arose during isolation, and that pairing was largely dependent upon the responses of the females to mating calls, with overlapping distributions of the two populations the females of each would be expected to respond with equal readiness to the calls of the other. Under these circumstances, with chance dictating the formation of pairs producing offspring, approximately half of the matings would be unproductive. Selection would tend to favor any slight differences in the mating calls of the two populations that antedated their becoming partly sympatric in their distributions. Among females the carriers of genotypes for indiscriminate responses to mating calls would be eliminated.

Selection would favor gene combinations for behavioral traits that either brought together pairs capable of producing offspring, or inhibited heterospecific matings. Divergence in mating calls, coupled with adaptive modifications in the behavior limiting the responses of females, could not enhance the effectiveness of existing isolation mechanisms. Such changes might, as Littlejohn (1959b) suggests, be looked upon as increasing the efficiency of genetic isolation. Because of the advantages premating isolation mechanisms confer on sympatric species, it also seems probable that reinforcement would occur during an early stage in the encroachment of ranges. As a result of this reinforcement in premating isolation mechanisms the sympatric association of species might be more rapidly extended, particularly under conditions where ecological divergence reduced competition.

Owing to the reinforcement of mating call differences, it is impossible to determine how often genetically incompatible species become sympatric in the absence of appreciable differences in their mating calls. Any competent student familiar with the Anura in any one area can ordinarily distinguish the voices of the species as readily as he can identify species by visual examination of individual frogs. Littlejohn (1959b) describes a situation in Australian frogs in which seven species of *Crinia* show marked differentiation in mating call despite similarities in their external morphology. Differences in morphology may occur in the absence of genetic incompatibility or significant differentiation in mating calls in allopatric populations, as indicated by Wasserman (1957, 1958) and confirmed by W. F. Blair (1958a). It is exceptional, nevertheless, for sympatric species to have similar calls.

A. P. Blair (1955) reports one of the few examples known among the Anura in the United States. He describes the situation in southwestern Utah where *Bufo punctatus* and *Bufo microscaphus microscaphus* occur together: "The two species breed at the same time, in the same bodies of water to a very considerable extent, they have very similar mating calls, the males of one species at least occasionally clasp females of the other species, and they are capable of producing viable offspring if the mating involves the female of *Bufo microscaphus* and the male of *Bufo punctatus* (it is to be noted, also, when the relative sizes of the two are considered, that this is a more likely clasping combination than female *B. punctatus* and male *B. microscaphus*). Yet, for unknown reasons, hybrids are completely lacking."

Human beings unquestionably find it difficult to distinguish the calls, but spectrograms disclose differences that may well provide the basis for discrimination in the responses of the toads. W. F. Blair (1957b) provides a spectrogram as well as a description of the call of *Bufo microscaphus,* recorded at Baker Reservoir in Utah. This spectrogram shows a call that differs somewhat from that of *Bufo microscaphus californicus*

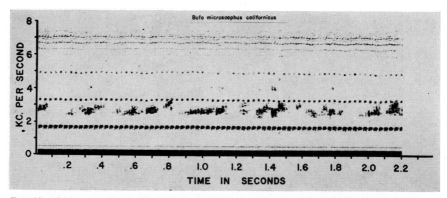

Fig. 15. Mating call of *Bufo microscaphus californicus,* with *Hyla regilla* in the background. Middle of trill, recorded at the edge of the Mojave River near Victorville, California, by R. C. Stebbins.

(Fig. 15). Spectrograms of the mating calls of three populations of *Bufo punctatus* (Figs. 16, 17, 18) reveal similarities. It should be noted, however, that the spectrogram of the call of the population sympatric with *B. microscaphus* shows marked differences between this call and those of populations of *Bufo punctatus* in Texas and Arizona (the call of the population inhabiting the Chiricahua Mountains of Arizona differs from others thus far recorded in the diminishing intensity and pulsation rate at the end, a characteristic exaggerated in the call of the individual represented in the spectrogram).

If we compare the calls of toads comprising the two sympatric populations, that of *B. m. microscaphus*, as described by W. F. Blair who re-

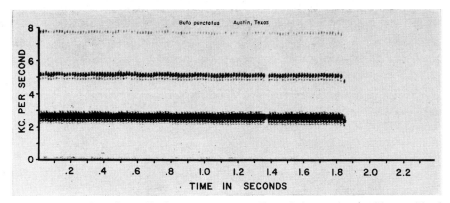

FIG. 16. End of mating call of *Bufo punctatus*. Recorded near Austin, Texas. Toad calling from shallow water at a temperature of 21.5°C.

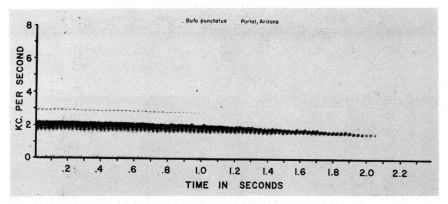

FIG. 17. Mating call of *Bufo punctatus*, showing lower pulsation rate, accompanying the drop in pitch at the termination of the trill. Though exaggerated in the individual producing this call, calls of other toads in the population at Portal, Arizona, do not cease abruptly as they do in other populations thus far recorded.

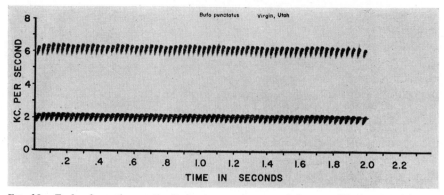

Fɪɢ. 18. End of mating call, *Bufo punctatus,* recorded near Virgin, Washington County, Utah. Both air and water temperatures 22.5°C.

corded it at 16° C, varies from 3.3 to 3.4 seconds in duration, with emphasized frequencies ranging from 1,250 to 1,350 cps, and pulsation rates of 49 at the beginning of the call, diminishing to 44 to 45 at the end. In contrast, the call of *Bufo punctatus* at 21.5° C varies from 7.2 to 8.7 seconds in duration, with a mean of 7.84, with emphasized frequencies at 2,000 cps; there are 37 to 38 pulsations per second at the beginning of the call, with a drop to 34 pulsations at the end.

At temperatures that differ by 5.5° C, there are, therefore, conspicuous differences between the calls in duration, pitch, and pulsation rates, all of which might be even greater were the two recorded at the identical temperatures. If discrimination depends upon any one of these characteristics of the mating calls or combinations of characteristics, the absence of hybrids A. P. Blair reports can be attributed to an array of isolation mechanisms, among which differences in mating calls may be important. Hybrids were not backcrossed by Blair. Hence the extent of the genetic isolation is unknown, as Mecham (1959) emphasizes.

Of greater interest in connection with the present discussion, however, are the differences that exist between the calls of conspecific populations outside the area of sympatry. A disjunct population of the larger toad, *Bufo microscaphus californicus,* occurs in the coastal area as well as along the western periphery of the deserts in southern California. Recordings of these toads obtained by Dr. Robert C. Stebbins along the Mojave River, near Victorville, reveal this population to have a call that lasts for 8.9 to 10 seconds, with emphasized frequencies that vary from 1,300 to 1,600 cps, and pulsation rates ranging from 40 at the beginning to 31, 33 or 34 at the end.

If we compare the call of *Bufo punctatus* in southwestern Utah with conspecific populations to the south and east we find emphasized frequencies at higher levels, but the calls are similar in duration in a population at Austin, Texas, where W. F. Blair (1956a) reports a range of 7.4 to 9.7 seconds. The population in the Chiricahua Mountains of Arizona is comprised of larger toads, but the dominant frequency approximates that of the population in Utah, with mating calls varying in length from 4.8 to 7.8 seconds. The harmonic structure the spectrograms reveal differences in each population. Pulsation rates at a water temperature of 26° C very from 51 to 53 per second in the population at Austin, Texas, according to Blair, but the spectrogram (Fig. 16) representative of toads recorded near a reservoir scarcely five miles northeast of Austin discloses pulsation rates of 61 to 62 per second, when the water temperature is 22.5° C. Approximately the same rate characterizes the beginning of the call in the Chiricahua Mountain population, although pulsations diminish to 40 to 42 per second at the end. W. F. Blair (1956a) reports a pulsation rate of 59 at a water temperature of 28° C in a population farther west in Arizona, at Scottsdale.

The data are insufficient to document this example adequately, but the greater divergence of calls, particularly in pulsation rates, in the area where species with similar calls are sympatric, suggests that call differences have been reinforced by natural selection. If reliable inferences can be drawn from comparisons of populations outside the area of sympatry, pulsation rates have diminished in *punctatus* but increased in *microscaphus,* in which the call has, however, materially decreased in duration. An alternative explanation must be mentioned. The larger toad, *Bufo m. microscaphus,* hybridizes with *Bufo woodhousei* in the area near the reservoir where W. F. Blair recorded the call of *B. microscaphus* described above. Introgression cannot be ruled out, therefore, although A. P. Blair (1955) reports finding large numbers of *B. microscaphus* but no *B. woodhousei* or evidence of hybridization at the site.

Another situation in which divergence in calls can possibly be attributed to reinforcement under conditions of sympatry concerns toads in Texas and Mexico. H. M. Smith (1947) reviews the taxonomy of toads referred to *Bufo compactilis.* On the basis of seemingly minor morphological characters Smith recognizes a nominate subspecies, *Bufo compactilis compactilis,* inhabiting central Mexico, and a second subspecies, *Bufo compactilis speciosus,* mapped as having a disjunct range extending from Oklahoma southward to the drainage basin of the lower Rio Grande River in Texas and adjacent parts of Mexico. Stebbins (1954) ignores the subspecies, but maps the distribution of the species as extending northward to New Mexico but not so far westward in northern Chihua-

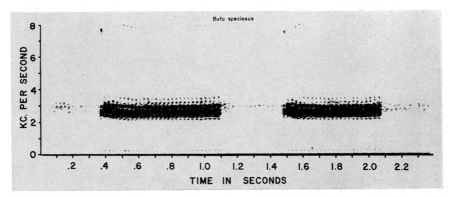

Fɪɢ. 19. Mating call of *Bufo speciosus*. Recorded in Caldwell County, Texas. Air temperature 20.0°, water temperature 21.0°C. Courtesy of W. Frank Blair.

hua. Apparently he considers the population in western Texas to be referable to the nominate subspecies rather than to *speciosus*.

W. F. Blair (1956a) provides a description and a spectrogram of the call of individuals from two localities in Texas. As shown by Blair, the call has a dominant frequency varying from 2,400 to 2,820 cps; it varies from 0.4 to 0.7 seconds in duration, with 39 to 40 pulsations per second at water temperatures ranging from 23° to 27° C. Dr. W. Frank Blair generously provided a taped recording of the mating call of an individual from Caldwell County, Texas. The spectrogram made from Dr. Blair's tape is reproduced as Figure 19. The name *Bufo speciosus* is applied, however, because of the extensive differences that exist between the call of the population in Texas and the calls of *Bufo compactilis* recorded in the Mexican state of Jalisco, near Chapala and Ajijic. Toads from the latter area are virtually indistinguishable from those in the Valley of Mexico, the approximate type locality of *B. compactilis*.

Spectrographic analysis of the mating calls of *Bufo cognatus* (Fig. 20) and *Bufo compactilis* (Fig. 21) reveals similarities that confirm aural impressions. Most human beings would find it difficult if not impossible to distinguish the mating calls of the two species. W. F. Blair (1956a) describes the calls of *Bufo cognatus* recorded near Tulia, Texas at air and water temperatures of 18.5° and 18° C, respectively, as ranging in emphasized frequencies from 1,775 to 2,075, varying from 5 to 53.8 seconds in duration, but averaging approximately 20 seconds, with 13 to 15 pulsations per second. Mean frequencies ranging up to 2,725 cps with 16 to 18 pulsations per second occur in Minnesota populations W. F. Blair (1957a) describes. There are 16 to 18 pulsations per second at the beginning of calls recorded near Tucson, Arizona when air temperatures

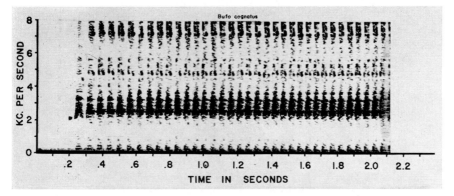

FIG. 20. Beginning of mating call of *Bufo cognatus*. Recorded in Tanque Verde Valley, 7.5 miles east of Tucson, Arizona. Air temperature 19.0°C.

were 19.0° C, but the rate rises to 20 pulsations per second as the call continues. Calls in the Arizona population vary in duration from 5.7 to 11.0 seconds. Spectrograms reveal structural differences between calls of populations in Arizona and Texas.

The mating calls of *Bufo compactilis* recorded in Jalisco when air and water temperatures were 17.8° C vary in duration from 12 to 37 seconds, with dominant frequencies between 2,300 and 2,800 and 12 to 13 pulsations per second. The calls of the Jalisco population, therefore, bear much greater resemblance to those of the larger toad, *Bufo cognatus*, than they do to the supposedly closer relative, *Bufo speciosus*. It seems probable that *B. cognatus* and *B. compactilis* retain voices approximating that of a common ancestor. An ancestral population was perhaps widely

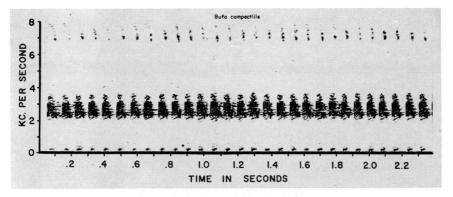

FIG. 21. Middle of mating call of *Bufo compactilis*. Recorded one mile east of Ajijic, Jalisco, Mexico. Air and water temperatures 19.8°C.

distributed, from which at least three populations became isolated, not necessarily at the same time, however. Detailed knowledge of distributions, particularly where ranges extend across the arid portions of northern Mexico is lacking. It is extremely doubtful, nevertheless, whether *B. cognatus* and *B. compactilis* ever occur sympatrically. It may be inferred from Stebbins's (1954) maps that *B. speciosus* and *B. cognatus* exist sympatrically in western Texas and the adjacent areas. The differences in the mating calls of *B. compactilis* and *B. speciosus* are so extensive, however, that it is improbable, if not impossible, that toads with intermediate voices will be found in the region between Jalisco and Texas. H. M. Smith (1947) may very well be right in assuming that the two smaller toads occupy ranges that are not contiguous.

If these various assumptions prove to be approximately correct, the divergence in the voices of *B. speciosus* and its morphologically similar relative, *Bufo compactilis,* can be attributed to the following phenomena: 1) Fragmentation of a widely distributed ancestral stock, giving rise to two populations, one of which was the forerunner of *B. cognatus,* and the other an ancestral population of *Bufo compactilis.* 2) Disruptions in the distribution of the latter resulting in the isolation of two populations, one at the north that gave rise to *B. speciosus* while the other occupied a range to the south. 3) Despite morphological divergence of the larger derivative, *B. cognatus,* it retained most elements of an ancestral voice closely approximating those of the other two populations. 4) With expansions in their respective distributions the range of *B. cognatus* extended eastward to overlap the range of *B. speciosus* expanding toward the northwest. 5) Differences in size or behavior may have inhibited interbreeding. (W. F. Blair, 1959b reports F_1 hybrids between *B. cognatus* and *B. speciosus* that reached maturity, but limited compatibility is indicated for some crosses. Reduced fertility would be expected in backcrosses.) Mismatings must have occurred with sufficient frequency, however, to bring selective forces into play that eliminated genotypes of both sexes with behavioral traits responsible for "mistakes" in amplexus. Because of the role of mating calls in the formation of breeding aggregations or possibly the attraction of females to males, existing differences in mating calls became emphasized, largely (and inexplicably unless differences arose fortuitously) through the effects of selection on the voice of *B. speciosus.* 6) Owing to the antecedent disjunction in the ranges of *B. compactilis* and *B. speciosus,* genotypes favoring the shorter call with higher pulsation rates in *B. speciosus* are confined to this isolated population.

It is problematical whether *B. speciosus* and *B. compactilis* would interbreed were their ranges to expand to the point of overlapping.

Hybridization experiments can, of course, reveal the presence or absence of genetic incompatibility, but laboratory investigation of behavioral patterns might fail to disclose differences that would inhibit or prevent interbreeding under natural conditions.   Pending the acquisition of additional information, it seems preferable to regard the two as distinct species on the assumption that differences in the mating call might be nearly as effective in discouraging mismatings between *B. compactilis* and *B. speciosus* as these differences presumably are in discouraging amplexus between *B. speciosus* and *B. cognatus*.   Size differences between the latter species, however, may augment the effectiveness of other mechanisms.

Specificity in Responses to Mating Calls.

When 14 species of frogs simultaneously assemble around a single spawning site, as occasionally happens in Florida, 14 distinctive calls issue from the chorus.   The vast majority of females in the breeding aggregation undoubtedly mate with males of their own species.   If diversification in mating calls is crucial to the effectiveness of behavioral patterns as isolation mechanisms, specificity in responses to calls is equally necessary.   Manifestly the first prerequisite is fulfilled under natural conditions, but it can seldom be ascertained from field observations whether a frog responds to auditory stimuli or whether other sensory mechanisms mediate behavior preceding amplexus.

Even though behavioral differences between males and females are basically dependent upon the interactions between genes that determine sex, differentials in the responses of males and females are attributable to internal secretions.   The complexity of the situation in a mixed chorus is apparent if it be recalled that in some species mating behavior is coupled with territorial responses to auditory stimuli at spawning sites. Territorial calls or mating calls with dual functions "advertise the ownership" of calling sites, and discourage the encroachment of conspecific males.   Mating calls attract members of one or both sexes to spawning sites, or the calls of one or both sexes attract individuals of the other.   If either territorial or mating behavior depends upon auditory stimuli, responses to calls also depend upon discrimination and localization.   For a call to attract only conspecific individuals of the opposite sex, it should be sufficiently distinctive in one or more characteristics to permit discrimination and be uttered often enough to provide a means of orientation.

Specificity in the responses of frogs to mating calls can be effective in inhibiting or preventing interbreeding under any one of three situations:

1) when the calls of a few males at an isolated spawning site elicit responses, including attraction and orientation of movements, that bring together both males and females in breeding aggregations; 2) when the calls of the individual male orient the movements of the female and attract her to the male; or 3) when the female calls in response to the call of the male, thereby providing a means of orientation and a stimulus eliciting motor responses in the male that lead to amplexus.

The first situation, perhaps characteristic of many toads, is effective in preventing interbreeding only when ecological divergence permits the formation of seasonally or spatially isolated choruses. When breeding aggregations of sympatric species assemble at the same pond at the same time they may not interbreed if there are differences in size, calling sites, or perhaps differences in other behavioral patterns dependent upon visual cues. When species similar in size are brought together at the same breeding site, differences in call or other aspects of their behavior may be ineffective in discouraging interbreeding. This appears to be the simplest explanation for the interbreeding known to occur among toads, *Bufo*. Although the evidence suggesting that toads are attracted to spawning sites rather than to individuals producing mating calls is inconclusive, experiments and field observations are in accord with this tentative conclusion.

The conditions described in the second situation perhaps characterize the majority of the Anura. Unless the observer takes precautions to eliminate visual cues, however, field observations do not necessarily reveal which sensory mechanisms are of paramount importance in the formation of pairs at spawning sites. Few published accounts provided sufficiently critical appraisals of the evidence to substantiate the conclusions reported, or they supply so few details that the reader cannot determine whether females are attracted to individual males, or clasped by males in response to visual or tactile cues after reaching spawning sites. Hylids commonly assemble at breeding pools, but females in other families may respond to the calls of males in isolated terrestrial situations, as indicated by the information Jameson (1955b) supplies for frogs in a leptodactylid genus, *Syrrhophus*.

The third situation outlined above, wherein both males and females call, appears to be restricted to frogs that deposit their eggs in terrestrial spawning sites. This is true of *Tomodactylus angustidigitorum*, in which Dixon (1957) reports the male to orient his movements in response to the calls of the female whose voice is higher in pitch than that of the male. Oviposition also occurs on land in *Alytes*. The accounts of Boulenger (1897) and Gadow (1901), however, do not mention the role of the voice in the mating activities of the species, but both authors assert that several males cluster around a single female. Dähne (1914) reports the voice of the female to be louder than that of the male. It may also be higher in pitch, although reliable inferences cannot be drawn from spectrographic analysis of the calls of *Alytes obstetricans* in a commercial recording released in Switzerland. The record, which became available through the kindness of Dr. Konrad Klemmer of the Senckenberg Museum, reveals differences in the pitch of alternate calls in some sequences, but without more detailed information than that provided by the company releasing the record, it is uncertain whether both sexes are represented or whether the differences result from discrepancies in the size of two males.

Discrimination and orientation are implicit rather than adequately demonstrated in the behavior Dixon describes for *Tomodactylus*. The mating call the male issues elicits a vocal response in a female 10 feet distant, but it is not clear from Dixon's account whether the female continues to call. Perhaps the male, calling from an elevated position, makes use of visual cues after the female reveals her presence by means of her call. As Dixon describes the situation, however, the male localizes the source of the call before approaching the female. Such patterns of mating behavior could be extremely effective as isolation mechanisms. Distinctive but similar calls in males and females of a species provide the means for localization, orientation, and discrimination, between sexes as well as between species.

Martof and Thompson (1958b), whose account is summarized earlier in this review, show conclusively that the mating calls of male chorus frogs, *Pseudacris nigrita,* attract conspecific females, but no tests were made that supply critical evidence of discrimination. Littlejohn and Michaud (1959), however, provide such evidence for *Pseudacris streckeri.* Females taken in amplexus and assumed to be receptive were released in an enclosure less than a meter in width and somewhat over two meters in length. Loudspeakers 62 mm in diameter, installed near each end of the enclosure, and connected to separate amplifying systems, enabled the investigators to provide separate sources of auditory stimuli that could be interchanged at will. The voices of two sympatric species, *Pseudacris streckeri* and *Pseudacris clarki,* previously recorded on loops of tape, were reproduced at intervals approximating those under which the voices were recorded in the field. Temperatures maintained in the laboratory were within two degrees of those prevailing when the calls were originally taped. Two 15-watt red lamps provided the illumination required for observations.

In preliminary experiments Littlejohn and Michaud released three females of *Pseudacris streckeri* in the enclosure. Apparently the call of

P. streckeri issued from one speaker while that of *P. clarki* issued from the other. Although the account states that calls of the two species were played from "each end," this evidently was not intended, for after 30 minutes all three females are described as being at the end of the enclosure where the voice of *P. streckeri* issued from the speaker. The account continues, "after some minutes of searching, around the *P. streckeri* speaker, probably in search of the male, a female would swim to within 1-2′ of the *P. clarki* speaker, pause, appear to listen, then turn away and move directly back to the *P. streckeri* speaker, usually contacting the speaker again." When the voices issuing from the speakers were interchanged, the females left the source of the call of the sympatric species and assembled near the speaker issuing the mating calls of their own species. One of the three females returned to the other speaker, however, and remained for at least a minute. The other two behaved in a manner suggesting that one expected to be clasped by the other.

In these preliminary tests frogs were also exposed to the calls of *Pseudacris triseriata,* another species sympatric with *P. streckeri* in eastern Texas. When calls of one species issued from one speaker while calls of the other issued from the speaker at the opposite end, only the calls of the conspecific male evoked a positive response. Females of *P. streckeri* from at least three sources employed in subsequent tests were released at the center of the enclosure, and the voices of the two species, *P. streckeri* and *P. clarki,* were interchanged between loudspeakers prior to each of several trials. Littlejohn and Michaud allowed frogs to remain in the enclosure for a thirty-minute period during which the calls were not interchanged. This "adaptation period" supposedly provided the frogs an opportunity to become familiar with their surroundings, although records were kept of the movements of the females during such periods.

With distinctive calls issuing from opposite ends of the enclosure, females would alternately move and then pause, supposedly orienting their movements in response to the reproductions of the calls issuing from the direction in which they headed, until they were within 10 to 25 cm of a speaker. Thereupon the females would either 1) encircle the speaker at a radius of ten to twenty-five centimeters, 2) sit facing the speaker at a distance of about five centimeters, 3) leap toward the speaker but continue fifteen to twenty centimeters after touching it, or 4) sit on the speaker or climb over it. In tabulating observations any one of these four maneuvers was considered a "contact," as long as the female moved at least 15 cm away from the speaker before returning.

During trials on four separate occasions 66 "contacts" were recorded, in 5 of which the females of *P. streckeri* went to the speaker issuing the voice of *P. clarki.* Littlejohn and Michaud believe that little importance should be attached to contacts with the speaker issuing the call of the other species because four of these contacts occurred during "adaptation periods" before the females were accustomed to their surroundings, whereas the fifth was momentary. In this instance the frog continued moving until she reached the speaker issuing the calls of a conspecific male.

This explanation the authors offer apparently stems from assumptions that pairing depends entirely upon auditory cues. The behavior Martof and Thompson (1958b) describe for males and females of *Pseudacris nigrita,* released together in an enclosure during preliminary observations, points to the use of both tactile and visual stimuli in pair formation. Littlejohn and Michaud mention two females that "assumed the position of amplexus" near a speaker and speak of females moving around a speaker as though they were "in search of the male." Investigators of anuran vocalizations tend to center their attention exclusively on auditory stimuli, but it is questionable whether frogs do so.

Had Littlejohn and Michaud placed models or even dead or anesthetized males in the vicinity of each speaker, the combination of form and sound might have been even more attractive. It is questionable whether visual discrimination is important in pair formation. It would be of interest, however, to ascertain whether the female when stimulated by mating calls can be induced to nudge or to leap on the back of any frog or object remotely resembling a male of her own species if it is situated close to the source of the sound. Perhaps a completely motionless object would be undetected, and it may prove necessary to simulate vibrations of the vocal sac, or provide some sort of movement that attracts the attention more effectively than a lifeless object. Terrestrial frogs employ visual cues in locating their prey, but immobile and quite edible insects escape detection.

Nevertheless, the differentials in the response Littlejohn and Michaud describe provide satisfactory evidence of discrimination in females of *P. streckeri.* It is also apparent from the observations of these investigators that the female localizes the source and orients her movements in response to the mating calls of her own species. The specificity of the response, essential to the effectiveness of behavioral mechanisms that inhibit interbreeding between sympatric species of *Pseudacris,* is assuredly part of the normal pattern of behavior in at least one species.

Because the voices of sympatric species seldom, if ever, differ in but a single characteristic, it is not astonishing that Littlejohn and Michaud report three differences between the voices of *P. streckeri* and *P. clarki.* Under comparable environmental temperatures, with both air and water temperatures within a range of 3.3° C, the call of *clarki* is 0.20 seconds in duration, with 75 trills per second, and the dominant frequency is 2,850 cps. The call of *streckeri* is much shorter, only 0.04 seconds in duration, and the dominant frequency of 2,200 cps is appreciably lower. The call of *streckeri* is described as "not trilled," but this implies a dichotomy in human hearing that may not exist in frogs.

As McAlister observes, the sound spectrograph (the instrument with the trade name, Sona-Graph, manufactured by the Kay Electric Company) will resolve no more than approximately eighty pulsations per second. Pulsation rates exceeding this can readily be determined, however, by making spectrograms from the sound on tape when it is reproduced at speeds slower than those used in recording it. Counts indicating pulsation rates of 132 and 184, respectively, for *Bufo kelloggi* and *Bufo retiformis* in the area where they occur sympatrically were obtained from tapes reproduced at one-fourth the normal speed. The differences in the pulsation rates of those two voices, though not aurally apparent to human beings, may nevertheless provide the means for discrimination in females of the two species. The important distinction in the voices of the *Pseudacris* is probably not that one is trilled and the other is not, but that they differ significantly in pulsation rates.

Pulsation rates, and the durations of calls, are influenced by temperature, whereas the number of pulsations comprising individual calls is unaffected by thermal changes. All three characteristics vary from one local population to another in some species, but ordinarily there are greater differences between sympatric but congeneric species in one or the other of these characteristics. The situation Crenshaw and Blair (1959) describe for *Pseudacris nigrita* and *Pseudacris triseriata,* species with overlapping distributions in the southeastern portion of the United States, is reviewed in the section dealing with hearing in frogs. It will be recalled that mating calls of these species overlap in dominant frequencies and durations, but the pulsation rate in *triseriata* is approximately four times that of *nigrita.* The spectrograms Crenshaw and Blair provide indicate that the shorter call of *triseriata* contains approximately three times as many pulsations as the call of *nigrita.* Limited hybridization is believed to occur despite ecological differences supplementing those between calls.

Conant (1958) depicts representatives of each of the seven species of *Pseudacris,* and maps their distributions. The range of one species, *P. triseriata,* with three races, extends from the Gulf Coast northward to New York and northwestward almost to the Arctic Circle. The other six species, as may be seen from Conant's maps, are distributed from Texas and Florida northward to Pennsylvania. The ranges of all other species overlap that of *P. triseriata* and five of the species also occur sympatrically with a second species. No two sympatric species are known to have calls that cannot readily be distinguished in the field. Even when the area of overlap is limited so that the vast majority of the frogs in each species never hear the voice of the other, their mating calls are distinct. It is particularly significant, therefore, that the voices of genetically incompatible allopatric species may be indistinguishable, whereas sympatric populations with different voices are not necessarily incompatible.

Pseudacris clarki occupies an area extending from the Gulf Coast of eastern Texas northward through central Oklahoma to Kansas. Conant's distributional maps of the species indicate that it occurs sympatrically with *P. triseriata* only in portions of Oklahoma and Kansas. Lindsay (1958) reports evidence of ecological divergence where they occur together, and says also that their mating calls are "distinct." Nevertheless, "breeding experiments in the laboratory showed no loss of viability or fertility in the hybrids." The summary of Lindsay's investigation does not indicate whether backcrosses were attempted. Detailed comparisons of the calls of the two species have not been published.

Mecham's (1959) experimental hybridization of two allopatric species, *Pseudacris streckeri* and *Pseudacris ornata,* reveals a situation of particular interest. W. F. Blair (1958f) reports no detectable differences between the calls of the two species other than a difference in dominant frequencies of 400 cps. The two are morphologically similar, although both similarities and differences are apparent in the illustrations in color that Conant (1958) provides. Mecham notes that differences in size, habitus, and pattern serve to distinguish the two species. Blair suggests that an early stage in speciation is represented in these allopatric populations, and he doubts whether they would behave as separate species were they to become sympatric. This inference was not without foundation before more detailed information was supplied by Mecham. His investigation reveals normal development of embryos resulting from crosses between P. *ornata* females and P. *streckeri* males, and in an earlier investigation he found no indication of genetic incompatibility in the reciprocal cross. Nevertheless, his attempts to backcross the hybrids with P. *ornata* females failed, and Mecham concludes that hybrids are sterile, perhaps because of abnormal development of the gonads.

It is evident, therefore, that populations geographically isolated may retain similar calls while differentiating physiologically to such an extent that gene exchange becomes impossible. Should these reproductively isolated species with similar mating calls become sympatric, selection would almost certainly reinforce any small differences exisiting in their mating calls and behavior that would tend to discourage males of one from clasping females of the other species. This is quite possibly what happened when an ancestral population of *Hyla versicolor* became fragmented, with two daughter populations later becoming sympatric. W. F. Blair (1958f) summarizes the complex situation in populations currently assigned to a single species. Blair's analysis of recordings reveals extensive variations in trill rates, with "fast trillers" and "slow trillers" ordinarily occurring in separate populations. In some areas, however, the two calls may be heard in the same aggregation in the absence of intermediate calls. Johnson (1959) found no morphological differences between frogs uttering the distinctive calls. Despite the absence of such differences, hybridization experiments reveal such extensive genetic incompatibility that Johnson, though speaking of "call races," concludes that "fast trillers," and "slow trillers" in Texas appear to represent separate species.

Viscount Chaplin, quoted in an unsigned account (Anonymous, 1954), calls attention to differences between the voices of northern and southern populations of European treefrogs long regarded as subspecies of *Hyla arborea*. As visualized by Viscount Chaplin, *H. arborea*, with an eastern subspecies, *savignyi*, is widely distributed in central Europe, whereas in the Iberian Peninsula *H. arborea* coexists with *H. meridionalis*. The voices "of *arborea* and *savignyi* are undistinguishable, while that of *meridionalis* is entirely distinct." Parker (1956), who reviews the situation in more detail, delineates the range of *H. meridionalis* as extending from southern France, across northwestern Italy to the Iberian Peninsula, with a disjunct population in the adjacent portion of northern Africa. Where *H. meridionalis* occurs sympatrically with *H. arborea* in northern Spain and southern France, the two species do not interbreed.

Though Parker does not mention the call, he describes the sympatric populations as being "discontinuous by behavior." The differences in the mating calls to which Viscount Chaplin refers are readily apparent in a commercial recording (previously mentioned in the discussion of the mating calls of *Alytes*) released in Switzerland. Spectrographic analysis of the undocumented calls on the record reveals extensive differences between the calls of *H. arborea* and *H. meridionalis*, despite similarities in dominant frequencies. The call of *H. arborea* consists of a series of pulsations, nine to eleven per second, with the individual pulsations 0.07 to 0.08 in duration. In contrast, *Hyla meridionalis* utters a short call, approximately 0.40 seconds in duration; at intervals of 0.8 to 0.9 seconds. Spectrograms, made from calls reproduced at one-fourth the normal speed, show that each pulsation of the call of *H. arborea* consists of what might be called micropulsations, of which there are ten to twelve. The call of *H. meridionalis,* with no pulsations discernible to the human ear, proves to be comprised of 48 to 50 micropulsations similar in structure and frequency to the few contained in each pulsation of the call of *H. arborea.* There are 58 micropulsations per second in the trilled call of *H. arborea* and 48 micropulsations per second in the untrilled call of *meridionalis.* In the absence of information concerning the temperatures of the individuals whose calls were analyzed, however, it is possible that a difference of this small magnitude can be ascribed to environmental influences. It is uncertain whether the reproductive isolation of these two sympatric hylids depends to some extent upon differences between their respective calls. The divergence indicated by spectrographic analysis would, however, appear to be adequate to account for differentials in the responses of females.

Variations in the mating calls of frogs in representative populations of *Hyla eximia* will be discussed in connection with their taxonomic implications. Pulsation rates and the number of pulsations per call in this Mexican hylid are extremely variable, as may be seen from Table 3 as well as from spectrograms (Figs. 32-38). We do not know, however, whether mating calls of individuals in one local population serve to attract females from another. Toads similar in size but with calls that differ extensively in duration and pulsation rates often interbreed. As emphasized in earlier discussions, however, it is questionable whether the mating calls of toads attract females to the individuals uttering the calls. Discrimination and differences between pulsation rates may enter into the responses of toads, without necessarily being effective in discouraging mismatings. The inadequacy of isolation mechanisms dependent upon the formation of separate breeding assemblages explains what might otherwise be interpreted as evidence that discrimination in female toads cannot be dependent upon differentials in pulsation rates. When pair formation is more directly dependent upon mating calls in that the female orients her movements in response to an individual rather than to a chorus, differences in pulsation rates, durations of individual calls, or the number of pulsations per call, may provide the means for discrimination that insure the effectiveness of behavioral patterns as premating isolation mechanisms.

VOICE STRUCTURE IN ANURAN HYBRIDS

During the last two or three decades numerous authors, including Dobzhansky (1935, 1937, 1951), Mayr (1940, 1942), and Huxley (1942), stress the importance of reproductive isolation in definitions of species. Mayr (1957a) traces the history of the various concepts leading to a biological concept of species that emphasizes gene flow on the one hand and discontinuities in nature on the other. Despite their general acceptance of these concepts, biologists also realize that there are varying degrees of reproductive isolation. There is no simple relationship between the systematic position of two species and their ability to hybridize. Virtually all students of the Anura agree that valid species may occasionally hybridize under natural conditions.

Despite the occurrence of hybrids, in nearly every instance where species freely interbreed, there is little if any evidence of gene flow outside the zone of contact. Littlejohn (1959b) believes that the abrupt intergradation in call structure in a region where the ranges of *Crinia pseudinsignifera* and *Crinia insignifera* narrowly overlap is indicative of introgression, although he considers the two populations to represent species. A. P. Blair (1946) summarizes the literature dealing with hybrid toads in eastern North America, and describes a hybrid produced by crossing a female *Bufo woodhousei* from Oklahoma with a male of *B. terrestris americanus*. The hybrid survived for nearly six years, during which it clasped other toads placed in the same container. It uttered the warning chirp, accompanied by the male release vibration, but it did not call, even when males of one parental species, *B. t. americanus*, called in its vicinity.

A. P. Blair (1941b) describes intermediate voices attributed to hybrid toads, but spectrographic analysis awaited the work of W. F. Blair (1956b). A hybrid between *Bufo w. woodhousei* and *Bufo t. americanus* taken in Oklahoma produced calls intermediate between those of the parental species, as shown in the spectrograms illustrating Blair's account. Hybrids resulting from laboratory crosses of less closely related species, *Bufo valliceps* and *Bufo w. woodhousei*, were released following metamorphosis and recorded when they were approximately two years old. One individual uttered a weakly-developed call unlike that of either parent, but the calls of other individuals more closely resembled those of *Bufo valliceps*, although none was perfect. Where *Bufo microscaphus* and *Bufo woodhousei* are known to hybridize in southwestern Utah, W. F. Blair (1957b) recorded intermediate voices, including one illustrated with a spectrogram that he describes as a "possible recombination type."

Recordings of hybrids obtained within the last five years are of interest for reasons in addition to their being intermediate between the calls of the parental species. As indicated in a preceding discussion, the individuals uttering the intermediate call were taken with choruses of one or the other of the parental species. The calls described below are those of sympatric species in three genera representing as many families, the Pelobatidae, Bufonidae, and Hylidae.

Scaphiopus.   Observations in 1953 disclosed evidence of interbreeding between *Scaphiopus hammondi* and *Scaphiopus bombifrons* in southeastern Arizona and the contiguous area in New Mexico.   Calls of the hybrids were not detected until 1955, however, when several males were found calling at the middle of a deep pool near Rodeo, New Mexico.   In this areas *S. bombifrons* has a characteristic pattern on the dorsum in contrast to the relatively unicolored appearance of *S. hammondi.*   The hybrids had the pattern of *bombifrons,* although they uttered their intermediate calls in a chorus comprised entirely of *S. hammondi.*   Three years later Dr. Richard G. Zweifel, who obtained a better recording, found the hybrids in a chorus of *S. bombifrons* in the same area, near Rodeo, New Mexico.

As shown in the spectrogram (Fig. 24) the call of *S. bombifrons* from near Rodeo, New Mexico is a short call, approximately 0.12 seconds in duration.   No pulsations are evident, although they become discernible when spectrograms are made of recordings reproduced at one-fourth the original speed.   The call of *S. hammondi* (Fig. 22) is strongly pulsated, however, and similar trills or pulsations at a more rapid rate occur in the call of the hybrid (Fig. 23).   The calls of the parental species and the hybrid, which may be heard on Side I, Band 3 of the Demonstration Record, are readily compared in tabular form:

	Duration Of Call In Seconds	*Pulsations Per Call*	*Intervals Between Calls* In Seconds
Scaphiopus bombifrons	0.12	30	0.38
S. bombifrons × *S. hammondi*	0.42	(21) 22 (23)	0.26
Scaphiopus hammondi	0.97	25	0.30

All three calls were recorded at similar temperatures within a few miles of Rodeo, New Mexico in San Simon Valley.   Calls of *S. bombifrons* virtually identical with those of the population in San Simon Valley were also recorded in Mexico near Chihuahua, Chihuahua during June, 1959.   The call W. F. Blair (1955c) illustrates with spectrograms and describes for *S. bombifrons* near Tulia, Texas bears considerable resemblance to the call of the hybrid from New Mexico, but consists of 22 to 40 pulsations.   The call of *S. hammondi* from Tulia, however, is similar to those for the New Mexican population.

There are obviously mean differences in the number of pulsations between local populations of *S. hammondi.*   Even so, there are few important differences between the calls of a population at Chapala, Jalisco,

Mexico (representative of a southern subspecies, *S. h. multiplicata*) and those of populations in Arizona, or the call of the individual from Tulia. Recordings of the calls of *S. hammondi* from California, Arizona, New Mexico, and the Mexican states of Coahuila and Jalisco do not, however, reveal variations in the number of trills so extensive as those Blair reports for the calls of the single population at Tulia identified as *bombifrons*. Blair identifies the call of one individual taken at Tulia as that of a hybrid between *hammondi* and *bombifrons*, but the characteristics tabulated for this call indicate that it overlaps those of the calls identified as *bombifrons*. It seems to be exceptional only in having the emphasized frequencies at somewhat higher levels.

The variations in the Tulia population are perhaps attributable to extensive interbreeding between *bombifrons* and *hammondi*, with recombinations in the hybrids resulting in the variable calls identified as those of *bombifrons*. Or perhaps there are sympatric populations of "slow trillers" and "fast trillers" among Texas populations of *S. hammondi*, as Blair (1958f) describes for *Hyla versicolor*. *S. hammondi* and *S. bombifrons* cannot be described as interbreeding freely in Arizona; so few hybrids are encountered that it seems safe to say that they comprise an extremely small percentage of the population. The same species may, nevertheless, interbreed with much greater frequency in Texas.

The individuals in the population near Rodeo that are intermediate in morphology as well as in call structure can scarcely be identified as anything other than hybrids between *S. hammondi* and *S. bombifrons*. Evidently hybrids participate in choruses of either of the parental species. No *S. bombifrons* called from the vicinity of the pool where hybrids were calling in 1955, but those taken by Zweifel in 1958 called with a chorus consisting largely of *bombifrons*, but a few *hammondi* were present. Thus, one species may have been absent in the chorus Blair recorded near Tulia, and those identified as *bombifrons* are actually hybrids, or at the eastern extremity of its range *bombifrons* may possess a voice that more closely resembles that of *hammondi* owing to the recency of the overlapping distributions. Reinforcement of differences in calls has perhaps taken place in Arizona and Chihuahua but not farther east, if this assumption is correct. Additional recordings are needed to obtain a solution to the problem.

Mating calls of the few species of *Scaphiopus* are fundamentally less divergent than they seem to be on the basis of aural comparisons or from comparisons of spectrograms of calls analyzed at normal speed. Spectrograms of the short call of *Scaphiopus bombifrons* reproduced at half the normal speed bear considerable resemblance to the spectrogram W. F. Blair (1955c) provides for the call of *S. hurteri*. The pulsations do not

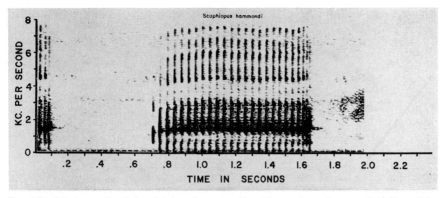

Fɪɢ. 22. Mating call of *Scaphiopus hammondi*, with portion of one call followed by the next complete call in the sequence, (sounds of insects in the background). Recorded at Portal, Arizona. Air temperature 22.6°C.

become evident in spectrograms of the call of *bombifrons* until it is reproduced at one-fourth the normal speed; spectrographic analysis will then disclose resemblances to the call of the hybrid (Fig. 23). It requires little imagination to derive the call of *hammondi* from this, or to prolong the call of *hurteri* to obtain one closely resembling that of *couchi*, which varies in length from one local population to another. The call of *intermontanus* is closer to that of *bombifrons*, as W. F. Blair (1956d) suggests, but in duration as well as trill rate it is intermediate between *hammondi* and *bombifrons*, if the latter name is applied to spadefoots with the call illustrated (Fig. 24).

Bufo. Mating calls of *Bufo terrestris americanus*, *Bufo woodhousei*

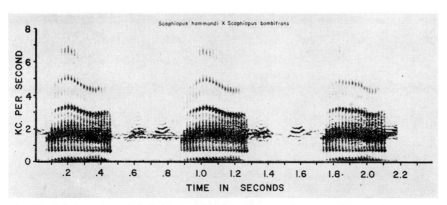

Fɪɢ. 23. Mating call of hybrid, *Scaphiopus hammondi* × *Scaphiopus bombifrons*. Recorded near Rodeo, New Mexico, with chorus of *Scaphiopus bombifrons* in background. Air temperature 22.0°, water temperature 20°C.

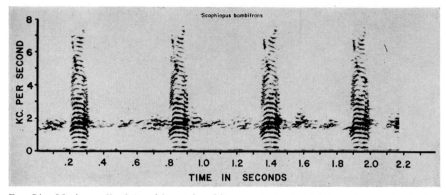

Fig. 24. Mating call of *Scaphiopus bombifrons*. Recorded near Rodeo, New Mexico. Air temperature 22°C, water temperature 20°C.

fowleri and the hybrid between the two were recorded by Dr. William Tavolga and Dr. Richard G. Zweifel at Closter, New Jersey during the spring of 1959. The hybrids obtained on this occasion are morphologically indistinguishable from *B. w. fowleri* taken the same night. *B. w. fowleri* called from one side of a pond, and the hybrids called from the other, apparently at the same site utilized earlier by *B. t. americanus*. This is uncertain, however, for hybrids calling earlier may have been mistaken for *americanus*.

As shown by spectrograms (Figs. 25, 26 and 27), the call of the hybrid is intermediate between calls of the parental species in some respects. The shorter calls of *fowleri* are easily encompassed in spectrograms, but the calls of the hybrids and of *americanus* are too long to be shown on one spectrogram. The following tabulation, in which data for *B. t.*

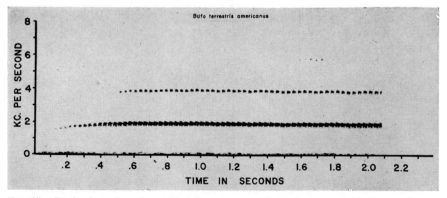

Fig. 25. Beginning of mating call of *Bufo terrestris americanus*, recorded near Closter, New Jersey. Body temperature 21.6°C.

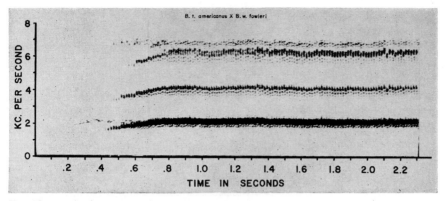

Fɪɢ. 26. Beginning of mating call of hybrid, *Bufo terrestris americanus* × *Bufo woodhousei fowleri.* Recorded at Closter, New Jersey. Body temperature 21.7°C.

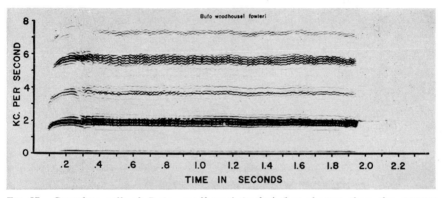

Fɪɢ. 27. Complete call of *Bufo woodhousei fowleri* (but shorter than the average call). Recorded at Closter, New Jersey. Body temperature 21.6°C.

terrestris are included for reasons explained below, will facilitate comparisons:

	Duration in Seconds Means and Extremes	Pulsations Per Second, Range	Pulsations Per Call
B. t. americanus	8.5 (6.4-9.2)	35-39	314
Hybrid	3.7 (1.9-5.4)	64 to 80	241
B. w. fowleri	1.7 (1.5-1.8)	146-151	244
B. t. terrestris	4.8 (3.2-5.8)	70-74	346

The call of the hybrid proves to be somewhat closer to that of *B. w. fowleri* than to *B. t. americanus,* as might also be inferred from the spectrograms of the three calls. The similarity between the hybrid and *B. w.*

fowleri is particularly striking if comparisons are made of the number of pulsations included in the call. These have been calculated by multiplying averages for the duration of the call by the mean number of pulsations per second. The results obtained from comparisons on this basis indicate that differences between the calls of the parental species consist largely in pulsation rates. The average call of *americanus* includes more pulsations, but the calls of the hybrid are comprised of almost the same number of pulsations as the calls of *fowleri*. Their rate of production, but not the number of pulsations per call, is apparently influenced by genes from *americanus*. In essence, therefore, the call of *fowleri* is little more than the call of *americanus* (with a small portion omitted) compressed into a narrower time interval.

Spectograms of the call of the hybrid compared with spectrograms of calls of *Bufo terrestris terrestris* (Fig. 28) reveal remarkable similarities

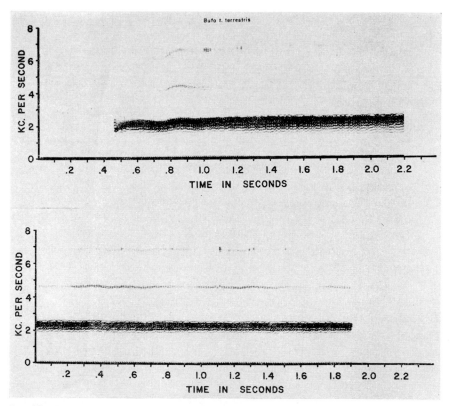

Fɪɢ. 28.   Mating calls of *Bufo terrestris terrestris,* beginning of call recorded near East Lake, Putnam County, Florida (upper), end of call recorded at Archbold Biological Station, Highlands County, Florida (lower).

borne out in part by figures supplied in the tabulation.   With more extensive data, and with corrections for the influences of temperature, mean pulsation rates may prove to be identical.   In the number of pulsations per call in the population at Closter, New Jersey, however, *B. t. terrestris* more closely resembles *B. t. americanus*.   On the basis of hybridization experiments Volpe (1959) reaches conclusions in accord with implications of these counts.   W. F. Blair (1957a) provides data and spectrograms for the call of *Bufo hemiophrys* and suggests that its affinities are with the *americanus*.   The data provided for the durations and pulsation rates of the calls, however, show that the range of variation in the totals for pulsations comprising the call of *B. hemiophrys* encompasses that of both *fowleri* and *americanus*.   There is some doubt, therefore, whether *hemiophrys* is necessarily more closely related to one than to the other.   Distinctions between trilled or untrilled calls are not entirely academic, but the presence of toads with intermediate pulsation rates resembling those of the hybird described above shows plainly that the differences are not dichotomous.

W. F. Blair (1957a) discusses other members of the assemblage and in an earlier paper (1956a) he provides data for various populations of *B. w. woodhousei* and *B. w. fowleri,* from which pulsation rates are omitted.   Spectrographic analysis of the mating calls of populations in Arizona and Utah shows that pulsation rates vary extensively.   The call of *B. w. australis* recorded near Phoenix when the air temperature was 24.0° C has a mean duration of 1.7 seconds, and a pulsation rate of 142. Calls of toads belonging to the smaller subspecies, *B. w. woodhousei,* were recorded at higher elevations and lower air temperatures, 9 to 10° C, in southern Utah.   At Moab calls had a mean duration of 2.8 seconds, and a pulsation rate of 108, but at Kanab calls were slightly shorter, averaging 2.3 seconds, with pulsation rates ranging from 98 to 104.   The average number of pulsations per call in the larger toads at Phoenix is 245, dropping to 233 at Kanab, but rising to 303 at Moab.

Temperature presumably influences pulsation rates and the durations of calls in these toads, but presumably the number of pulsations is unaffected by temperature changes.   This should be verified experimentally, but it is certainly true of the shorter calls of some hylids.   The differences noted in the average number of pulsations in the calls of toads cannot be attributed to temperature, and variations in the number do not appear to be correlated with other features of the environment.

Hyla.   A higher-pitched call (to be heard on Band 3 of Side I on the Demonstration Record) detected in a small chorus of *Hyla gratiosa* near Hicoria, Florida on July 16, 1957, proved to be that of an individual in-

termediate in size between *Hyla gratiosa* and *Hyla cinerea,* although its
pattern is not strikingly different from that of *H. cinerea.* Its voice is
intermediate between the two species in the dominant frequency. The
distinct bands in spectrograms (Fig. 29) representing the harmonics in
the mating calls of *H. gratiosa* and *H. cinerea,* however, are ill-defined
and diffuse in the hybrid. There is little doubt that the frog that produced these calls is a hybrid. Despite its superficial resemblance to the
smaller species, its calling habits were identical with those of a dozen or
more *Hyla gratiosa* in the chorus in which it was found. When induced
to call in a sound-proofed room at the Archbold Biological Station the
night it was collected, it alternated its call with that of *H. gratiosa,* re-
peating it at the same intervals as the larger of the two parental species.

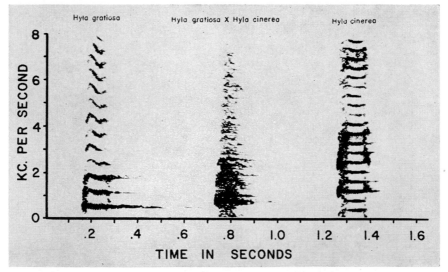

Fig. 29. Mating calls of *Hyla gratiosa* (left), hybird, *Hyla gratiosa* × *Hyla cinerea*
(center), and *Hyla cinerea* (right). All recorded near Archbold Biological Station,
Highlands County, Florida. Illustrations above show patterns and relative sizes of
parental species and the hybrid.

When calling alone, however, the repetition rate was nearly identical with that for the calls of *Hyla cinerea* recorded under the same conditions in the sound-proofed room. Since the hybrid modified its call-rate to conform to that of the larger species, it seems improbable that call rates under these circumstances depend wholly upon temperature, even though it may influence rates in the absence of auditory stimuli.

In the hybrids of *Scaphiopus, Bufo* and *Hyla*, mating calls are intermediate between those of the parental species, but in some characteristics, calls may more closely resemble those of one parent or differ from those of both parental species. Thus the number of pulsations in calls of the hybrid between the two species of toads is virtually the same as the number in calls of *Bufo w. fowleri*, whereas the interval between calls in the *Scaphiopus* hybrid is shorter than it is in the vocalizations of either parental species at similar temperatures.

The calling habits of hybrids apparently resemble those of either parent. *Scaphiopus* hybrids apparently join choruses of either parental species. It is uncertain, however, whether the presence of hybrids in choruses depends upon their responses to the calls of parental species. In *Bufo* there is a tendency for hybrids to form separate choruses, as Cory and Manion (1955) describe the situation in *Bufo t. americanus* and *B. w. fowleri*. This may result in part from seasonal differences in the mating of the parental species, but the observations imply a blending of physiological responses under genetic control. If hybrids respond to their own calls or those of parental species, however, there is nothing to indicate that either parent responds to the call of the hybrid. Even when hybrids are genetically compatible with parental species, their mating calls may elicit no response. Hybrids, at least among toads, do not appear to be at a disadvantage in competing with the parental species as far as survival is concerned. W. F. Blair (1956c) provides the only experimental evidence to confirm this assumption, but the prevalence of hybrids in other situations is in accord with the results obtained.

Whether intermediate voices in hybrids can be attributed to modifications in the vocal apparatus, to intermediate neural mechanisms, as McAlister (1959b) implies, or to a combination of the two, remains to be ascertained. Characteristics of the voice would appear to depend entirely upon what a frog inherits rather than upon influences attributable to learning. Schneirla (1956) discusses the interplay of maturation and learning and the problems entailed in disentangling their influences. Where earlier experiments suggested swimming in salamander larvae to be merely a matter of neural determination of functional development, results obtained by Fromme (1941) indicate that coordination of movement is partially dependent upon practice. Schneirla, however, points out the shortcomings of the experimental procedures employed.

MATING CALL ANALYSIS AS AN ADJUNCT TO SYSTEMATIC STUDIES

Our knowledge of anuran mating calls, though still in a rudimentary stage, has advanced to the point where complexities are beginning to become apparent. The integration of vocality and responses in the intricate patterns of behavior associated with reproduction and hence also with isolation mechanisms and speciation is manifest. Nevertheless, the information thus far assembled is quite possibly inadequate to assess the full significance of differences or similarities in mating calls. The adaptive phenomena associated with reinforcement of differences in mating calls in sympatric species, and the genetic incompatibility of allopatric populations with mating calls so nearly identical that they must have stemmed from the call of a common ancestor, should be borne in mind by any systematist who labors under the illusion that spectrograms of mating calls are going to settle all problems of relationships.

The spectrograms reproduced in Figure 30 will perhaps emphasize the point that similarity in call is not of necessity an indication of close relationship. The structures of call B and call C disclosed in spectrograms (which might have shown even greater resemblances had they been produced on the same spectrograph) suggest that these two possess characteristics in common that neither shares with A. The frogs producing calls A and C, however, are sufficiently close to produce viable hy-

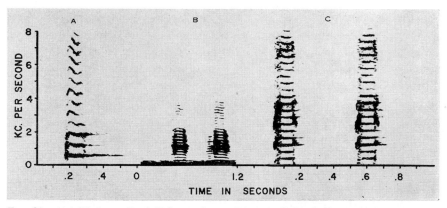

FIG. 30. (A.) Mating call of *Hyla gratiosa*. (B.) Sound signal of emperor goose, *Anser canagicus*, (note different time scale). (C.) Mating call of *Hyla cinerea*. Spectrogram of goose from Vibralizer, others from Sona-Graph, both manufactured by Kay Electric Company. Goose signal used by courtesy of Dr. Peter H. Klopfer.

brids, whereas the sound signal with the structure designated as B is produced by an animal so distantly related that it is placed in a separate Class.

With knowledge in its present state, it is equally uncertain whether divergence in call is necessarily indicative of distant relationship. Spectrograms of the calls of canyon treefrogs from Arizona and California (Fig. 31) show such conspicuous differences that it is certainly to be doubted that females of one would respond to the calls of the other. Morphologically the frogs in these two populations are so similar that they have been regarded as the same species for over a hundred years. They occupy separate ranges separated by the Mojave and Sonoran deserts. The disjunction in their distribution may not antedate the Pleistocene pluvial periods, or it may date from a much earlier period in the Tertiary as increasingly arid conditions supposedly arose in the area now termed desert. If the canyon treefrogs on opposite sides of the desert descended from a common ancestor, it seems questionable in this instance whether the divergence should be attributed to conditions of sympatry existing in California, where the canyon treefrog occurs side by side with only one other congener, *Hyla regilla*. In some respects the calls of the sympatric species more closely resemble each other than either resembles the call of *H. arenicolor* in Arizona and Utah, with a range southward into Mexico, where it may be sympatric with several species of *Hyla*. Relatively little modification would be required to derive the split call of *H. regilla* (Fig. 39) from the undivided call of the canyon treefrogs in California.

As shown in the analysis of the calls of hybrids between species of

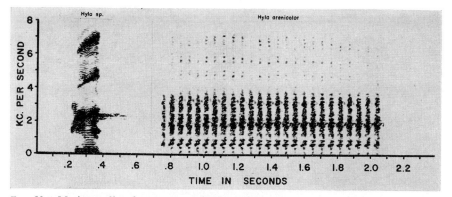

FIG. 31. Mating calls of canyon treefrogs, undescribed species recorded in Sentenac Canyon, San Diego County, California (left), and one complete mating call of *Hyla arenicolor* (right). Recorded near Virgin, Washington County, Utah. Air and water temperatures 21.5°C.

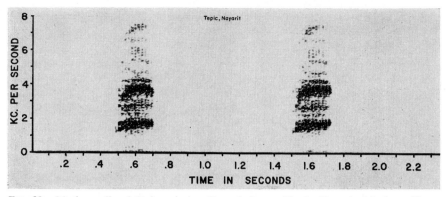

FIG. 32. Mating calls of *Hyla eximia*. Recorded near Tepic, Nayarit, Mexico. Elevation 3,000 feet. Air temperature 20.0°C.

Bufo and *Scaphiopus,* the differences between trilled and untrilled calls are not actually dichotomous, as might be inferred from aural impressions or from spectrograms of calls reproduced at normal speeds. Even with the limited information thus far obtained for a few representative populations of *Hyla eximia* (Figs. 32 to 37, inclusive) in Mexico, it is possible to show that intermediate stages ranging from an un-trilled to trilled calls may occur within populations currently assigned, and correctly so in all probability, to a single species. The variations within these populations, summarized in Table 3, (and discussed and illustrated on Side I, Band 3 of the Demonstration Record) do not appear to be clinal in nature. On the contrary, the variations more closely resemble

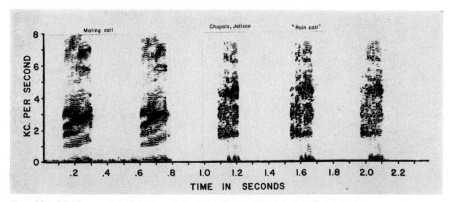

FIG. 33. Mating calls (left), and "rain calls," probably territorial calls, uttered with the vocal sac partially inflated (right). Recorded at Chapala, Jalisco, Mexico. Elevation 5,000 feet. Air temperatures 20.0°, and 16.0°C, respectively.

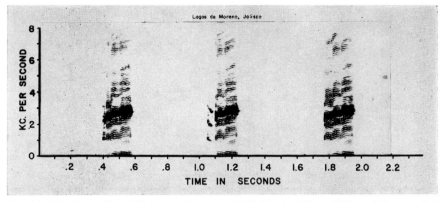

FIG. 34. Mating calls of *Hyla eximia*, single individual. The middle call is preceded by a chirp that accompanied the majority of calls uttered by the same individual. Recorded near Lagos de Moreno, Jalisco, Mexico. Elevation 6,300 feet. Air temperature 16.5°C.

a mosaic pattern of distribution, insofar as can be judged by representative calls from seven populations.

The calls within this single species exemplify the pitfalls confronting the investigator who is faced with the problem of drawing reliable inferences from a single sample. To complicate the situation further, the investigator must distinguish between mating calls and "rain calls" (compared in Fig. 33), those uttered with the vocal sac partly inflated that may prove to be territorial calls. There are also individual variants. Only one frog was calling at the site near Lagos de Moreno, and this individual

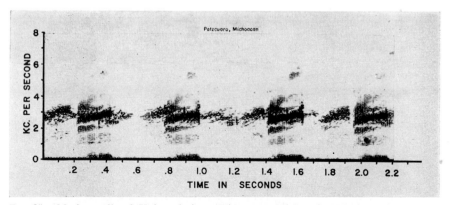

FIG. 35. Mating calls of *Hyla eximia* at Pátzcuaro, Michoacán, Mexico (with calls of other individuals of the same species in the background). Elevation 7,100 feet. Air temperature 16.5°C.

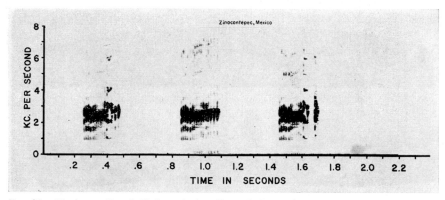

FIG. 36. Mating calls of *Hyla eximia*. Recorded at Zinacantepec, México, Mexico. Elevation 8,800 feet. Air temperature 15.0°C.

uttered series of calls, each of which was preceded by a chirp. The chirp was sometimes omitted in a long series of calls. In the section of the tape from which the spectrogram (Fig. 34) was made, a chirp is present in one call between two supposedly normal calls. It will be noted, however, that the inclusion of the chirp does not change the duration of the call. Spectrographic analysis reveals little variation in the duration of calls, or in the total pulsations per call. Those including the chirp, however, invariably have four fewer pulsations. Variations in individual calls are apparent in the spectrogram (Fig. 36) illustrating calls in the population at Zinacantepec.

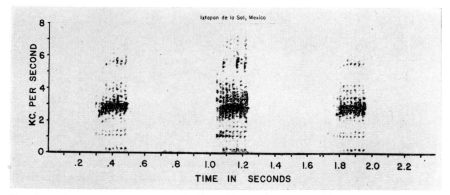

FIG. 37. Mating calls (two individuals) of *Hyla eximia*. Recorded at Ixtápan de la Sal, México, Mexico. Elevation 5,300 feet. Air temperature 20.0°C. The call in the center of the spectrogram comes from the individual closer to the microphone. Each issued calls at nearly the identical interval of 1.3 seconds.

There is a positive correlation between pulsation rates and the number of pulsations comprising calls, but neither of these characteristics is correlated with the duration of calls.   Variation in the intervals between calls is extensive, more so than becomes apparent from hasty examination of spectrograms.   The frogs in the population at Ixtápan de la Sal, in the state of México, call at intervals exceeding a second, but when two individuals are within a meter of each other they alternate their calls with such precision that the series uttered by one frog dovetail almost perfectly with the calls of the other frog.   When the individual uttering the middle call in the spectrogram (Fig. 37) illustrating this population was removed, the other frog continued to emit calls at the identical rate.

Frogs with calls similar to those recorded at Ixtápan de la Sal were recorded in chorus north of this locality, and therefore closer to Zinacantepec.   Within an air-line distance of less than 25 miles, but with a difference in altitude of approximately 3,000 feet, there is an abrupt change in the calls of these treefrogs.   In the population at Zinacantepec at 15.0° C the call with rapid pulsations is repeated at intervals of less than half a second.   When the air temperature was 18.5° C at Ixtápan de la Sal, frogs uttered a call in which the pulsation rate is so much lower that the call becomes a trill to human ears.   The trilled mating calls of these frogs is so much more widely spaced, at intervals exceeding a second, that it bears little superficial resemblance to the calls of the populations at either Zinacantepec or Toluca a few miles away.   In most characteristics the call of the frogs at Ixtápan approximates that of the most distant population, at Tepic, Nayarit, over 300 miles to the west.   These two populations share the distinction of having the lowest pulsation rates, as well as the lowest rates of repetition in the samples recorded.

With only seven populations represented in the sample, it is perhaps uncertain whether mating calls with fewer pulsations, lower pulsation rates, and longer intervals between calls are restricted to the warmer climates that characterize Ixtápan and Tepic.   Frogs in other genera utter increasingly shorter calls more frequently as temperatures rise. Thus Bellis (1957) reports that a rise in temperature of 10° C increases repetition rates in the call of *Pseudacris triseriata* from 18 per minute to 36 per minute, whereas the call decreases in duration from 1.2 to 0.06 seconds.   According to Zweifel (1959), the call-rate of *Bombina variegata* increases from 62 to 123 calls per minute when the body temperature (with an extrapolation 1.2 degrees at the upper level) rises from 16.8° to 26.8° C, but the duration of the call decreases from 0.32 to 0.22 seconds. The Q_{10} value for repetitions of the call, therefore, is about two in each instance, or approximately the same as that reported by Frings and Frings (1957) for repetition rates in the chirp of a cone-headed grasshopper.

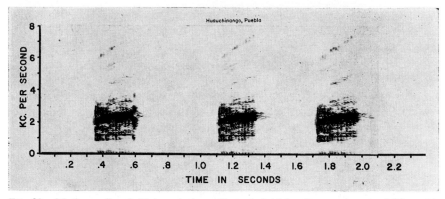

F<small>IG</small>. 38.   Mating calls of *Hyla eximina*.   Recorded 10.5 miles southwest of Huauchinango, Puebla.   Elevation 7,500 feet.   Calling from shallow water at 17.0°C.

The calls of the populations of *Hyla eximia* at Tepic and Ixtapan de la Sal, however, were recorded at slightly higher temperatures than those of populations inhabiting the plateau at higher elevations.   Nevertheless, the differences in pulsation rates and repetition rates in the call are the reverse of what might be expected if they were the result of thermal influences.   The modifications in the calls of the populations in warmer climates may, of course, be associated with physiological adaptations, but if there are compensations for temperature influencing pulsation and repetition rates, they are the opposite of what might be expected.   Were these treefrogs from warmer climates transferred to cooler environments inhabited by their relatives at higher elevations on the plateau, the differences between their calls would become emphasized.

Possibly the populations with the most divergent mating calls represent separate species.   It is pertinent to note, however, that the calls overlap in nearly all quantitative characteristics.   Larger samples from more localities would undoubtedly disclose even more extensive overlaps. The degree of divergence in some characteristics of the call in sympatric species of other genera, pulsation rates in *Pseudacris* for example, suggests that differences in the populations of *Hyla eximia* somewhat greater in magnitude would be required before isolation mechanisms dependent upon mating calls became effective.   Levels of divergence prerequisite for discrimination are a matter of conjecture.   Ratios of one to four in pulsation rates, and of one to three in the number of pulsations per call are reported by Crenshaw and Blair (1959) for two sympatric species of *Pseudacris*.

The most divergent calls represented by the data in Table 3 are those recorded in Chapala and Ixtápan de la Sal.   Comparison of the mating calls of treefrogs at the two localities reveals that those in Chapala are comprised of nearly twice as many pulsations, with a pulsation rate more than doubled, and a rate of repetition that is more than tripled. It cannot be stated with assurance that these differences are adequate for discrimination by females were the two populations to become sympatric. If any degree of genetic incompatibility existed, reinforcement of such differences might result from selection. Spectrograms provide evidence of differences that may be correlated with mean differences in morphological characters, but the systematist is still faced with the problem of deciding whether interbreeding would occur were the populations sympatric. At first thought it may seem that spectrographic analysis of mating calls merely provides an additional character upon which to base an opinion concerning the level of divergence. In some situations, however, this additional character can be extremely important.

It is doubtful whether the same criteria can be applied to all genera in evaluating differences between mating calls. For reasons explained earlier, differences in the mating calls of toads may be less effective in preventing interbreeding than similar differences in hylids. Differences in size, breeding seasons, habitats or behavior should, of course, be taken into account when the systematist attempts to ascertain whether allopatric populations warrant recognition, and if so, whether they are species or subspecies. Without more detailed knowledge of auditory discrimination in the Anura, the procedure employed in evaluating differences or similarities in mating calls is much the same as that followed in evaluating morphological characters. In some instances, however, there is a tremendous advantage in being able to use one more character.

When the mating calls (those in Figure 31, for example) of allopatric populations are approximately as divergent as those of sympatric species, in the absence of any other criterion, it is reasonable to assume that divergence has reached the species level. Genetic divergence in allopatric populations with nearly identical mating calls may, however, reach the species level, as Mecham (1959) shows. Experimental hybridization may demonstrate that allopatric populations with divergent calls are also genetically incompatible, but if they are readily crossed as well as backcrossed, this in itself is no proof that speciation has not occurred. Any of several other isolation mechanisms might prevent interbreeding were the two populations sympatric.

Spectrographic analysis of mating calls, therefore, can reveal the existence of species overlooked by systematists once dependent upon descriptions of calls or morphological criteria. Similarly, the analysis of mating calls of sibling species, or sympatric frogs so similar morphologically that systematists may have questioned their status, may reveal

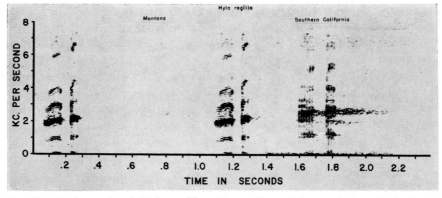

FIG. 39. Mating calls of *Hyla regilla*. Two calls at left recorded at Rock Creek, Montana. One call at right recorded at Lake Fulmor at an elevation of 5,500 feet in the San Jacinto Mountains of southern California. Air temperatures 15.0° and 12.8°C, respectively.

differences that serve to establish their validity, as W. F. Blair (1958f) demonstrates for *Acris gryllus* and *Acris crepitans*.

When the data obtained from spectrographic analysis of mating calls are interpreted in conjunction with the information obtained from experimental hybridization, they provide solutions to systematic problems unobtainable by other means. Sympatric populations usually pose relatively simple problems, whereas the status of allopatric populations may or may not be easily established. If they are genetically incompatible or if there are vast differences between mating calls, specific status is indicated. If they are genetically compatible and there is no appreciable divergence in mating calls, it is usually assumed that the populations are conspecific. There are, however, borderline cases. Spectrograms (Fig. 39) reveal pulsations in the mating call of *Hyla regilla* from the San Jacinto Mountains in southern California that are absent in a representative population from Montana. Despite the distance between the two populations, there is reason to suspect that the two populations are conspecific. Greater divergence is apparent when spectrograms (Figs. 31 and 40) of two populations of *Hyla arenicolor* are compared. The call of an individual near Virgin, Utah is 1.25 seconds in duration and comprised of 25 pulsations issued at a rate of 20 pulsations per second, with the temperature of the air and water at 21.5° C. The call of an individual recorded at a similar temperature in Cave Creek, near Portal, in the Chiricahua Mountains of southeastern Arizona is only 0.73 seconds in duration, and the 21 pulsations comprising the call were issued at the higher rate of 28 pulsations per second. Different frequencies are emphasized in the respective calls, but the similarities in the two calls are also manifest.

Detailed comparisons of the morphology of the two populations of *Hyla arenicolor* unquestionably would disclose other differences. Recordings of calls from localities in the intervening area might disclose intermediate calls. If tests demonstrate that frogs from the two populations can readily be crossed and backcrossed, there is little doubt that the two populations are conspecific, and the systematist may have no difficulty in deciding from other data whether it is worth while to recognize subspecies. If the populations in Utah and southeastern Arizona prove to be genetically incompatible, however, the possibility remains that any two adjacent populations from the area in between may be capable of interbreeding, as J. A. Moore demonstrated for *Rana pipiens.*

Such similarities as those shown in the spectrograms for the two populations of *Hyla arenicolor* can be construed as evidence of relationship. Greater differences between mating calls may make it impossible to decide whether any real affinity is indicated. Techniques entailing reproduction of mating calls at reduced speeds may reveal similarities not otherwise evident. Such methods have not yet been employed in analyzing the calls of the two populations of canyon treefrogs represented in the spectrogram (Fig. 31), but such analysis may show that the short call of the treefrogs in the California population could be derived from a longer call merely by compressing a similar number of pulsations into less space. Spectrograms of the call of *Hyla eximia* in Ixtapan de la Sal (Fig. 37) made from a recording at double the normal speed bear considerable resemblance to the spectrogram of the Chapala population (Fig. 33).

Clues to relationships do not necessarily require such procedures. The mating call of *Hyla squirella,* an inhabitant of the southeastern portion of the United States, closely resembles the mating call of *Hyla eximia* at Chapala. Spectrograms of the call of *H. squirella* W. F. Blair (1958a, 1958c) provides could easily be included in the series published herewith to illustrate the variations within *H. eximia,* and few would suspect that it did not belong in the series. The Floridian and Mexican frogs are sufficiently similar morphologically to suggest that *H. squirella* was derived from *H. eximia.* The call of the canyon treefrog in California is astonishingly similar to that of *squirella* as well as to the *eximia* population in Chapala. Comparisons of spectrograms for the calls of *Hyla arenicolor* with those for the *H. eximia* population in Ixtapan de la Sal, or even those of the population in Tepic, in both of which the pulsations are apparent, reveal manifest differences. It requires relatively little imagination, however, to derive the longer call of *arenicolor* from the trilled calls of *H. eximia* at Ixtápan de la Sal. With pulsations apparent

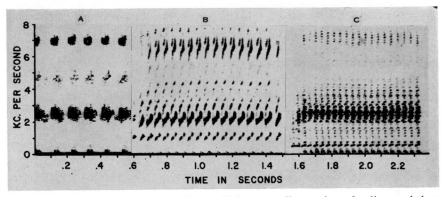

FIG. 40. Mating calls of three hylids, A. *Hyla femoralis*, portion of call recorded at Orange Springs, Florida; B. *Hyla versicolor*, entire call recorded at Hazelhurst, Wisconsin; and C. *Hyla arenicolor*, entire call recorded in Cave Creek, Arizona.

or absent in the call of *Hyla regilla* (Fig. 39) in California and the Northwest, it could easily be derived from one or another of the *H. eximia* calls merely by splitting the call, or omitting a portion of it, a tendency apparent in some of the calls of the individual recorded at Zinacantepec (Fig. 36).

It is within the realm of possibility that all of these frogs (as well as some others) were derived from an ancient and adaptable ancestral stock. Uncertainties arise, however, when somewhat more divergent calls are compared. The call of *Hyla versicolor* is extremely variable, with scarcely two populations having the identical call. A spectrogram (Fig. 40) of the call of an individual from Wisconsin discloses resemblances as well as differences when compared with the call of *H. arenicolor* shown in the same figure. Frogs of the two species also bear considerable resemblance in external characters. W. F. Blair (1958a, 1958f), however, considers *H. arenicolor* to be related to *H. femoralis*. The call of this species also varies extensively from one locality to another, averaging 3.8 seconds in duration at Orange Springs, Putnam County, Florida, but only 1.8 seconds in another population recorded near Lake Okeechobee. Only a small portion of the call from an individual from Orange Springs is included in the spectrogram (Fig. 40).

W. F. Blair supplies spectrograms for *Hyla femoralis* and *H. arenicolor* in each of the two publications cited above, but those in the spectrogram of *H. femoralis* from Taylor County, Florida (W. F. Blair, 1958f) bear little resemblance to that of another individual from Perry County, Mississippi. Neither bears much resemblance to the spectrogram of the call from Putnam County, Florida. By comparing spectrograms of one population or another, therefore, it is possible to reach quite different decisions. On the basis of the spectrogram of the calls of the three species illustrated in Figure 40, the call of *arenicolor* (C) bears greater resemblance to that of *versicolor* (B) than either does to the call of *femoralis* (A). *Hyla versicolor* and *H. arenicolor* unquestionably are closer morphologically. Neither resembles *H. femoralis* in habitus, coloration or size as closely as they resemble each other.

Frogs with totally different mating calls may or may not be genetically compatible, for reasons discussed in detail by J. A. Moore (1955, 1957b, 1958). Unless two species have similar mating calls, resemble each other morphologically, or occur sympatrically, experimental hybridization may not reveal any information that is readily interpreted in meaningful terms.

ACKNOWLEDGMENTS

Critical summarization of our knowledge of anuran vocalizations as elements of behavior linked closely to speciation might seem to be a modest task. Nevertheless, the preparation and documentation of this review incurred numerous obligations.

Mr. Richard Archbold provided both facilities and services during 1954 and 1957 at the Archbold Biological Station, where members of his staff, particularly Mr. Leonard Brass and Mr. Frank Rinald, were extremely helpful. Miss Alice G. C. Grandison of the British Museum (Natural History) participated in the work entailed in recording, assembling, and testing the responses of toads at the Archbold Station in 1957. The hospitality of Dr. Eugenie Clark and Dr. and Mrs. William Tavolga at the Cape Haze Laboratory contributed materially to the success of our work at the Archbold Station.

Dr. Richard G. Zweifel, Dr. Robert C. Stebbins of the University of California at Berkeley, and Dr. William Tavolga of the College of the City of New York recorded some of the sounds utilized in the preparation of this review. Dr. W. Frank Blair of the University of Texas generously provided the tape from which the spectrogram of *Bufo speciosus* was prepared. Mr. Harry C. James made it possible to record the frogs in the San Jacinto Mountains in California, and Dr. Raymond B. Cowles of the University of California at Los Angeles, Dr. Frederick Shannon of Wickenburg, Arizona, Dr. Archie Carr of the University of Florida, Dr. Arnold Grobman of the Florida State Museum, Dr. Rodolfo Ruibal of the University of California at Riverside, Dr. Paulo Vanzolini of the Department of Agriculture, São Paulo, Brazil, Señor Carlos Gomez, Señor Jorge Guiterrez, of Tepic, and Señor Pedro García Ribera of Pátzcuaro, all assisted in obtaining recordings in the field.

Drawings reproduced herein (in Figures 6 and 29) were prepared by Mr. Kenneth Gosner, and are used with his approval and the permission of the editor of Natural History Magazine, Mr. John Purcell. Figure 12 is reproduced through the kindness of Dr. Paul Anderson of Columbia University. The spectrogram of the call of the emperor goose, kindly supplied by Dr. Peter Klopfer of Duke University, is used with his permission.

Mr. Moses Asch of Folkways Records and Service Corporation granted permission to reproduce a portion of the record, *Sounds of North American Frogs.* Mr. Asch also provided the portable recorder and tapes used during the summer of 1953. Mr. Alexander Rota was most accommodating in preparing photographs of materials used as illustrations. All spectrograms, with the exception of that of the emperor goose, were made on the Sona-Graph (Kay Electric Company) by Dr. Richard G. Zweifel and Mr. George Foley.

Dr. John A. Moore, Dr. William Tavolga, Dr. Richard G. Zweifel, and Martha R. Bogert read portions of the manuscript and provided criticisms that clarified obscure or doubtful statements. Mrs. Margaret Shaw was both patient and efficient in deciphering illegible copy and typing the manscript. Mrs. Shaw and Mrs. Theresa McKnight both assisted in solving bibliographic problems.

Sincere thanks are extended to all these individuals for their invaluable assistance in assembling and documenting the information contained in this review.

LITERATURE CITED

Abbott, C. C. 1884. Recent studies of the spade-foot toad. Amer. Nat. *18:* 1076–1080.

Adrian, E. D., K. J. W. Craik, and R. S. Sturdy. 1938. The electrical response of the auditory mechanism in cold-blooded vertebrates. Proc. Roy. Soc. London. Ser. B. *125:* 435–455.

Alexander, R. D. 1957. Sound production and associated behavior in insects. Ohio Jour. Sci. *57:* 101–113.

Allee, W. C., A. E. Emerson, O. Park, T. Park, and K. P. Schmidt. 1949. Principles of animal ecology. Philadelphia and London: W. B. Saunders Co. xii + 837 pp.

Anderson, P. K. 1954. Studies in the ecology of the narrow-mouthed toad, *Microhyla carolinenis carolinensis.* Tulane Studies Zool. *2:* 15-46.

Andrewartha, H. G., and L. C. Birch. 1954. The distribution and abundance of animals. Chicago: Univ. of Chicago Press. xv + 782 pp.

Anonymous. 1954. [*In* Meetings of the Society for scientific business.] Proc. Zool. Soc. London. *124:* 196.

Archer, W. H. 1959. Have toads a strong homing instinct? African Wild Life. *13:* 246–248.

Aronson, L. R. 1943a. The sexual behavior of Anura. 5. Oviposition in the green frog, *Rana clamitans,* and the bull frog, *Rana catesbeiana.* Amer. Mus. Novitates. *1224:* 1–6.

————. 1943b. The sexual behavior of Anura. IV. Oviposition in the mink frog, *Rana septentrionalis* Baird. Amer. Midland Nat. *29:* 242–244.

————. 1943c. The "release" mechanism and sex recognition in *Hyla andersonii.* Copeia. *4:* 246–249.

————. 1944. The sexual behavior of Anura. 6. The mating pattern of *Bufo americanus, Bufo fowleri,* and *Bufo terrestris.* Amer. Mus. Novitates. *1250:* 1–15.

————, and G. K. Noble. 1945. The sexual behavior of Anura. 2. Neural mechanisms controlling mating in the male leopard frog, *Rana pipiens.* Bull. Amer. Mus. Nat. Hist. *86:* 83–140.

Axtell, R. W. "1958" [1959]. Female reaction to the male call in two anurans (Amphibia). Southwestern Nat. *3:* 70–76.

Babcock, H. L. 1926. A time-table of New England frogs and toads. Bull. Boston Soc. Nat. Hist. *38:* 11–14.

————, and I. Hoopes. 1940. An almanac of frogs and toads. New England Nat. *6:* 7–9.

Bajandurov, B. I., and W. A. Pegel. 1933. Der bedingte Reflex bei Fröschen. Ztschr. wiss. Biol. *18(C):* 284–297.

Balcells, E. 1957. Datos para el estudio del ciclo biologico de *Rana t. temporaria* del Pirineo. Pirineos. *13:* 327–346.

Banta, A. M. 1914. Sex recognition and the mating behavior of the wood frog, *Rana sylvatica.* Biol. Bull. *26:* 171–183.

Barbour, T. 1916. A note on two interesting New Jersey amphibians. Copeia. *26:* 5–7.

Bartlett, A. D. 1896. Notes on the breeding of the Surinam water-toad *(Pipa americana)* in the Society's Gardens. Proc. Zool. Soc. London. pp. 595–597.

Bates, M. 1950. The nature of natural history. New York: Scribner's Sons. 308 pp.

Beach, F. A. 1944. Responses of captive alligators to auditory stimulation. Amer. Nat. *78:* 481–505.

Bellis, E. D. 1957. The effects of temperature on salientian breeding calls. Copeia. *2:* 85–89.

————. 1958. An ecological study of the wood frog, *Rana sylvatica* Le Conte. Diss. Abstr. *18:* 1537.

Berger, K. 1924. Sound perception in reptiles. Ztschr. vergleich. Physiol. *1:* 517–540.

Birkenmeier, E. 1952. Uber die Lautauserungen der Gattung *Bombina.* Mitt. Naturh. u. Vorgesch., Magdeburg. *3:* 81–88. [Not seen]

Blair, A. P. 1941a. Isolating mechanisms in tree frogs. Proc. Natl. Acad. Sci. *27:* 14–17.

————. 1941b. Variation, isolation mechanisms, and hybridization in certain toads. Genetics. *26:* 398–417.

————. 1942. Isolating mechanisms in a complex of four species of toads. Biol. Symposia. *6:* 235–249.

————. 1943. Population structure in toads. Amer. Nat. *77:* 563–568.

————. 1946a. The effects of various hormones on primary and secondary sex characters of juvenile *Bufo fowleri.* Jour. Expt. Zool. *103:* 365–400.

————. 1946b. Description of a six-year-old hybrid toad. Amer. Mus. Novitates. *1327:* 1–3.

————. 1947a. Field observations on spadefoot toads. Copeia. *1:* 67.

————. 1947b. The male warning vibration in *Bufo.* Amer. Mus. Novitates. *1344:* 1–7.

————. 1947c. Defensive use of the parotoid secretion by *Bufo marinus.* Copeia. *2:* 137.

————. 1955. Distribution, variation, and hybridization in a relict toad (*Bufo micro-scaphus*) in southwestern Utah. Amer. Mus. Novitates. *1722:* 1–38.

Blair, W. F. 1955a. Mating call and stage of speciation in the *Microhyla olivacea-M. carolinensis* complex. Evolution. *9:* 469–480.

————. 1955b. Size difference as a possible isolation mechanism in *Microhyla*. Amer. Nat. *89:* 297–301.

————. 1955c. Differentiation of mating call in spadefoots, genus *Scaphiopus*. Texas Jour. Sci. *7:* 183–188.

————. 1956a. Call difference as an isolation mechanism in southwestern toads (genus *Bufo*). Texas Jour. Sci. *8:* 87–106.

————. 1956b. The mating calls of hybrid toads. Texas Jour. Sci. *8:* 350–355.

————. 1956c. Camparative survival of hybrid toads (*B. woodhousei* × *B. valliceps*) in nature. Copeia. *4:* 259–260.

————. 1956d. Mating call and possible stage of speciation of the Great Basin spade-foot. Texas Jour. Sci. *8:* 236–238.

————. 1957a. Mating call and relationships of *Bufo hemiophrys* Cope. Texas Jour. Sci. *9:* 99–108.

————. 1957b. Structure of the call and relationships of *Bufo microscaphus* Cope. Copeia. *3:* 208–212.

————. 1958a. Mating call and stage of speciation of two allopatric populations of spadefoots (*Scaphiopus*). Texas Jour. Sci. *10:* 484–488.

————. 1958b. Response of a green treefrog (*Hyla cinerea*) to the call of the male. Copeia. *4:* 333–334.

————. 1958c. Call difference as an isolation mechanism in Florida species of hylid frogs. Quart. Jour. Florida Acad. Sci. *21:* 32–48.

————. 1958d. Distributional patterns of vertebrates in the southern United States in relation to past and present environments. *In* Zoogeography, Amer. Assoc. Adv. Sci. pp. 433–468.

————. 1958e. Breeding congresses of the Mexican toad (*Bufo valliceps*) in relation to environmental variations. Bull. Ecol. Soc. Amer. *39:* 75.

————. 1958f. Mating call in the speciation of anuran amphibians. Amer. Nat. *92:* 27–51.

————. "1958" [1959a]. Call structure and species groups in U. S. treefrogs (*Hyla*). Southwestern Nat. *3:* 77–89.

————. 1959b. Genetic compatibility and species groups in U. S. toads (*Bufo*). Texas Jour. Sci. *11:* 427–453.

————, and D. Pettus. 1954. The mating call and its significance in the Colorado River toad (*Bufo alvarius*) Girard. Texas Jour. Sci. *6:* 72–77.

Blankenagel, F. 1931. Untersuchungen über die Grosshirnfunktionen von *Rana tem-poraria*. Zool. Jahrb., Zool. Physiol. *49:* 271–322.

Bles, E. J. 1901. On the breeding habits of *Xenopus laevis* Daud. Proc. Cambridge Philos. Soc. *11:* 220–222.

————. 1905. The life-history of *Xenopus laevis*, Daud. Trans. Roy. Soc. Edinburgh. *41:* 789–821.

Bogert, C. M. 1947. Results of the Archbold Expeditions. No. 57. A field study of homing in the Carolina toad. Amer. Mus. Novitates. *1355:* 1–24.

————. 1949. Thermoregulation in reptiles, a factor in evolution. Evolution. *3:* 195–211.

————. 1952. Relative abundance, habitats, and normal thermal levels of some Virginian salamanders. Ecology. *33:* 16–30.

————. 1953. The tuatara: why is it a lone survivor? Sci. Monthly. *86:* 163–170.

————. 1954. Commentary for recording of "Sounds of the American Southwest." N. Y.: Folkways Records and Service Corp., Sci. Ser. *FX-6122:* 12 pp.

————. 1958. Commentary for recording of "Sounds of North American frogs." N. Y.: Folkways Records and Service Corp., Sci. Ser. *FX-6166:* 17 pp.

————. 1959. How reptiles regulate their body temperature. Sci. Amer. *200:* 105–108, 111–112, 115–116, 118, 120.

————, and J. A. Oliver. 1945. A preliminary analysis of the herpetofauna of Sonora. Bull. Amer. Mus. Nat. Hist. *83:* 297–426.

Boulenger, G. A. 1882. Catalogue of the Batrachia Salientia S. Ecaudata in the collection of the British Museum. 2nd ed. London: British Museum. xvi + 503 pp.

————. 1897. The tailless batrachians of Europe, Part I. London: The Ray Society. iii + 210 pp.

————. 1898. The tailless batrachians of Europe, Part II. London: The Ray Society. pp. 211–376.

————. 1912. Some remarks on the habits of British frogs and toads, with reference to Mr. Cummings's recent communication on distant orientation in Amphibia. Proc. Zool. Soc. London. pp. 19–22.

————. 1920. A monograph of the south Asian, Papuan, Melanesian and Australian frogs of the genus *Rana.* Rec. Indian Mus. *20:* 1–226.

Bragg, A. N. 1940a. Observations on the ecology and natural history of Anura. I. Habits, habitat and breeding of *Bufo cognatus* Say. Amer. Nat. *74:* 322–349, 424–438.

————. 1940b. Observations on the ecology and natural history of Anura. II. Habits, habitat, and breeding of *Bufo woodhousii woodhousii* (Girard) in Oklahoma. Amer. Midland Nat. *24:* 306–321.

————. 1942. Further field notes on the initiation of breeding behavior of Anura. Turtox News. *20:* 12.

————. 1959. Response of a female *Pseudacris nigrita triseriata* to the call of a male. Copeia. *4:* 341.

Breder, C. M. 1946. Amphibians and reptiles of the Rio Chucunaque drainage, Darien, Panama, with notes on their life histories and habits. Bull. Amer. Mus. Nat. Hist. *86:* 375–436.

————, R. B. Breder, and A. C. Redmond. 1927. Frog tagging: a method of studying anuran life habits. Zoologica. *9:* 201–229.

Bruce, H. M., and A. S. Parkes. 1947. Observations on *Discoglossus pictus* Otth. Proc. Roy. Soc., B. *134:* 37–56.

Bruyn, E. M., and C. H. van Nifterik. 1921. Influence du son sur la réaction d'une excitation tactile chez les grenouilles et les crapauds. Arch. néerlandaises Physiol. Ser. 3C. *5:* 363–379.

Buddenbrock, W. von. 1956. The love-life of animals. London: Frederick Muller Limited. 207 pp.

————. 1958. The senses. Ann Arbor: Univ. of Mich. Press. 167 pp.

Bushnell, R. 1957. Some notes on the breeding of Amphibia, 1952. Brit. Jour. Herpetol. *2:* 56–59.

Buytendijk, F. J. J. 1918. L'instinct d'alimentation et l'expérience chez les crapauds. Arch. néerlandaises Physiol. Ser. 3C. *2:* 216–228.

Cagle, F. R. 1956. An outline for the study of an amphibian life history. Tulane Studies Zool. *4:* 79–110.

Carpenter, C. R. 1958. Territoriality: a review of concepts and problems. *In* Roe, A., and G. G. Simpson (eds.), Behavior and evolution. New Haven: Yale Univ. Press. pp. 224–250.

Carr, A. F., Jr. 1934. A key to the breeding-songs of the Florida frogs. Florida Nat. New Ser. 7: 19–23.

————. 1940a. Dates of frog choruses in Florida. Copeia. 1: 55.

————. 1940b. A contribution to the herpetology of Florida. Univ. Florida Pub., Biol. Sci. Ser. 3: 1–118.

Caruso, M. A. 1949. Sobre el ciclo sexual anual de algunos "Hylidae" del Norte Argentino. Acta Zool. Lilloana. 8: 83–103.

Cei, G. 1944. Analisi biogeografica e ricerche biologiche e sperimentali sul ciclo sessuale annuo delle Rane rosse d'Europa. Monitore Zool. Italiano. 54: (suppl.) 1–117.

Cei, J. M., and S. Espina Aguilera. 1957a. La vibración sexual preventiva ("warning vibration") en Pleurodema chilenas. Invest. Zool. Chilenas. 4: 15–21.

————, and ————. 1957b. La vibración sexual preventiva en poblaciones de Bufo spinulosus de Chile. Invest. Zool. Chilenas. 4: 62–65.

Chapman, B. M., and R. F. Chapman. 1958. A field study of a population of leopard toads (Bufo regularis regularis). Jour. Animal Ecol. 27: 265–286.

Collias, N., and M. Joos. 1953. The spectrographic analysis of sound signals of the domestic fowl. Behaviour. 5: 175–188.

Conant, R. 1958. A field guide to reptiles and amphibians of eastern North America. Boston: Houghton Mifflin Co. xv + 366 pp.

Copeland, M. 1913. The olfactory reactions of the spotted newt, Diemyctylus viridescens (Rafinesque). Jour. Animal Behavior. 3: 260–273.

Cory, L., and J. J. Manion. 1955. Ecology and hybridization in the genus Bufo in the Michigan-Indiana region. Evolution. 9: 42–51.

Courtis, S. A. 1907. Response of toads to sound stimuli. Amer. Nat. 41: 677–682.

Crenshaw, J. W., and W. F. Blair. 1959. Relationships of the Pseudacris nigrita complex in southwestern Georgia. Copeia. 3: 215–222.

Cummins, H. 1920. The role of voice and coloration in spring migration and sex recognition in frogs. Jour. Expt. Zool. 30: 325–343.

Dähne, C. 1914. Alytes obstetricans und seine Brutpflege. Blatt. Aquar.-Terrar.-Kde. 25: 227–229.

Darwin, C. 1839. Journal of researches into the geology and natural history of the various countries visited by H. M. S. Beagle under the command of Captain FitzRoy, R. N. from 1832 to 1836. London: Henry Colburn. xiv + 629 pp. + index.

————. 1859. On the origin of species by means of natural selection or the preservation of favoured races in the struggle for life. London: John Murray. ix + 502 pp.

Dice, L. R. 1952. Natural communities. Ann Arbor: Univ. of Mich. Press. x + 547 pp.

Dickerson, M. C. 1906. The frog book. N. Y.: Doubleday, Page and Co. xvii + 253 pp.

Diebschlag, E. 1935. Zur Kenntnis der Grosshirnfunktionen einiger Urodelen und Anuren. Ztschr. vergleich. Physiol. 21: 343–394.

Dixon, J. R. 1957. Geographic variation and distribution of the genus Tomodactylus in Mexico. Texas Jour. Sci. 9: 379–409.

Dobzhansky, T. 1935. A critique of the species concept in biology. Phil. Sci. 2: 344–355.

————. 1937. Genetic nature of species differences. Amer. Nat. 71: 404–420.

————. 1951. Genetics and the origin of species. 3rd ed., rev. N.Y.: Columbia Univ. Press. xix + 446 pp.

Duellman, W. E., and A. Schwartz. 1958. Amphibians and reptiles of southern Florida. Bull. Florida State Mus. 3: 181–324.

Dunn, E. R. 1931. The amphibians of Barro Colorado Island. Occas. Papers Boston Soc. Nat. Hist. *5:* 403–421.

————. 1941. Notes on *Dendrobates auratus*. Copeia. *2:* 88–93.

Dye, W. J. P. 1921. The relation of the lateral line organs to hearing. Jour. Comp Psychol. *1:* 469–471.

Eaton, T. H., Jr. 1959. The ancestry of modern Amphibia: a review of the evidence. Univ. Kansas Pub., Mus. Nat. Hist. *12:* 157–180.

Eibl-Eibesfeldt, I. 1950. Ein beitrage zur paarungsbiologie der erdkröte (*Bufo bufo* L.). Behaviour. *2:* 217–236.

Einem, G. E., and L. D. Ober. 1956. The seasonal behavior of certain Floridian Salientia. Herpetologica. *12:* 205–212.

Ferhat-Akat, S. 1939. Untersuchungen über den Gehörsinn der Amphibien. Zeitschr. vergleich. Physiol. *26:* 253–281.

Fish, M. P. 1956. Animal sounds in the sea. Sci. Amer. *194(4):* 93–102.

Fitch, H. S. 1956. Early sexual maturity and longevity under natural conditions in the Great Plains narrow-mouthed frog. Herpetologica. *12:* 281–282.

————. 1958. Home ranges, territories, and seasonal movements of vertebrates of the Natural History Reservation. Univ. Kansas Pub., Mus. Nat. Hist. *11:* 65–326.

Fraenkel, G. S., and D. L. Gunn. 1940. The orientation of animals, kineses, taxes and compass reactions. Oxford: The Clarendon Press. viii + 352 pp.

Frings, H., and M. Frings. 1956. A simple method for producing visible patterns of tape recorded sounds. Nature. *178:* 328–329.

————, and ————. 1957. The effects of temperature on the chirp-rate of male cone-headed grasshoppers, *Neoconocephalus niger*. Jour. Expt. Zool. *134:* 411–425.

Fromme, A. 1941. An experimental study of the factors of maturation and practice in the behavioral development of the embryo of the frog, *Rana pipiens*. Genet. Psychol. Monogr. *24:* 219–256.

Gadow, H. 1901. Amphibia and reptiles. *In* Cambridge Natural History, vol. 8. N.Y.: MacMillan Co. xiii + 668 pp.

Gallardo, J. M. 1958. Observaciones sobre el comportamiento de algunos anfibios argentinos. I.—Referidas especialmente a la defensa, retorno y alimentación en *Bufo arenarum* Hensel y *Leptodactylus ocellatus* (L.). Cien. Invest. *14:* 291–302.

Gans, C., and N. D. Richmond. 1957. Warning behavior in snakes of the genus *Dasypeltis*. Copeia. *4:* 269–274.

Garner, R. L. 1892. The speech of monkeys. London: Heinemann. 260 pp.

Geyer, H. 1927. Uber Lautäusserunger der Molche. Blatt. Aquar.-Terrar.-Kde. *39:* 27–28.

Girard, C. 1854. A list of North American bufonids, with diagnoses of new species. Proc. Acad. Nat. Sci. Phila. *7:* 86–88.

Goin, C. J. "1948" [1949]. The peep order in peepers; a swamp water serenade. Quart. Jour. Florida Acad. Sci. *11:* 59–61.

————, and O. B. Goin. 1957. Remarks on the behavior of the squirrel treefrog, *Hyla squirella*. Ann. Carnegie Mus. *35:* 27–36.

Goldsmith, G. W. 1926. Habits and reactions of *Scaphiopus hammondii*. Year Book Carnegie Inst. Wash. *25:* 369–370.

Gosner, K. L., and I. H. Black. 1955. The effects of temperature and moisture on the reproductive cycle of *Scaphiopus h. holbrooki*. Amer. Midland Nat. *54:* 192–203.

Greenberg, B. 1942. Some effects of testosterone on the sexual pigmentation and other sex characters of the cricket frog (*Acris gryllus*). Jour. Expt. Zool. *91:* 435–446.

Griffin, D. R. 1958. Listening in the dark. New Haven: Yale Univ. Press. xviii + 413 pp.

Hansen, K. L. 1958. Breeding pattern of the eastern spadefoot toad. Herpetologica. *14:* 57–67.

Hardy, D. F. 1959. Chorus structure in the striped chorus frog, *Pseudacris nigrita.* Herpetologica. *15:* 14–16.

Harris, J. P., Jr. 1959. The natural history of *Necturus:* II. Field and Lab. *27:* 71–77.

Herter, K. 1941. Beiträge sur Physiologieund sur Entw-Mech. der Amphibien. *In* Kukenthal Handbook der Zoologie. Amphibia. Berlin.

Heusser, H. 1958. Ueber die Beziehungen der Erdkröte *(Bufo bufo* L.) zu ihrem Laichplatz. I. Behaviour. *12:* 208–232.

Hinckley, M. H. 1883. On some differences in the mouth structure of tadpoles of the anourous batrachians found in Milton, Mass. Proc. Boston Soc. Nat. Hist., 1882. *21:* 307–315.

————. 1884. Notes on the peeping frog, *Hyla pickeringii* Le Conte. Mem. Boston Soc. Nat. Hist. *3:* 311–318.

Hinsche, G. 1926. Uber Brunst-und Kopulationsreaktionen des *Bufo vulgaris.* Ztschr. vergleich. Physiol. *4:* 564–606.

Hoffman, R. L. 1946. The voice of *Hyla versicolor* in Virginia. Herpetologica. *3:* 141–142.

Holmes, S. J. 1906. The biology of the frog. N. Y.: The Macmillan Co. ix + 370 pp.

Houssay, B. A. 1954. Hormonal regulation of the sexual function of the male toad. Acta Physiol. Latino Amer. *4:* 1–41.

Howard, H. E. 1920. Territory in bird life. London: Murray. xiii + 308 pp.

Huxley, J. 1942. Evolution. The modern synthesis. N. Y. and London: Harper and Brothers. 645 pp.

Inger, R. F. 1954. Systematics and zoogeography of Philippine Amphibia. Fieldiana: Zool. *33:* 183–531.

————. 1956. Morphology and development of the vocal sac apparatus in the African frog *Rana (Ptychadena) porosissima* Steindachner. Jour. Morph. *99:* 57–72.

————. 1958. The vocal sac of the Colorado River toad *(Bufo alvarius* Girard). Texas Jour. Sci. *10:* 319–324.

————, and B. Greenberg. 1956. Morphology and seasonal development of sex characters in two sympatric African toads. Jour. Morph. *99:* 549–574.

Jahn, T. L., and V. J. Wulff. 1950. Phonoreception. *In* Prosser, C. L. (ed.), Comparative animal physiology. Philadelphia and London: W. B. Saunders Co. pp. 471–501.

Jameson, D. L. 1954. Social patterns in the leptodactylid frogs *Syrrhophus* and *Eleutherodactylus.* Copeia. *4:* 36–38.

————. 1955a. Evolutionary trends in the courtship and mating behavior of Salientia. Syst. Zool. *4:* 105–119.

————. 1955b. The population dynamics of the cliff frog, *Syrrhophus marnocki.* Amer. Midland Nat. *54:* 342–381.

Johnson, C. 1959. Genetic incompatibility in the call races of *Hyla versicolor* Le Conte in Texas. Copeia. *4:* 327–335.

Jordan, H. D. 1954. Homing toads. Niger. Field. *19:* 189.

Juszczyk, W. 1951. The migrations of the aquatic frog *Rana esculenta* L. Bull. Internatl. Acad. Polonaise Sci. Lett. Sér. B. pp. 341–369.

Kikuchi, T. 1958. On the residentiality of a green frog, *Rana nigromaculata* (Hallowell) (I). Japanese Jour. Ecol. *8:* 20–26.

Klauber, L. M. 1956. Rattlesnakes, their habits, life histories, and influence on mankind. Berkeley and Los Angeles: Univ. of California Press. 2 vols. *1:* xxx+ 708 pp.; *2:* xviii + pp. 709–1476.

Kleerekoper, H., and K. Sibabin. 1959. A study on hearing in frogs *(Rana pipiens and Rana clamitans).* Ztschr. vergleich. Physiol. *41:* 490–499.

Kramer, G. 1933. Die Sinnesleitungen und das Orientierungsverhalten von *Xenopus laevis.* Zool. Jahrb., Zool. Physiol. *52:* 629–676.

Lankes, K. 1928. Zur Biologie des Korrallensingers, *Hyla caerulea.* Blatt. Aquar.-Terrar.-Kde. *39:* 6–7.

Lindsay, H. L., Jr. 1958. Analysis of variation and factors affecting gene exchange in *Pseudacris clarki* and *Pseudacris nigrita* in Texas. Diss. Abstr. *18:* 2268.

Littlejohn, M. J. 1958a. Mating behavior in the treefrog, *Hyla versicolor.* Copeia. *3:* 222–223.

————. 1958b. A new species of frog of the genus *Crinia* Tschudi from south-eastern Australia. Proc. Linnean Soc. New South Wales. *83:* 222–226.

————. 1959a. Artificial hybridization within the Pelobatidae and Microhylidae. Texas Jour. Sci. *11:* 57–59.

————. 1959b. Call differentiation in a complex of seven species of *Crinia* (Anura, Leptodactylidae). Evolution. *13:* 452–468.

————, and A. R. Main. 1959. Call structure in two genera of Australian burrowing frogs. Copeia. *3:* 266–270.

————, and T. C. Michaud. 1959. Mating call discrimination by females of Strecker's chorus frog *(Pseudacris streckeri).* Texas Jour. Sci. *11:* 86–92.

Liu, C. C. 1931. Sexual behavior in the Siberian toad, *Bufo raddei,* and the pond frog, *Rana nigromaculata.* Peking Nat. Hist. Bull. *6:* 43–60.

————. 1935. Types of vocal sac in the Salientia. Proc. Boston Soc. Nat. Hist. *41:* 19–40.

————. 1941. Natural history studies of west China Amphibia. IV. Life history of *Rana adenopleura (Rana musica?).* Peking Nat. Hist. Bull. *15:* 285–290.

————. 1950. Amphibians of western China. Fieldiana: Zool. Mem. *2:* 1–400.

Loveridge, A. 1947. Revision of the African lizards of the family Gekkonidae. Bull. Mus. Comp. Zool. *98:* 1–469.

————. 1953. Zoological results of a fifth expedition to East Africa. IV. Amphibians from Nyasaland and Tete. Bull. Mus. Comp. Zool. *110:* 325–406.

Lowe, C. H., Jr. 1954. Isolating mechanisms in sympatric populations of south-western anurans. Texas Jour. Sci. *6:* 265–270.

Lutz, B. 1947. Trends toward aquatic and direct development in frogs. Copeia. *4:* 242–252.

Lutz, F. E. 1941. A lot of insects; entomology in a suburban garden. N. Y.: G. P. Putnam's Sons. 304 pp.

Main, A. R. 1957. Studies in Australian Amphibia. I. The genus *Crinia* Tschudi in south-western Australia and some species from south-eastern Australia. Australian Jour. Zool. *5:* 30–55.

————, A. K. Lee, and M. J. Littlejohn. 1958. Evolution in three genera of Australian frogs. Evolution. *12:* 224–233.

Martof, B. S. 1953a. Territoriality in the green frog, *Rana clamitans.* Ecology. *34:* 165–174.

————. 1953b. Home range and movements of the green frog, *Rana clamitans.* Ecology. *34:* 529–543.

————, and E. F. Thompson, Jr. 1958a. Reproductive behavior of the chorus frog, *Pseudacris nigrita.* Bull. Ecol. Soc. Amer. *39:* 92. (Also published in Animal Behavior, 1958, *6:* 244)

————, and ————. 1958b. Reproductive behavior of the chorus frog, *Pseudacris nigrita.* Behaviour. *13:* 243–258.

Maslin, T. P. 1950. The production of sound in caudate Amphibia. Univ. Colorado Studies, Ser. Biol. *1:* 29–45.

————. 1957. *Hyla microeximia* sp. n., Hylidae, Amphibia, from Jalisco, Mexico. Herpetologica. *13:* 81–86.

Maynard, E. A. 1934. The aquatic migration of the toad, *Bufo americanus* Le Conte. Copeia. *4:* 174–177.

Mayr, E. 1940. Speciation phenomena in birds. Amer. Nat. *74:* 249–278.

————. 1942. Systematics and the origin of species: from the viewpoint of a zoologist. N. Y.: Columbia Univ. Press. xiv + 334 pp.

————. 1955a. The species as a systematic and as a biological problem. Biol. Syst., Proc. 16th Ann. Biol. Colloquium, Oregon State College, Corvallis. pp. 1–12.

————. 1955b. Summation: systematics and modes of speciation. Biol. Syst., Proc. 16th Ann. Biol. Colloquium, Oregon State College, Corvallis. pp. 45–51.

————. 1957. Difficulties and importance of the biological species concept. *In* The species problem, Amer. Assoc. Adv. Sci. pp. 371–388.

————. 1958. Behavior and systematics. *In* Roe, A., and G. G. Simpson (eds.) , Behavior and evolution. New Haven: Yale Univ. Press. pp. 341–362.

McAlister, W. H. "1958" [1959a]. Species distribution in a mixed *Scaphiopus-Bufo* breeding chorus. Southwestern Nat. *3:* 227–229.

————. 1959b. The vocal structures and method of call production in the genus *Scaphiopus* Holbrook. Texas Jour. Sci. *11:* 60–77.

McIlhenny, E. A. 1935. The alligator's life history. Boston: Christopher Publishing House. 117 pp.

Mecham, J. S. 1959. Experimental evidence of the relationship of two allopatric chorus frogs of the genus *Pseudacris.* Texas Jour. Sci. *11:* 343–347.

Merzbacher, L. 1900. Ueber die Beziehungen der Sinnesorgane zur den Reflex bewegingen des Frosches. Pflügers Arch. *81:* 222–262.

Miller, N. 1909. The American toad *(Bufo lentiginosus americanus,* Le Conte) , Amer. Nat. *43:* 641–688, 730–745.

Misdorf, H. 1928. Zur Physiologie der Phonorezeption bei den Batrachiern. Ber. Verhandl. Sächs Akad. Wiss. Leipzig, Math.-Phys. *80:* 209–216.

Moore, H. J. 1954. Some observations on the migration of the toad *(Bufo bufo bufo).* Brit. Jour. Herpetol. *1:* 194–224.

Moore, J. A. 1942. The role of temperature in speciation of frogs. Biol. Symposia. *6:* 189–213.

————. 1955. Abnormal combinations of nuclear and cytoplasmic systems in frogs and toads. Adv. Genet. *7:* 139–182.

————. 1957a. Principles of zoology. N.Y.: Oxford Univ. Press. xiv + 667 pp.

————. 1957b. An embryologist's view of the species concept. *In* The species problem, Amer. Assoc. Adv. Sci. pp. 325–338.

————. 1958. Hybridization as an adjunct to the systematics of amphibians. 15th Internatl. Cong. Zool. Sect. 2, Paper *11:* 1–2.

Moriya, K. 1951. On isolating mechanisms between the two subspecies of the pond frog, *Rana nigromaculata.* Jour. Sci. Hiroshima Univ. Ser. B, div. 1. *12:* 47–56.

Myers, G. S. 1951. Notes on salamander voices. Copeia. *1:* 76.

Negus, V. E. 1949. The comparative anatomy and physiology of the larynx. London: W. Heinemann. 230 pp.

Neill, W. T. 1952. Remarks on salamander voices. Copeia. *3:* 195–196.

Nice, M. M. 1941. The role of territory in bird life. Amer. Midland Nat. *26:* 441–487.

Noble, G. K. 1921. Snakes that inflate. Nat. Hist. *21:* 166–171.

————. 1923. Voice as a factor in the mating of batrachians. Science, N. S. *58:* 270–271.

————. 1931. The biology of the Amphibia. N. Y. and London: McGraw-Hill Book Co. xiii + 577 pp.

————, and L. R. Aronson. 1942. The sexual behavior of Anura. I. The normal mating pattern of *Rana pipiens.* Bull. Amer. Mus. Nat. Hist. *80:* 127–142.

————, and E. J. Farris. 1929. The method of sex recognition in the wood-frog, *Rana sylvatica* Le Conte. Amer. Mus. Novitates. *363:* 1–17.

————, and R. C. Noble. 1923. The Anderson tree frog (*Hyla andersonii* Baird), observations on its habits and life history. Zoologica, 2: 416–455.

————, and P. G. Putnam. 1931. Observations on the life history of *Ascaphus truei* Stejneger. Copeia. *3:* 97–101.

Oliver, J. A. 1955. The natural history of North American amphibians and reptiles. Princeton, N. J., D. Van Nostrand Co., Inc. ix + 359 pp.

Oordt, P. G. W. J. van. 1956. The role of temperature in regulating the spermatogenetic cycle in the common frog (*Rana temporaria*). Acta Endocrinol. *23:* 251–264.

Orton, G. L. 1943. The tadpole of *Rhinophrynus dorsalis.* Occas. Papers Mus. Zool. Univ. Mich. *472:* 1–7.

Park, O., A. Barden, and E. Williams. 1940. Studies in nocturnal ecology. IX. Further analysis of Panama rain forest animals. Ecology. *21:* 122–134.

Parker, H. W. 1956. Species transgressions in one horizon. Syst. Assoc. Pub. *2:* 9–15.

Pearson, P. G. 1955. Population ecology of the spadefoot toad, *Scaphiopus h. holbrooki* (Harlan). Ecol. Monogr. *25:* 233–267.

————. 1957. Further notes on the population ecology of the spadefoot toad. Ecology. *38:* 580–586.

Perdeck, A. C. 1958. The isolating value of specific song patterns in two sibling species of grasshoppers (*Chorthippus brunneus* Thunb. and *C. biguttulus* L.). Behavior. *12:* 1–75.

Pettus, D. 1955. Notes on the breeding behavior of the common tree-frog (*Hyla versicolor*). Texas Jour. Sci. *7:* 345–346.

Piatt, J. 1941. Observations on the breeding habits of *Bufo americanus americanus.* Copeia. *4:* 264.

Pittendrigh, C. S. 1958. Adaptation, natural selection, and behavior. *In* Roe, A., and G. G. Simpson (eds.), Behavior and evolution. New Haven: Yale Univ. Press. pp. 390–416.

Pope, C. H. 1944. Amphibians and reptiles of the Chicago area. Chicago: Chicago Natural History Museum Press. pp. 1–275.

Pumphrey, R. J. 1950. Hearing. *In* Physiological mechanisms in animal behaviour. Symposia Soc. Expt. Biol., Cambridge, 1949. pp. 3–18.

Pyburn, W. F. 1958. Size and movements of a local population of cricket frogs (*Acris crepitans*). Texas Jour. Sci. *10:* 325–342.

Raney, E. C. 1940. Summer movements of the bullfrog, *Rana catesbeiana* Shaw, as determined by the jaw-tag method. Amer. Midland Nat. *23:* 733–745.

Rengel, D. 1948. Sobre la vivración sexual preventiva ("warning vibration") en los sapos machos del Norte argentino. Acta Zool. Lilloana. *6:* 279–282.

——. 1949. La vibración "preventiva" como carácter ambosexual en algunos batracios de la Provincia de Tucumán. Acta Zool. Lilloana. 7: 353–358.

Risser, J. 1914. Olfactory reactions in amphibians. Jour. Expt. Zool. 16: 617–652.

Roe, A., and G. G. Simpson (eds.). 1958. Behavior and evolution. New Haven: Yale Univ. Press. viii + 557 pp.

Romer, A. S. 1945. Vertebrate paleontology. 2nd Ed. Chicago: Univ. of Chicago Press. ix + 687 pp.

Rose, W. 1950. The reptiles and amphibians of southern Africa. Cape Town: Maskew Miller, Limited. xxv + 378 pp.

Ruibal, R. 1955. A study of altitudinal races in Rana pipiens. Evolution. 9: 322–338.

Ryan, R. A. 1953. Growth rates of some ranids under natural conditions. Copeia. 2: 73–80.

Sato, S. 1939. Beiträge zur experimentellen Untersuchung der Resonanztheorie der Gehörempfindung. (I. Mitteilung.) Untersuchungen über die Gehörempfindung des Frosches. Ztschr. Otol. Rhinol. Laryngol., Tokyo. 45: 40–41. [Not seen]

Savage, R. M. 1932. The spawning, voice, and sexual behaviour of Bombina variegata variegata. Proc. Zool. Soc. London. 4: 889–898.

——. 1934. The breeding behaviour of the common frog, Rana temporaria temporaria Linn., and of the common toad, Bufo bufo bufo Linn. Proc. Zool. Soc. London. pp. 55–70.

——. 1935. The influence of external factors on the spawning date and migration of the common frog, Rana temporaria temporaria Linn. Proc. Zool. Soc. London. pp. 49–98.

Schmalhausen, J. J. 1957. The sound-transmitting mechanism of amphibians. Zool. Zhur. 36: 1044–1063.

Schneirla, T. C. 1956. Interrelationships of the "innate" and the "acquired" in instinctive behavior. In Masson et Cie (eds.), L'instinct dans le comportement des animaux et de l'homme. Paris. pp. 387–452.

Sexton, O. 1958. Observations on the life history of a Venezuelan frog, Atelopus cruciger. Acta Biol. Venezuelica. 2: 235–242.

Simpson, G. G. 1958. The study of evolution: methods and present status of theory. In Roe, A., and G. G. Simpson (eds.), Behavior and evolution. New Haven: Yale Univ. Press. pp. 7–26.

——, C. S. Pittendrigh, and L. H. Tiffany. 1957. Life. An introduction to biology. N. Y.: Harcourt, Brace and Co. xiv + 845 pp.

Smith, H. M. 1947. Subspecies of the Sonoran toad (Bufo compactilis Wiegmann). Herpetologica. 4: 7–13.

Smith, M. A. 1954. The British amphibians and reptiles. Rev. Ed. London: Collins. xiv + 322 pp.

Stebbins, R. C. 1951. Amphibians of western North America. Berkeley and Los Angeles: Univ. of California Press. ix + 539 pp.

——. 1954. Amphibians and reptiles of western North America. N. Y.: McGraw-Hill Book Co., Inc. xxii + 528 pp.

——, and J. R. Hendrickson. 1959. Field studies of amphibians in Colombia, South America. Univ. California Pub. Zool. 56: 497–540.

Stephenson, E. M., and N. G. Stephenson. 1957. Field observations of the New Zealand frog, Leiopelma Fitzinger. Trans. Roy. Soc. New Zealand. 84: 867–882.

Storer, T. I. 1925. A synopsis of the Amphibia of California. Univ. California Pub. Zool. 27: 1–342.

Strother, W. F. 1959. The electrical response of the auditory mechanism in the bullfrog (Rana catesbeiana). Jour. Comp. Physiol. Psychol. 52: 157–162.

Strübing, H. 1954. Uber Vorzugstemperaturen von Amphibien. Ztschr. Morph. Ökol. Tiere. *43*: 357–386.

Taylor, E. H. 1931. Notes on two specimens of the rare snake *Ficimia cana* and the description of a new species of *Ficimia* from Texas. Copeia. *1*: 4–7.

Test, F. H. 1954. Social aggressiveness in an amphibian. Science. *120*: 140–141.

Thompson, E. F., Jr., and B. S. Martof. 1957. A comparison of the physical characteristics of frog calls *(Pseudacris)*. Physiol. Zool. *30*: 328–341.

Thornton, W. A. 1955. Interspecific hybridization in *Bufo woodhousei* and *Bufo valliceps*. Evolution. *9*: 455–468.

Tumarkin, A. 1955. On the evolution of the auditory conducting apparatus: a new theory based on functional considerations. Evolution. *9*: 221–243.

Turner, F. B. 1959. Some features of the ecology of *Bufo punctatus* in Death Valley, California. Ecology. *40*: 175–181.

Twitty, V. C. 1959. Migration and speciation in newts. Science. *130*: 1735–1743.

Volpe, E. P. 1956. Reciprocal mis-matings between *Hyla squirella* and *Microhyla carolinensis*. Copeia. *4*: 261–262.

————. 1957. Embryonic temperature adaptations in highland *Rana pipiens*. Amer. Nat. *91*: 303–309.

————. "1957" [1958]. Genetic aspects of anuran populations. Amer. Nat. *91*: 355–371.

————. 1959. Hybridization of *Bufo valliceps* with *Bufo americanus* and *Bufo terrestris*. Texas Jour. Sci. *11*: 335–342.

Walker, C. F. 1946. The amphibians of Ohio. Part 1, the frogs and toads (Order Salientia). Ohio State Mus. Sci. Bull *1(3)*: 1–109.

Wasserman, A. O. 1957. Hybridization in three species of spadefoot toads. Copeia. *2*: 144–145.

————. 1958. Relationships of allopatric populations of spadefoots (genus *Scaphiopus*). Evolution. *12*: 311–318.

Wellman, G. B. 1917. Notes on the breeding habits of the American toad. Copeia. *51*: 107–108.

Wever, E. G., and J. A. Vernon. 1957. Auditory responses in the spectacled caiman. Jour. Cell. Comp. Phys. *50*: 333–340.

Winston, R. M. 1955. Identification and ecology of the toad *Bufo regularis*. Copeia. *4*: 293–302.

Wright, A. H. 1914. North American Anura. Life-histories of the Anura of Ithaca, New York. Carnegie Inst. Wash. Pub. *197*: vii + 98 pp.

————, and A. A. Wright. 1949. Handbook of frogs and toads of the United States and Canada. 3rd Ed. Ithaca, N. Y.: Comstock Publishing Co., Inc. xii + 640 pp.

Yerkes, R. M. 1903. The instincts, habits and reactions of the frog. Psychol. Rev. Monogr. *4*: 579–638.

————. 1905. The sense of hearing in frogs. Jour. Comp. Neurol. Psychol. *15*: 279–304.

Zweifel, R. G. 1956. Two pelobatid frogs from the Tertiary of North American and their relationships to fossil and recent forms. Amer. Mus. Novitates. *1762*: 1–45.

————. 1959. Effects of temperature on call of the frog, *Bombina variegata*. Copeia. *4*: 322–327.

TABLE 1

SUMMARY OF RELEASES AND RECOVERIES OF TOADS, *Bufo terrestris*, COLLECTED AT RANDOM

Exp. No.	Sound Source	Total Released	Number Recovered		No Movement	Not Recovered	Air Temperatures	R.H.
			Toward Sound	Away from Sound				
Males								
1	(no sound source)	68	(North) 35	(South) 31	0	2	26.0°C	87%
2	North	50	21	25	0	4	23.5°C	81%
3	South	92	34	44	4	10	24.0°C	92%
4	North	67	19	48	0	0	25.0°C	96%
Totals		277	109	148	4	16		
Females								
5	South	24	14	6	0	4	26.5°C	78%
6	North	24	16	7	0	1	23.5°C	93%
7	South	24	19	4	0	1	28.5°C	78%
Totals		72	49	17	0	6		

TABLE 2

SUMMARY OF RELEASED AND RECOVERIES OF TOADS TAKEN FROM A BREEDING AGGREGATION

Exp. No.	Sex	Total Released	Number Recovered		No Movement	Not Recovered	Air Temperature	R.H.
			Toward Sound	Away from Sound				
8	♂♂	39	25	12	0	2	23.5°C	96%
9	♀♀	14	7	3	0	4	23.5°C	96%
	Totals	53	32	15	0	6		

TABLE 3

SUMMARY OF VARIATIONS IN MATING CALLS IN REPRESENTATIVE POPULATIONS OF *Hyla eximia* IN MEXICO

Locality	Elevation in Feet	Air Temp. °C	Duration of Call in Seconds	Intervals Between Calls in Seconds	Total Pulsations	Pulsations per Second
Tepic, Nayarit	3000	20.0	0.20–0.21	0.80–0.95	11–12	60
Chapala, Jalisco	5000	20.0	0.16–0.18	0.29–0.35	19–21	120–140
Lagos de Moreno, Jalisco	6300	16.5	0.18–0.20	0.39–0.68	15 + chirp 19 (no chirp)	110–113
Pátzcuaro, Michoacán	7100	16.5	0.21–0.22	0.29–0.42	20	90–100
Zinacantepec, México	8800	15.0	0.22–0.23	0.34–0.48	13–17	70–80
Ixtapan de la Sal, México	5300	18.5	0.20–0.21	1.25–1.32	8–11	40–50
10 mi. S.W. of Huauchinango, Puebla	7500	16.0	0.25–0.28	0.29–0.50	12–15	65–70

CAPTIONS FOR SELECTIONS OF ANURAN MATING CALLS

Side I

Band 1. To illustrate the variability of the mating call from population to
population within a single species, as exemplified by *Hyla eximia* at the
following localities in Mexico:

Selection No.	Locality	Elevation	Air Temp. °C
1.	Tepic, Nayarit	3,000'	20.0
2.	Chapala, Jalisco	5,000'	20.0
3.	Lagos de Moreno, Jalisco	6,300'	16.5
4.	Pátzcuaro, Michoacán	7,100'	16.5
5.	Zinacantepec, México	8,800'	15.0
6.	Ixtapan de la Sal, México	5,300'	20.5

Band 2. To illustrate modifications in mating calls resulting from hybridization of species under natural conditions:

Selection No.	Identity of Individual	Locality
8.	*Scaphiopus hammondi*	Near Portal, Arizona
9.	*Scaphiopus bombifrons*	Near Portal, Arizona
10.	*S. hammondi* × *S. bombifrons*	Near Portal, Arizona
11.	*Hyla gratiosa* × *Hyla cinerea*	Hicoria, Florida
12.	*Hyla cinerea*	Hicoria, Florida
13.	*Hyla gratiosa* and hybrid	Hicoria, Florida

The Ontogeny Of Vocalizations In Birds [1,2]

WESLEY E. LANYON

Department of Birds, American Museum of Natural History, New York

INVESTIGATIONS of the development of animal sounds have recently achieved a welcome degree of objectivity, largely as the result of technological advances in sound recording and analysis. In no group has progress been greater than with birds, though even there the number of species for which there are meaningful data is still small.

Earlier investigations of the ontogeny of avian vocalizations were largely in the nature of observations by aviculturists who witnessed the response of hand-reared birds. The interpretations were necessarily subjective, usually without adequate controls, and consequently inconclusive and often contradictory. The extent of the earlier literature in this field has been adequately reviewed elsewhere (Sanborn, 1932; Nice, 1943; Poulsen, 1951; Thorpe, 1951).

It was my good fortune to travel through Europe recently and visit with many of the more active workers in this field. The need for a greater exchange of information and a coordination of research between laboratories was most apparent. It was further apparent that the experimentation during the past decade constitutes a "break through" in our efforts to understand the intricate processes whereby avian vocalizations develop and become manifest. The present review examines the approach of contemporary workers, synthesizes recent advancements in the field, and suggests areas where future research would be profitable.

METHODS

Experimentation within this field during the past decade has shown vast improvement over earlier studies, particularly with respect to three features: 1) more carefully controlled conditions, 2) documentation of results, and 3) a more objective analysis of these results.

A combination of observational and experimental procedures involving free-living birds, wild birds maintained in captivity, and hand-reared birds has been most productive in recent studies. Observation of

---

[1] Manuscript received October 1959.
[2] Recordings illustrating this chapter are on Side II, Band 3 of the Demonstration Record.

the development of vocalizations of wild birds serves as a natural control for experiments with captive individuals. The maintenance of wild birds, trapped during critical periods of development, has been a valuable technique in some studies. Conversely, the maintenance of hand-reared birds in enclosures in natural and artificial environments has been useful.

The hand-rearing of passerine birds from the egg (A) is a difficult task and has been accomplished by very few workers. In the Zoological Institute at the University of Freiburg, one of the leading laboratories in this field, young passerines have been reared from eggs artificially incubated for up to four days prior to hatching. Hartshorne (pers. comm.) has successfully raised eastern bluebirds (*Sialia sialis*) from artificially incubated eggs removed from the nest only a few hours after laying occurred. For the most part, however, individuals have been reared from the nestling stage (B), at ages varying from several hours to just prior to fledging.

Experimental birds have been maintained under varying conditions of "isolation". These can be arbitrarily classified as follows:

1) isolated from all sound (deafened).
2) isolated from all other birds (but can hear itself).
3) isolated from all experienced birds but can hear siblings.
4) isolated from experienced birds of own species, but can hear experienced individuals of other species.

Isolation of type 4) is easily accomplished and has been used by many workers. Conditions (2) and (3) can be achieved with assurance only with "sound-proof" rooms, of the type described by Sauer (1954) and by Thorpe and Hinde (1956). Metfessel (1940) was perhaps the first to adapt this experimental procedure for research in this field. The laboratories of Koehler at Freiburg and of Thorpe at Madingley are currently using such rooms for this purpose. The term "sound-proof" as used by these laboratories essentially means audio-insulation against the sounds of birds from without, but allows for the possibility that extraneous low frequency noises may be heard. The workers at Freiburg have adopted the term "Kaspar Hauser" for a bird hand-reared in such a room. An individual reared under conditions A2 above is a Kaspar Hauser of the first order; one meeting conditions B2 is a Kaspar Hauser of the second order; and one meeting conditions B3 is a Kaspar Hauser of the third order.

From the classification above, it is apparent that the ultimate experiment in "isolation" is one that meets conditions A1: the development of vocalizations in a bird deafened before it can receive auditory stimulation (presumably several days prior to hatching). This has not been attained as yet. Using blackbirds *(Turdus merula)* reared from the nestling stage, Messmer and Messmer (1956) successfully removed the auditory organs as early as 18 days of age, thus approaching conditions B1 above.

A prerequisite for all modern work has been the use of magnetic tape and sound recorders to permit the accurate documentation of the responses of wild and experimental birds. Methods of transcription from auditory to visual patterns have become more practical and objective during this same period. The techniques used by Sauer (1954) and Messmer and Messmer (1956), involving musical notations and oscilloscopic films, have now been replaced by the sound spectrograph. The reader is referred to the discussion by Borror in this symposium for an account of this machine and its application to zoological research.

From earlier observations there emerged a controversy over the "acquired" and the "inborn", and a tendency of many observers to favor the one or the other of these "alternatives". Such a dichotomous treatment of ontogenetic phenomena and the weighing of the relative roles of heredity and environment were destined to lead to misunderstanding and confusion, and did. Modern workers, well-grounded in the basic principles of genetics, recognize the fallacy of this approach.

The freedom with which such terms as "innate" and "learned" were used by different workers to describe vocal responses achieved under quite dissimilar experimental conditions has been a further source of confusion, and makes a synthesis of facts and a formulation of principles extremely difficult. Unfortunately the practice still continues (this reviewer includes himself among the guilty) and represents one of the serious hurdles to our general advancement in the field.

The difficulty arises in part from the widely variable criteria that have been used to justify the use of such terms, and in part from differences in connotation actually intended by the authors. Heinroth (1924-1926) undoubtedly knew what he meant when he characterized the song of the chaffinch *(Fringilla coelebs)* as "inborn", but the recent studies of Poulsen (1951) and Thorpe (1954) clearly reveal that such a term is seriously misleading. Sauer (1954) concluded that the song of the whitethroat *(Sylvia communis)* is "completely innate". Many readers have understandably interpreted this to mean that imitation of experienced birds plays no role in the normal ontogeny of whitethroat song, but such an interpretation is clearly erroneous (Sauer, pers. comm.).

The following examples have been selected to demonstrate that discrepancies in connotation may arise when a term such as "innate" is used rather freely to describe responses under different experimental conditions. In Thorpe's work with the chaffinch (1954) and in my own work with meadowlarks, *Sturnella* (Lanyon 1957), the term "innate" was used to indicate development of normal vocalizations in individuals isolated from their own species from the nestling stage but permitted to hear other birds. Sauer (1954) eliminated the possibility that the white-throat learns certain utterances from other birds and concluded that "its utterances must then be innate, for it has only heard itself." But Messmer and Messmer (1956) recognized a need to eliminate self-learning before a vocal response of the blackbird could be considered as "innate".

The use of simple terms and phrases to describe complex situations arises from a desire to clarify through brevity and from editorial pressure to condense for economic reasons. But when this practice develops misleading interpretations and unreconcilable differences in connotation, it is not to be condoned. Recent recognition of the imprudent usage of such terms has been most encouraging (Tinbergen 1957).

DISCUSSION

Birds can be conveniently divided into two groups of nearly equal numbers on the basis of the degree of development of the syrinx or vocal apparatus: 1) the non-passerines, typically without intrinsic syringeal muscles, and 2) the passerines, having up to seven pairs of intrinsic syringeal muscles. A direct correlation exists between the degree of development of the syrinx, with respect to muscles and attachments, and the variety of vocal patterns that characterize a particular species (Miskimen, 1951). As one might predict, the vocalizations of the passer-ines, as a group, are more diversified and complex than those of the non-passerines, and are conventionally divided into two general categories: a) call notes, and b) song. The distinction here is based upon the complexity and function of the sounds but, in terms of knowledge extant, is one more of convenience than of fact. Arbitrary as this division may be, it is indeed applicable in the majority of passerines. No such division of complexity of vocal patterns exists among the non-passerines for in these lower forms the vocalizations are all of the simple call note variety.

References to seasonal aspects of developmental processes are made with regard to the birds of the north temperate latitudes.

NON-PASSERINES

There are no studies of the ontogeny of vocalizations of non-passerine birds in which machine analyses of vocal patterns have been made. This is paradoxical, for there are two very great advantages in working with these lower forms in contrast to passerines: 1) they have smaller and less variable vocal repertoires, making analysis easier; and 2) they are, as a group, more easily reared from the egg than passerines.

The subjective observations made at game bird hatcheries, zoological parks, and by aviculturists in general suggest that individuals of most non-passerine orders, reared from artificial incubators, are capable of developing their species characteristic vocal patterns without benefit of post-hatching exposure to experienced individuals. Witchell (1896), Heinroth (1924, 1924-1926) and others have been impressed with the stereotypy of non-passerine vocalizations and the abilty of the young to develop them in isolation from other birds, and give examples from several orders. Perhaps the careful work of Schjelderup-Ebbe (1923) with the domestic fowl comes the closest to being objective evidence for this stereotypy in non-passerines.

The question arises whether it *is* essential for *any* non-passerine species to be exposed to experienced individuals of its own species in order to refine its vocalizations or even develop them completely. Goethe (1955) believes that the "kiaw" or "mau" call of the herring gull *(Larus argentatus),* used by adults to call the young, is learned shortly after hatching. The only conclusive evidence for the role of learning through vocal imitation among non-passerines is in the parrots and their allies. But it has been suggested (Heinroth, 1924; Thorpe, 1955) that parrots are known to mimic vocally only in captivity and that they probably do not do so in the wild. There are further cases where hand-reared non-passerines have *failed* to develop species characteristic vocal patterns, but such negative evidence is usually clouded with the possibility that such birds were not properly motivated or were maintained under sub-optimal conditions.

The available evidence of the stereotypy of vocalizations among the non-passerines is impressive, but should definitely be supported with machine analyses. The possibility that learning from experienced individuals may play a role in refining certain calls with regard to exact frequencies or patterns and that some calls may not become manifest *at all* without such exposure can only be investigated with carefully controlled experiments, using objective analytical techniques.

PASSERINES

As of the date of this review, there are only four passerine species for which spectrographic evidence for the ontogeny of vocalizations has been published: chaffinch (Thorpe, 1954, 1955; Marler, 1956a); eastern meadowlark, *Sturnella magna,* and western meadowlark, *Sturnella ne-glecta* (Lanyon, 1957) ; and canary, *Serinus canarius* (Poulsen, 1959). I am aware of spectrographic evidence, some of which will be published soon, for eleven other passerines: two tree creepers *(Certhia familiaris* and *C. brachydactyla),* blackbird, eastern bluebird, whitethroat, red-backed shrike *(Lanius collurio),* linnet *(Carduelis cannabina),* bullfinch *(Pyrrhula pyrrhula)* yellowhammer *(Emberiza citrinella),* corn bunting *(Emberiza calandra),* and reed bunting *(Emberiza schoeniclus).* Six families are represented by these species. In addition there are earlier published observations of a number of hand-reared passerines which merit consideration, especially those of Nice (1943), Scott (1901, 1902, 1904abc), Heinroth (1924, 1924-1926), Sanborn (1932) and Metfessel (1940).

Call Notes

In those passerines that have been studied to date, it is apparent that the simple vocal patterns conventionally termed "call notes" are as remarkably stereotyped and genetically fixed as the vocalizations of the non-passerines. Fortunately the experimental data in the case of the passerines is better and substantiates the subjective conclusions of many earlier investigators.

We now have spectrographic evidence that three species are capable of developing most of their species-characteristic calls without benefit of post-hatching aural stimulation from other birds. Individuals of the following species, hatched and raised individually in sound-proof rooms, developed most of their specific calls in the normal sequence and timing: blackbird (Messmer and Messmer, 1956, spectrograms not published); whitethroat (Sauer, 1954, spectrograms not published) ; and red-backed shrike (Blase, in Press).

Information about the age at which the avian embryo is first capable of registering aural stimulation is meager. Simms (1955) has sound recordings of the calls of unborn stone-curlew *(Burhinus oedicnemus)* chicks given in response to the conversational calls of the hen, on the day of hatching. Messmer and Messmer (1956) reported that their young blackbirds could differentiate and respond to a particular human whistle by their third day. They successfully reared one of their blackbirds in isolation from 81.5 hours prior to hatching, which would presumably eliminate the possibility of all aural stimulation from other birds. But even in the experiments conducted in sound-proof rooms, one must still allow for the possibility that certain types of self-induced or self-stimulated learning may be involved in the ontogeny of the call notes. Nor do the Messmers' remarkable experiments involving the removal of the auditory organs of blackbirds eliminate this possibility for nearly all of the calls of this species become manifest by 18 days of age, the age of the youngest bird so treated.

There is further spectrographic evidence that five other species of passerines, hand-reared from the nestling stage without opportunity to hear experienced individuals of their own species, are capable of developing most of their species characteristic calls in a normal manner (Fig. 1): two species of meadowlark (Lanyon, 1957), linnet and canary (Poulsen, pers. comm.), and chaffinch (Marler, 1956a). The number of species that have been hand-reared as nestlings for which there are subjective observations attesting to this stereotypy is much larger. No attempt will be made to list these references here.

A significant observation of many workers has been the failure of certain call notes to develop in a normal manner in hand-reared birds. A characteristic call of the male western meadowlark did not develop in hand-reared individuals until the latter were exposed to experienced males during their first spring (Lanyon, 1957). Ravens *(Corvus corax)* reared without exposure to experienced ravens fail to develop their entire vocal repertoire, while others reared with adults developed all of the specific notes (Kramer, pers. comm.). Lorenz (pers. comm.) has observed that one of the notes of the house sparrow *(Passer domesticus)* fails to develop when individuals are reared in isolation from experienced birds. Two calls of the blackbird failed to develop in individuals hand-reared from the egg (Messmer and Messmer, 1956; confirmed by Thielcke and Poltz, pers. comm.).

Here again, as in the case of the non-passerines, negative evidence of this type cannot be offered as proof that such call notes are necessarily learned from experienced birds. In addition to the possibility of dietary or other deficiencies, there is a more likely explanation for the inhibition or incomplete maturation of vocal patterns in captive birds. Endocrine balance is undoubtedly an important consideration here. Hand-reared male western meadowlarks habitually rendered a characteristic female call note, while wild males have rarely been heard to do so (Lanyon, 1957). Sauer (1955) noted that two alarm calls of his hand-reared whitethroats were not manifest until the birds approached their first period of reproduction, and this is correlated with the observation that these notes are normally heard from wild birds only during the breeding season. Differences in the development and manifestation of two alarm calls of hand-reared chaffinches, which are normally associated only with breeding males (Marler, 1956a), have been explained on the basis of variations in male sex hormone levels (Collard and Grevendal, 1946;

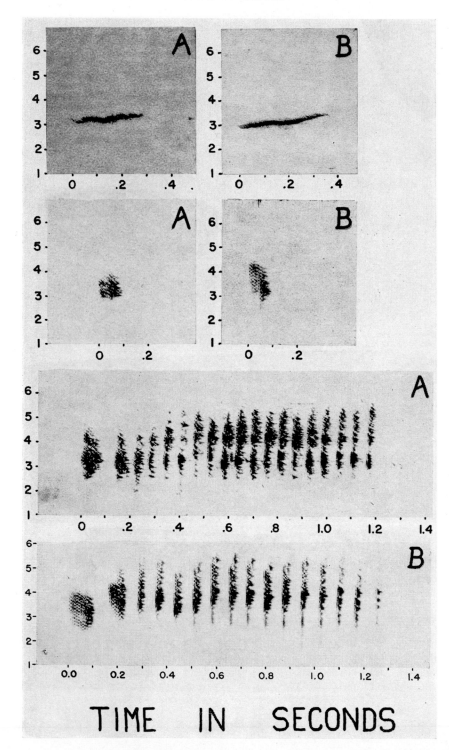

TIME IN SECONDS

Poulsen, 1951). Similar effects of testosterone upon the calls of non-passerines lends support to the importance of endocrine balance in the manifestation of vocalizations. Testosterone proprionate has been found to produce crowing in domestic chicks (Noble and Zitrin, 1942) and in domestic hens (Allee and Collias, 1938). Noble and Wurm (1940) demonstrated that injections of male sex hormone induced demonstrable changes in the voice of month-old and of female black-crowned night herons *(Nycticorax nycticorax)*.

Various workers have suggested that learning from experienced individuals may be essential for the refinement of certain calls with regard to exact pattern and frequency. The flight calls of the linnet developed imperfectly in hand-reared individuals (Poulsen, 1954). The characteristic social call of hand-reared chaffinches "is sometimes abnormal, as a result of the persistence of a developmental stage", and may be refined through learning (Marler, 1956b). Furthermore, the geographical modification of the common alarm call of the chaffinch may depend upon exposure to experienced individuals (Marler, 1956b). A hand-reared bullfinch, without opportunity to hear others of its own species, develops a location note that is only suggestive of that of its species. But if reared with a canary, the bullfinch will adopt the somewhat similar location note of the canary and use it in the appropriate stimulus situations (Nikolai, pers. comm.). Young willow tits *(Parus atricapillus)*, hatched and reared by great tits *(Parus major)*, adopted some of the characteristic call notes of the foster parents (Loehrl, pers. comm.).

The call notes of passerines are usually fully developed during the first three months of age, except for those dependent upon endocrine stimulation and associated with the reproductive period (Marler, 1956a; Lanyon, 1957). In the blackbird, all but three of 15 recognizable calls are expressed in their definitive form by the end of the third week of age (Messmer and Messmer, 1956). The majority of the calls of the whitethroat are fully developed during the first month of age (Sauer, 1955).

Certain call notes, such as begging and location notes, are normally associated only with the nestling and fledgling period. Of particular interest is the growing evidence that many of the later calls of adult birds are derived through processes of simplification and alteration of these earlier vocalizations. Marler (1956a) has suggested that three of the calls of the adult chaffinch may be derived from a single precursor

FIG. 1. Call notes of the eastern meadowlark: (A) Experimental male, reared in isolation from others of its species from 10 days of age; (B) Free-living adult, recorded in Dane Co., Wisconsin, May 1953.

in the repertoire of young birds. Adult blackbirds have an alarm note and also a social note that may develop, through transitional stages, from a juvenile location note (Messmer and Messmer, 1956). Likewise, adult meadowlarks have a social note that is believed to be a derivative of the location note of fledglings (Lanyon, 1957). Sauer (1954) presents evidence for a sequential pattern of call note development in white-throats. Blase (in press) has spectrographic evidence for the development of some of the calls of the red-backed shrike from the begging note of nestlings. Poulsen (1951) considers the crowing note of the linnet to be a derivative of the aggressive note of young birds. Improvements in observational and automatic recording techniques will be required in future studies to provide us with more precise data on the timing and transitional aspects of this very important aspect of ontogeny.

Song

Most of the attention given to the developmental aspects of avian vocalizations has been focussed upon the songs of passerine birds. This is understandable, for their musical quality, complexity of structure, and noticeable variability are at once attractive and challenging.

Since there is no agreement among workers as to a standardized terminology of bird song, the terms appearing in this review will be defined as used.

Following the terminology of Lister (1953), the most characteristic and most commonly rendered song of passerine species, usually confined to the male and usually associated with courtship and territorial behavior, is here considered as "primary song". We will be concerned especially with the developmental stages of primary song. Other categories designated by Lister as "secondary song", such as "flight song" and "whispering song" have not been sufficiently investigated to merit treatment at this time.

Recent investigations have revealed a general pattern of the sequential development of primary song that is common to all passerines studied thus far. Developmental differences between species appear to be limited to the timing of the various phases of development. The transition between phases is gradual and consequently any attempt to diagram this developmental process (Fig. 2) should not be interpreted too literally. Selections 1-4 further illustrate this process, as revealed in the development of a hand-reared western meadowlark.

The initial phase of this general pattern of development, considered here as "subsong", has the following characteristics: 1) it consists of random, subdued warbling, of greater duration than definitive primary

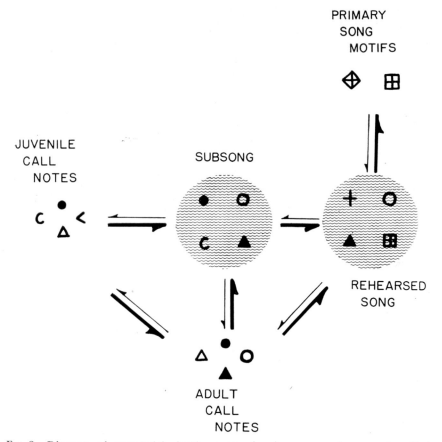

Fig. 2. Diagram of sequential development of primary song in passerine birds. Double arrows suggest the reversible nature of the developmental process.

song; 2) it usually contains recognizable call notes interspersed within the framework of warbling notes, but is typically without any phrases suggestive of definitive primary song; 3) it is often composed of a greater range of frequencies than later developmental stages; and 4) it shows greater similarity between species than does primary song. The age at which subsong first appears in experimental birds varies somewhat between species and even between individuals of the same species, presumably due to differences in motivation and experimental conditions. Typically, the juvenile call notes are incorporated into a framework of random warbling during the first month after fledging.

The next distinctive phase of development is termed "rehearsed song" here. The transition from subsong to rehearsed song is accomplished by the addition of distinguishable vocal patterns that are suggestive of definitive primary song. These primary song motifs are interspersed, along with the specific call notes, within the framework of random warbling, thus increasing the variability of the vocalizations during this period. It has been impossible for workers to always denote the exact age at which this transition occurs, though in most species rehearsed song is established by the first autumn.

The development of primary song from rehearsed song is accomplished by dropping out of the random warbling and call notes, with simplification of that total song repertoire and increased emphasis upon the definitive primary song motifs. This transition typically occurs during the first winter and early spring.

The sequential pattern as outlined above refers to the developmental process in the young bird. But in many species a similar process recurs each spring as the adult bird passes from a sexually quiescent phase into the reproductive cycle (Thorpe, 1954; Sauer, 1954; Messmer and Messmer, 1956; Lanyon, 1957; Curio, 1959). Sauer (1955) has observed that regression of this developmental process may occur in senile or sick whitethroats. This reversibility of the developmental process is indicated by the double arrows in Figure 2.

Just as we have indicated in the case of call notes, hormone levels probably play an important role in the development and manifestation of primary song. In the great majority of song birds, primary song is typically a male secondary sex characteristic and this is true of those species that have been best studied experimentally. Experimental females of these species typically develop a subsong similar to that of the male, but no rehearsed song or primary song (Poulsen, 1951; Sauer, 1954; Messmer and Messmer, 1956; Lanyon, 1957), and continue to render occasional subsong as adults. It has been shown that primary song may be induced in the female canary by appropriate amounts of male sex hormone (Leonard, 1939; Baldwin, Goldin and Metfessel, 1940; Herrick and Harris, 1957), but Poulsen (1951) was unable to elicit primary song from female chaffinches treated in this manner. That the rate of development of primary song in the male chaffinch is at least partially controlled by hormone levels has been demonstrated by Poulsen (1951) and Thorpe (1954). Though the injection of male sex hormone into month-old blackbirds induced a louder, more vigorous subsong, it did not accelerate the transition from subsong to rehearsed song (Thielcke and Poltz, pers. comm.).

But the females of a number of passerines habitually render typical primary song motifs (Nice, 1943). Very rarely females not normally considered to be songsters will render male-like motifs in the wild

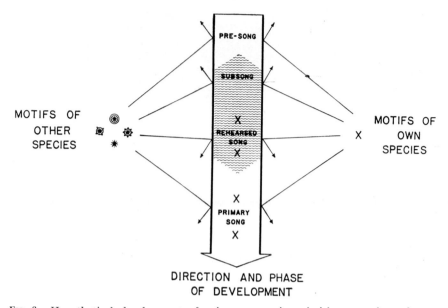

FIG. 3. Hypothetical development of primary song in primitive passerines, demonstrating a lack of receptivity to the motifs of other birds. Note the simplicity of the original motif and the reduced repertoire of primary song as compared with Fig. 4.

(Lanyon, 1957; Hartshorne, pers. comm. on the eastern bluebird), indicating that the developmental process proceeded as in the males but that manifestation of the definitive stages is inhibited or without proper motivation. Once again, we must beware of negative evidence as furnished by the observations of experimental females cited above.

The addition of the primary song motifs, *per se,* to the subsong framework, and the nature of their development constitute important aspects of current research. The extent to which exposure to experienced individuals is essential for the normal development of these motifs in a first year bird is still the challenging question that it was to Baron von Pernau (see Streseman, 1947) in the early 18th century. Craig (1943) and Thorpe (1956) have suggested that the more primitive condition is one in which no imitation of experienced birds is involved in the developmental process. This purely hypothetical pattern of development of primary song in the more primitive passerines is diagrammed in Figure 3.

Thorpe (pers. comm.) has unpublished spectrographic evidence that this primitive developmental pattern may apply to the corn bunting and reed bunting. Individuals hand-reared from the nestling stage in isolation from experienced individuals of their own species (but exposed to the songs of other species) developed primary song motifs identical with

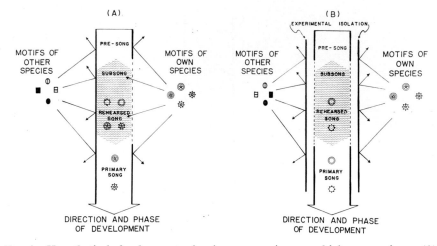

Fig. 4. Hypothetical development of primary song in some higher passerines: (A) Some free-living birds normally refine their original motifs by vocal imitation of other individuals of their own species; (B) Some experimental birds, reared in isolation from all other birds, develop original motifs which are suggestive of those of their own species but lacking in refinement.

those of wild individuals of their respective species. One wonders, however, if even in these species learning from experienced individuals does not normally account for some refinement of motifs as it surely does in all other species studied thus far. The spectrographic evidence necessary to assign this developmental pattern to any species has not as yet been published. When conclusive experimental evidence does establish this primitive developmental pattern for any species, one might predict that the repertoire of primary song motifs of that species will be very much limited and that the individual motifs will be simple in structure (Fig. 3). Experimentation with the sub-oscines, such as the tyrannid flycatchers and manakins, might be productive along these lines.

Of the three passerine species that have been reared from the egg in sound-proof rooms, it has been demonstrated that all three are capable of developing original primary song motifs in the absence of auditory stimuli from other birds: blackbird (Messmer and Messmer, 1956), whitethroat (Sauer, 1954), and canary (Metfessel, 1940). The chaffinch (Thorpe, 1954), reared from the nestling stage in a sound-proof room, also developed original motifs. These primary song phrases, developed in isolation, were only suggestive of the primary song of the respective species, the similarities being in such parameters as duration and general quality (Fig. 4B).

It is of particular interest that, in the experiments cited above, the original motifs developed by isolated individuals of the same species seldom had the same detail of structure unless the birds were given an opportunity to hear one another, in which case conformity occurred. We now have evidence that learning through imitation of other individuals is a normal feature of the development of primary song in all four of these species: blackbird (Messmer and Messmer, 1956; Thielcke and Poltz, pers. comm.), whitethroat (Sauer, pers. comm.), canary (Metfessel, 1940; Poulsen, 1959) and chaffinch (Thorpe, 1954). When given the opportunity to do so, the young of these species normally depend upon imitation of other individuals of their own species in order to refine their own original motifs and to complete their full repertoire of primary song. This agreement of results in experimentation to date suggests that this developmental pattern may be a prevalent one among many of our higher song birds, and it is presented in a hypothetical form in Figure 4A.

The role of self-learning in the development of primary song is difficult to assess experimentally. Messmer and Messmer (1956) reported that blackbirds, deafened as early as 18 days of age, developed original motifs in the same manner as did control birds in isolation. But the motifs of the deafened birds had a tonal quality recognizably different from those of the controls. It seems plausible that young birds may normally refine their own motifs to some extent by hearing themselves.

The developmental pattern presented in Figure 4A would not apply to true mimics. Mimicry, as defined here, implies imitation of motifs of another species and characterizes a number of passerines that habitually include such phrases within their primary song repertoire. The experimental evidence is insufficient to present even a hypothetical diagram of the development of primary song in these birds. Presumably the young mimic is as receptive to the motifs of other species (possibly there is a preference for certain species) as to those of his own, and gradually incorporates these into his primary song repertoire.

Blase (pers. comm.) has conducted some interesting experiments at the Freiburg laboratory with the red-backed shrike, a well-known European mimic. He considers this species to have no original primary song motifs—the entire repertoire must be learned through imitation of other birds. Experimental birds, reared in isolation in sound-proof rooms, developed normal subsong which they retained even as adults, but did not progress beyond the subsong phase of development. There was no transition from subsong to rehearsed song because of the failure of these birds to develop original primary song motifs in the manner observed in the other species studied at Freiburg (whitethroat and blackbird). Because of the negative type of evidence involved, these significant experiments should be repeated with appropriate examination of all alternative interpretations.

The developmental pattern postulated in Figure 4A implies that these free-living birds normally refine and supplement their own original motifs by imitating those motifs that they hear from other individuals of their own species. This phenomenal ability of hand-reared birds to imitate sounds in their environment was appreciated by the earliest bird fanciers. We now have spectrographic evidence from experimental birds. Thorpe (1954) has published spectrograms demonstrating the "uniform community patterns" of primary song motifs that are established among chaffinches reared together. Poulsen (pers. comm.) has spectrographic evidence of the ability of a canary to imitate the motif of an African green singing finch (Serinus mozambicus), which it added to its own repertoire of original motifs. Figures 5 and 6 and Selections 5-8 on the demonstration record demonstrate the ability of hand-reared western meadowlarks to imitate the motifs of other species (Lanyon, 1957). Thielcke and Poltz (pers. comm.) have similarly documented the imitation of a recording of a wood thrush (Hylocichla mustelina) by one of their hand-reared blackbirds.

Additional evidence for this important role of learning in the normal development of primary song comes from studies of wild populations. Distinct geographical communities of adults that have nearly identical motifs have been reported for many passerines. Figure 7 demonstrates the remarkably similar motifs recorded from four different western meadowlarks having adjacent breeding territories. Marler (1952) has reported this phenomenon with regard to the chaffinch, and further discusses "community song-characteristics" in his chapter in this volume. Nice (1943) has cited similar evidence for the song sparrow (Melospiza melodia).

The concept that the learning process associated with the development of primary song occurs only during a restricted period of the bird's life has attracted much attention in recent work. Though there is some variation in the timing between species and even between experimental individuals of the same species, the concept appears to be valid for those passerines studied thus far. In general, this learning period coincides with the developmental phases designated here as subsong and rehearsed song (see Figure 4A for graphic presentation of this concept). Our

---

FIG. 5. A Primary song motif of a redwinged blackbird (top spectrogram; from Selection 5, recorded in Dane Co., Wisconsin, April 1954) and imitations developed by three hand-reared western meadowlarks (second spectrogram from top made from Selection 6).

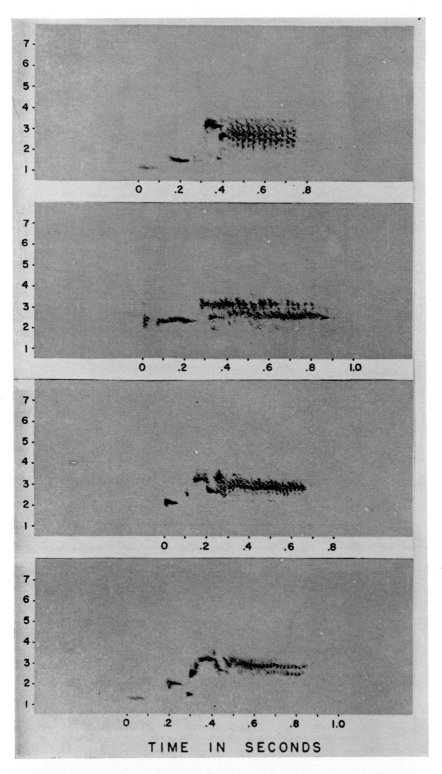

TIME IN SECONDS

data is presently insufficient to assess the relative receptivity of any species at various times during this period.   No one has yet demonstrated conclusively that a passerine has the ability to learn a primary song motif either during its nestling stage or after the full development of primary song in its first spring.

I have presented evidence (Lanyon, 1957) that the period of receptivity of juvenile meadowlarks extends from the onset of subsong (about the fifth week of age) through their first winter.   When definitive primary song has been established in late winter, the first year males are no longer receptive, even to the song of their own species.   Two months of exposure to a given motif, at any time from June through October, was sufficient time for a juvenile to learn that particular motif.   Poulsen (1954) arrived at similar conclusions in his studies on the linnet.

Some of the variation in timing between species can be explained on the basis of specific differences in the periods when the adults are actively singing.   Meadowlarks and linnets remain in full song throughout the autumn, accounting for the results cited above.   The chaffinch, on the other hand, is not in full song in autumn.   Thorpe (1954, 1958) and Poulsen (1951) have discovered that in addition to an early period of receptivity, correlated with subsong, the chaffinch is also receptive during the rehearsed song phase of its first spring when the refinement of motifs is completed through imitation of adult song.

Thielcke and Poltz (pers. comm.) of the Freiburg laboratory have attempted to better define the learning period of the blackbird, by exposing hand-reared birds to controlled auditory stimulation during the course of the developmental process.   They have demonstrated that learning of primary song motifs may occur as early as the 15th day (approximate time of fledging), but that there is no response to such stimulation during the nestling stage.   This species is still receptive during February of the first year, and at that time less than one minute of stimulation by a single primary song motif (that of the wood thrush of the New World!) was sufficient for an experimental blackbird to learn that motif and incorporate it into his primary song repertoire.   Poulsen (pers. comm.) has evidence that as little as five days of exposure to a particular motif is sufficient for a young canary to acquire that song pattern.

Most workers are in agreement that the juvenile passerine need not

FIG. 6.   Imitations of the primary song motifs of "tutors" by a hand-reared western meadowlark: (from top to bottom) (1) meadowlark; (2) wood pewee, *Contopus virens* (recorded at Ithaca, New York; courtesy of Dr. P. P. Kellogg); (3) meadowlark (from Selection 8); (4) yellowthroat, *Geothlypis trichas* (from Selection 7, recorded in Dane Co., Wisconsin, June 1954).

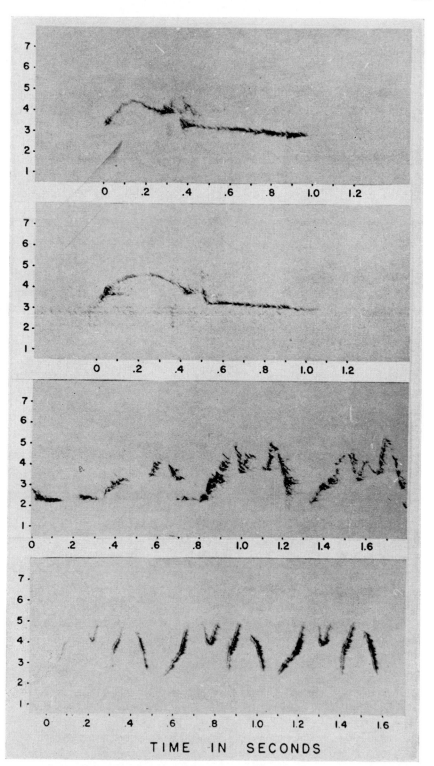

TIME IN SECONDS

necessarily learn its primary song motifs from its own "father." In many species, as in the meadowlarks (Lanyon, 1957), the juveniles are fully independent from their parents and disassociated from the territory in which they were fledged by the onset of subsong and the period of receptivity. They tend to remain in the general vicinity, however, thus giving rise to the community dialects discussed earlier.

Nikolai (pers. comm.) has some interesting observations made on experimental bullfinches which he interprets to mean that the refinement of the primary song motifs must be learned from the singing bird that actually rears the young of this species. His bullfinches developed original motifs which remained unimproved and unrefined unless the birds were permitted to hear the males that reared them. In choice experiments, young birds "preferred" to learn the motifs of the parent rather than those of other male bullfinches. In a control experiment a young bullfinch, reared by a canary but permitted to hear other bullfinches, learned the motifs of the canary! These experiments should be repeated with carefully designed controls for they raise some interesting points. The bullfinch is known to incorporate the complete motifs of alien species into its own repertoire (Thorpe, 1954)—one wonders when and under what circumstances this acquisition takes place.

Another interesting aspect of this learning process is that the actual manifestation of the motif acquired from another bird may be delayed up to several months from the time that the exposure occurred. Experimental meadowlarks exposed to particular songs during the subsong phase in June, at a time when they render no primary song motifs, do not begin to incorporate their acquired motifs into rehearsed song until early September (Lanyon, 1957). Similar observations have been made on the chaffinch (Thorpe, 1954) and blackbird (Thielcke and Poltz, pers. comm.). Thorpe (1951) cites a classical reference from Heinroth to a nightingale (*Luscinia megarhynchos*) that reproduced the song of a blackcap (*Sylvia atricapilla*) heard for only one week six or eight months before.

If many of the higher passerines have this period of receptivity during which they modify their original motifs and acquire new ones, one must pre-suppose a preferential receptivity for the motifs of their respective species during this period, except in the case of the true mimics already discussed. This has now been demonstrated experimentally for the chaffinch (Thorpe 1954, 1958), blackbird (Thielcke and Poltz, pers.

FIG. 7. Primary song motifs recorded from four western meadowlarks on adjacent territories in Dane Co., Wisconsin, April 1954. Note remarkable similarity in general pattern, but minute differences in detail.

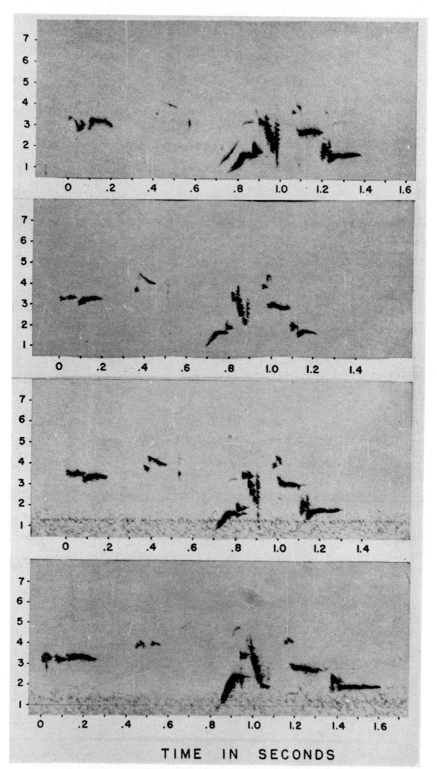

TIME IN SECONDS

comm.), and the two meadowlarks (Lanyon, 1957). But Thorpe (1955) has spectrographic evidence that even nonmimics, such as the chaffinch, may temporarily include imitations of the motifs of other species during the rehearsed song phase of the developmental process. These are dropped from the vocal repertoire in the transition to definitive primary song, however. Further evidence suggests that, should an experimental bird be isolated from his own species during this period, a secondary preference is shown for the motifs of a closely allied species when available (Loehrl, 1955; Lanyon, 1957).

The hand-rearing of birds in isolation from experienced individuals of their own species but with an opportunity to hear the songs of other species has been a popular research procedure. In some instances, the experimental birds develop a mixed repertoire of original motifs, suggestive of the patterns of their species, and motifs learned from other species (Fig. 8A). The blackbirds reared by Thielcke and Polz (pers. comm.) would come under this category. A garden warbler *(Sylvia borin)*, reared from the egg and isolated as above, developed some original motifs to which it added imitations of several species which it had heard during its first autumn (Sauer, pers. comm.).

More frequently the experimental birds have developed remarkably good imitations of the motifs of their "tutors", to the exclusion of any patterns characteristic of their own species (Fig. 8B). Examples of this are to be found in the studies of Scott (1901, 1902, 1904abc) and in my own work with the meadowlarks (Lanyon, 1957). Unfortunately the usual interpretations of these results have led to considerable confusion and should be reexamined here in light of the general pattern of song development that has emerged from recent studies. The positive response of these particular birds is, as I have suggested earlier, further confirmation of the ability of passerines to learn through vocal imitation. A natural corollary would be that learning from experienced individuals plays an important role in the normal development of their primary song. We are not justified, however, in assuming that these species are incapable of developing primary song motifs of their own, until that has been demonstrated by appropriate experimentation. Or, expressed in another way, these experiments *per se* give us no basis for the conclusion that primary song in these species is "entirely learned".

Thielcke and Poltz (pers. comm.) believe that the blackbird uses some of its original motifs as a basis or framework which, when completed through vocal imitation of experienced individuals, develop into the definitive primary song. The same theory has been applied to the chaffinch (Thorpe, 1954), whitethroat (Sauer, pers. comm.), linnet (Poulsen, pers. comm.) and canary (Poulsen, 1959). There is a pos-

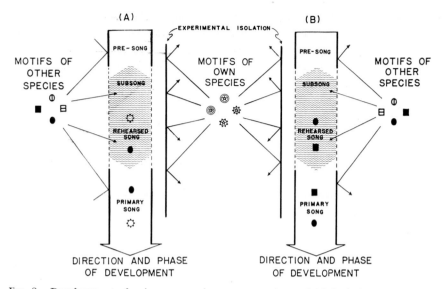

FIG. 8. Development of primary song in some experimental birds, isolated from their own species but exposed to other species: (A) Some birds develop a mixed repertoire of original motifs and of motifs learned from other species; (B) Some birds develop a repertoire comprised solely of the motifs learned from other species.

sibility that the original motifs of certain species may be obscured completely by the acquired motifs or possibly inhibited in their further development and manifestation by the learning process. This could be especially true in those experiments where the juvenile bird is permitted to hear only the songs of other species.

An integral feature of this developmental process is the species characteristic limitations placed upon the size of the repertoire of primary song motifs. Observations of wild populations of many song birds originally suggested this phenomenon, and there is now confirmation from recent experimental studies (Marler, 1956b; Messmer and Messmer, 1956). In my meadowlark studies I discovered that this limitation applies to "alien" motifs as well. A male western meadowlark normally has a repertoire of six to nine motifs. A hand-reared individual, permitted to hear red wing blackbirds (*Agelaius phoeniceus*) during the first two months of the receptive period (to the exclusion of meadowlark song) and the songs of its own species during the following two months, developed a repertoire of nine primary song motifs: two imitations of red-wing blackbirds and seven meadowlark songs (Lanyon, 1957).

Once incorporated into the bird's repertoire and manifested at the end of the first spring, the primary song motifs are remarkably stereotyped and reportedly "fixed for life" (Poulsen, 1951, 1954). There is spectrographic evidence to suggest that the chaffinch may shift emphasis, occasionally alter or omit a phrase, or shorten the length of the motif in subsequent years (Thorpe, 1954). A western meadowlark, whose complete repertoire of primary song was recorded and spectrographed in 1953, was singing the same nine motifs on his territory in 1955 (Lanyon, 1957).

The following points might be reiterated, then, to summarize the recent investigations into the developmental aspects of bird song: 1) There appears to be a general pattern of the sequential development of song common to all species studied thus far, which is at least partially controlled by endocrine factors. A gradual transition, differing primarily in timing between species, occurs from early subsong to intermediate rehearsed song and finally to definitive primary song. The latter is fully developed by the first spring, through a process of simplification and increased emphasis upon particular sound patterns. 2) The extent to which exposure to experienced birds is essential for the normal development of song is still the challenging question as it was to earlier workers. It has been suggested that the more primitive type of developmental process is one in which no learning through imitation of other birds takes place, but there is little experimental proof for this. Research on the lower families of passerine birds is needed to explore this thesis. We know that certain song birds that have been reared from the egg in sound proof rooms are capable of developing original song motifs, but these are only suggestive of the song of their respective species. These birds normally refine and supplement their own original motifs by imitating the sounds that they hear from other individuals. This important role of learning in the normal development leads to distinct geographical dialects of bird song. 3) The period of receptivity during which learning may occur extends from the time of fledging through the first spring. There is little evidence that birds continue to acquire new songs beyond this period. Most birds, except those that normally mimic others, show a preferential receptivity to the sounds of their own species. Once learned and incorporated into the vocal repertoire, these vocal patterns are remarkably stereotyped and fixed for life.

LITERATURE CITED

Allee, W. C. and N. Collias. 1938. Influence of injected male hormone on the social hierarchy in small flocks of hens. Anat. Rec. Sup. *72:* 60.

Baldwin, J. M., H. S. Goldin, and M. Metfessel. 1940. Effects of testosterone proportionate on the female roller canary under complete song isolation. Proc. Soc. Expt. Biol. and Med. *44:* 373–375.

Collard, J. and L. Grevendal. 1946. Etude sur les caracteres sexuels des pinsons, *Fringilla coelebs* et *F. montifringilla.* Gerfaut. *2:* 89–107.

Craig, W. 1943. The song of the wood pewee *Myiochanes virens* Linnaeus: A study of bird music. N.Y. State Mus. Bull. No. 334: 186 pp.

Curio, E. 1959. Verhaltensstudien am Trauerschnapper. Ztschr. f. Tierpsychol. Sup. *3:* 118 pp.

Goethe, F. 1955. Vergleichende Beobachtungen uber das Verhalten der Silbermowe *(Larus a. argentatus)* und der Heringsmowe *(Larus f. fuscus).* Proc. XI Internatl. Ornith. Cong. (1954): 577–582.

Heinroth, O. 1924. Lautausserungen der Vogel. Jour. Ornith. *72:* 223–244.

————, and M. Heinroth. 1924–1926. Die Vogel Mitteleuropas. 3 vols. Berlin.

Herrick, E. H. and J. O. Harris. 1957. Singing female canaries. Science *125:* 1299–1300.

Lanyon, W. E. 1957. The comparative biology of the meadowlarks *(Sturnella)* in Wisconsin. Pub. Nuttall Ornith. Club. No. 1. Cambridge, Mass. 67 pp.

Leonard, S. L. 1939. Induction of singing in female canaries by injections of male hormone. Proc. Soc. Expt. Biol. and Med. *41:* 229–230.

Lister, M. D. 1953. Secondary song: a tentative classification. Brit. Birds. *46:* 139–143.

Loehrl, H. 1955. Beziehungen zwischen Halsband—und Trauerfliegenschnapper *(Muscicapa albicollis* und *M. hypoleuca)* in demselben Brutgebiet. Proc. XI Internatl. Ornith. Cong. (1954): 333–336.

Marler, P. 1952. Variation in the song of the chaffinch *Fringilla coelebs.* Ibis. *94:* 458–472.

————. 1956a. The voice of the chaffinch and its function as a language. Ibis. *98:* 231–261.

————. 1956b. The voice of the chaffinch. New Biology 20: 70–87.

Messmer, E. and I. Messmer. 1956. Die Entwicklung der lautausserungen und Einiger Verhaltensweisen det Amsel *(Turdus merula merula* L.) unter naturlichen Bedingungen und nach Einselaufzucht in schalldichten Raumen. Ztschr. f. Tierpsychol. *13:* 341–441.

Metfessel, M. 1940. Relationships of heredity and environment in behavior. Jour. Psychol. *10:* 177–198.

Miskimen, M. 1951. Sound production in passerine birds. Auk. *68:* 493–504.

Nice, M. M. 1943. Studies in the life history of the song sparrow. II. Trans. Linn. Soc. N.Y. *6:* 1–328.

Noble, G. K. and M. Wurm. 1940. The effect of testosterone propionate on the black-crowned night heron. Endocrinology. *26:* 837–850.

————, and A. Zitrin. 1942. Induction of mating behavior in male and female chicks following injection of sex hormone. Endocrinology. *30:* 327–344.

Poulson, H. 1951. Inheritance and learning in the song of the chaffinch *(Fringilla coelebs* L.). Behavior. *3:* 216–228.

————. 1954. On the song of the linnet (Carduelis cannabina). Dansk Ornith. For. Tidsskr. 48: 32–37.

————. 1958. The calls of the chaffinch (Fringilla coelebs L.) in Denmark. Dansk Ornith. For. Tidsskr. 52: 89–105.

————. 1959. Song learning in the domestic canary. Ztschr. f. Tierpsychol. 16: 173–178.

Sanborn, H. C. 1932. The inheritance of song in birds. Jour. Compar. Psychol. 13: 345–364.

Sauer, F. 1954. Die Entwicklung der Lautausserungen vom Ei ab schalldicht gehaltener Dorngrasmucken (Sylvia c. communis Latham) im Vergleich mit spater isolierten und mit wildlebenden Artgenossen. Ztschr. f. Tierpsychol. 11: 10–93.

————. 1955. Entwicklung und Regression angeborenen Verhaltens bei der Dorngrasmucke (Sylvia c. communis). Proc. XI Internatl. Ornith. Cong. (1954): 218–226.

Schjelderup-Ebbe, T. 1923. Weitere Beitrage zur Sozial- und Individual-Psychologie des Haushuhns. Ztschr. f. Psychol. 92: 60–87.

Scott, W. E. D. 1901. Data on song birds: observations on the song of Baltimore orioles in captivity. Science. 14: 522–526.

————. 1902. Data on song in birds: the acquisition of new songs. Science. 15: 178–181.

————. 1904a. The inheritance of song in passerine birds. Remarks and observations on the song of hand-reared boblinks and red-winged black-birds (Dolichonyx oryzivorus andAgelaius phoeniceus). Science. 19: 154–155.

————. 1904b. The inheritance of song in passerine birds. Remarks on the development of song in the rose-breasted grosbeak Zamelodia ludoviciana (Linnaeus) and the meadowlark Sturnella magna (Linnaeus). Science. 19: 957–959.

————. 1904c. Inheritance of song in passerine birds. Further observations on the development of song and nest-building in hand-reared rose-breasted grosbeaks Zamelodia ludoviciana (Linnaeus). Science. 20: 282–283.

Simms, E. 1955. The conversational calls of birds as revealed by new methods of field recording. Proc. XI Internatl. Ornith. Cong. (1954): 623–626.

Streseman, E. 1947. Baron von Pernau: pioneer student of bird behavior. Auk. 64: 35–52.

Thorpe, W. H. 1951. The learning abilities of birds. Pt. II. Ibis. 93: 252–296.

————. 1954. The process of song-learning in the chaffinch as studied by means of the sound spectrograph. Nature. 173: 465.

————. 1955. The analysis of bird song with special reference to the song of the chaffinch (Fringilla coelebs). Proc. XI Internatl. Ornith Cong. (1954): 209–217.

————. 1956. Learning and instinct in animals. Methuen and Co. London. 1–493.

————. 1958. Further studies on the process of song learning in the chaffinch (Fringilla coelebs gengleri). Nature. 182: 554–557.

————, and R. A. Hinde. 1956. An inexpensive type of sound-proof room suitable for zoological research. Jour. Expt. Biol. 33: 750–755.

Tinbergen, N. 1957. Some aspects of instinct and learning in birds. Biol. and Human Affairs. 23: 15–20.

Witchell, C. 1896. The evolution of bird-song. Adams and Charles Black. London. 253 pp.

CAPTIONS TO SELECTIONS ON DEMONSTRATION RECORD

Selection 1. Th various stages in the sequential development of primary song in passerine birds are presented in detail in the text and in Fig. 2. The following recordings further illustrate this process, as revealed in the development of a hand-reared western meadowlark. First, subsong from a two months old male. Note that at this age there are no phrases suggestive of the definitive primary song, even though this individual had been exposed to meadowlark song during this period.

Selection 2. At three months of age the transition from a subsong to rehearsed song has taken place, for distinguishable vocal patterns that are suggestive of definitive primary song have been added to the framework of random warbling.

Selection 3. When this western meadowlark was ten months of age it had dropped the random warbling and was placing increased emphasis upon its definitive primary song motifs. Some of these are typical of its species, while others are imitations of redwinged blackbirds that it heard during the critical learning period.

Selection 4. At two years of age the primary song motifs remained essentially the same—there was no evidence of learning new patterns subsequent to the first spring.

Selection 5. Other meadowlarks, reared in isolation from experienced individuals of their own species but with an opportunity to hear the songs of other species, developed imitations of the motifs of their "tutors". Here, for example, is the primary song of a redwinged blackbird.

Selection 6. And here is an imitation of this species as learned by a hand-reared western meadowlark during its first summer.

Selection 7. Now, the primary song of a yellowthroat, one of our common warblers.

Selection 8. Here are the imitations of yellowthroat as learned by a hand-reared western meadowlark during its first summer.

Bird Songs and Mate Selection

Peter Marler

Department of Zoology, University of California, Berkeley

ALTHOUGH BIRD SONGS have been the subject of much attention, particularly in recent years, there is hardly any *direct* information about how they actually function. In this respect bird studies are less advanced than, for example, those on Orthoptera (e.g. Perdeck 1957, Walker 1957), and there is no doubt that the greatest single need in studies of avian communication is for experiment in this field and in particular, on the value of songs as reproductive isolating mechanisms. This subject must therefore be discussed at present in terms of indirect evidence, not all of which is as clear as is sometimes assumed.

Ornithologists are often impressed by the distinctiveness of the songs of species which live together. Often song is more useful for field identification than the morphology, and at least once has provided the first clue to the separation of new species (White, 1879) (Fig. 1). This fact of specific distinctiveness in songs seems to carry the implication that they serve as reproductive isolating mechanisms, either in establishing or perpetuating a bond between breeding birds, thus being subject to a selective pressure encouraging specific distinctiveness. Leaving aside for the moment the question whether specific distinctiveness of songs in sympatric species is in fact universal, we can make certain deductions about some of the characteristics which bird songs should have, when functioning in this way.

ACKNOWLEDGMENTS

Expeditions to the Canary Islands and to Mexico were made possible by grants from the Royal Society of London and from the Associates in Tropical Biogeography, for which the author is very grateful. Some of the work was accomplished as a research fellow at Jesus College and in the Department of Zoology at the University of Cambridge, under the direction of Dr. W. H. Thorpe.

---

[1] Manuscript received April 1959.

[2] Recordings illustrating this chapter are on Side II, Band 3 of the Demonstration Record.

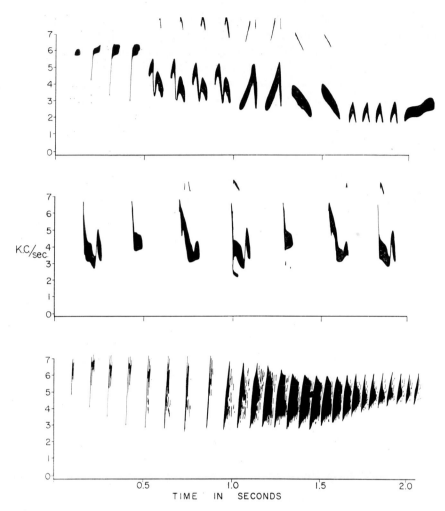

—FIG. 1. The songs of three European Phylloscopus warblers, used by Gilbert White as the first evidence that they are distinct species. The two upper birds, the willow warbler (*Phylloscopus trochilus*—top, May 1957) and the chiffchaff (*P. collybita*, May 1957) are particularly similar morphologically but have quite different songs. The first has a short regular song, repeated at intervals, while the second rambles on continuously, improvising on two basic notes. The lower record is a wood warbler song (*P. sibilatrix*, May 1954).

REPRODUCTIVE ISOLATION AND SPECIFIC DISTINCTIVENESS

We should not forget, as Ernst Mayr has often reminded us (1942), that there is a wide variety of methods of achieving reproductive isolation. In any one species several factors of varying importance may contribute and this must be as true of birds as of other animals. So the following discussion is based on the hypothesis, that *the structural characteristics of loud and conspicuous song play a dominant role in reproductive isolation of the species,* leaving aside for the moment the effects of such factors as *when* or *where* the song is given, and ignoring other functions of the song, such as defense of the territory.

This hypothesis implies that the kind of *sound environment* within which a bird lives, exerts a selective pressure on its song, encouraging the development of a type which is conspicuously different from the sounds making up the background against which it must be used. This in turn has important implications for the study of geographical song variation.

GEOGRAPHICAL VARIATION OF SONG

Although the geographical variation of bird songs has often been noted (Benson, 1948; Marler, 1952; Saunders, 1935) no explanation is usually advanced to suggest why variation takes a particular form in a given case. However many species live with different companions in different parts of their range, and from our hypothesis their songs would be expected to vary. If we know sufficient of the various *sound environments* it should even be possible to predict in detail the direction in which the song is likely to vary. The task of describing all the sounds in a given area during the course of a year is huge, though not insuperable. It has not yet been attempted in a normal mainland environment, but a start has been made in the simpler situation presented by small islands.

Lack and Southern (1949) drew attention to the interesting differences in songs of the same or closely related species between Britain and the Canary Islands, in the Atlantic off the coast of North Africa. Small island avifaunas are always poorer in species than those on the adjacent mainland, and the *sound environment* will therefore be simpler. Selection pressure on the songs of resident birds should be relaxed, compared with mainland, as the observations of Lack and Southern did indeed seem to imply. The single *Parus* species for example, as compared with six in Britain, has a very variable song, which seems to encompass many of the sounds made by the British species. In the Azores the goldcrest, *Regulus regulus,* also has much more varied calls than the British bird (Marler and Boatman, 1951).

BIRD SONGS IN THE CANARY ISLANDS

In 1956 the writer was able to visit the Canary Islands with a tape recorder, making possible a more detailed comparison of songs with the mainland. The situation proved to be more complex than had been expected. Some songs showed no significant change, some were simpler, and others were more variable, but none were more complex, in the sense of being more elaborate while still remaining reasonably stereotyped.

For example, the songs of the turtle dove, *Streptopelia turtur,* the great spotted woodpecker *Dryobates major,* the corn bunting *Emberiza calandra,* the blackcap, *Sylvia atricapilla,* and the blackbird, *Turdus merula,* do not seem to differ consistently from those of their close relatives in Britain, on the basis of the small samples examined. (Fig. 2.) Why some species should be unaffected by island conditions is not clear. Of the above, all but the turtle dove have sub-specific status, and presumably have been living on Tenerife long enough for changes in song to occur. It may be that we have to postulate an *inertia* in the mechanisms controlling song form in some species. Alternatively, the function of song may differ in species which show island variation and in those which do not.

Two species of chaffinch live on Tenerife, the endemic blue chaffinch, *Fringilla teydea* and *Fringilla coelebs tintillon,* a subspecies of the mainland form. Recordings were only obtained of blue chaffinch song, but Lack and Southern suggest that *tintillon* song is similar. The comparison with the British chaffinch shows a simpler song on the islands, which has a closer resemblance to the innate song of isolated chaffinches than to the more elaborate normal songs of wild birds (Thorpe, 1954, 1958).

The same applies to the song of the Azores chaffinch, *Fringilla coelebs moreletti* (Marler and Boatman, 1951). It looks as though island conditions have reduced the need for the learned elaboration of chaffinch song which takes place in Britain (Thorpe, 1954, 1958), and this in spite of the fact that two species of *Fringilla* are present instead of one. Perhaps the relative ecological isolation of the two Tenerife chaffinches is significant here.

The trend to increased variability is illustrated by the blue titmouse, *Parus caeruleus* and the chiffchaff, *Phylloscopus collybita*. The *Parus* has an extraordinary range of different songs or calls, one succeeding the other in the same individual with bewildering variety (Fig. 3). Many of these bear a resemblance to songs of the coal tit, *Parus ater,* in Britain but some are more like those of other *Parus* species. In the same way, the chiffchaff sometimes sounds like the corresponding species in Britain, but at other times sounds like its close relative, the willow warbler, *Phylloscopus trochilus,* which is not present in the Canary Islands (Fig. 4).

In seeking the reason for this increased variability in the island situation, which contrasts with the greater simplicity in the chaffinches, we can only speculate. It almost seems that while the chaffinch in Britain is under pressure to elaborate its song, the blue tit and chiffchaff must restrict themselves to a small portion of their potential repertoires. Under island conditions, with the selection pressure on specific distinctiveness relaxed, there are changes in opposite directions. Yet both of these would result in a loss of efficiency if they occurred in Britain.

At present the evidence reveals no correlation between island variation and the relative contributions of learning and inheritance to song development in the mainland forms. Both in the European corn bunting (Thorpe, 1956), and chiffchaff (Heinroth, 1924) the inherited elements seem to predominate in the song, yet the former hardly sounds different on Tenerife, while the other is distinctly changed. There may be considerable plasticity in the genetic mechanism controlling chiffchaff song, for variations are known to occur in other parts of Europe (Lynes, 1914). Learning plays a greater role in normal song development of the blackbird in Europe (Messmer, 1956) yet there is little difference between Britain and Tenerife. However, it may be significant that of all the species involved, it is in the development of chaffinch and blue tit song that learning is most important in Europe (Thorpe, 1954, 1958; Promptoff and Lukina, 1945). We should expect that learned song traditions would be the most ready to vary in response to change in selection pressure.

Much more information is needed here, but careful studies of geographical variation may eventually throw considerable light on the kind of selection pressures to which bird songs are subject. Other types of variation are also worthy of attention.

SONG DIALECTS

We must take care to distinguish between the broad geographical variation of the song of a species and the variations which can be observed between adjacent populations living under similar conditions. These are often considerable and have led to the proposal of an analogy with dialects in human speech. In the chaffinch for example, there are community song-characteristics which change as you pass into the next community, particularly if there is a barrier to hinder movement. The situation is well illustrated in some of the more isolated Scottish glens, each with its own chaffinch *dialect* (Marler, 1956).

FIG. 2. A comparison of songs of close relatives in Europe and on the Canary Islands. In each case the upper record is from Tenerife in the Canary Islands. Note the similar basic patterns of song in *Turdus merula* (top, April, 1956, April, 1953), *Sylvia atricapilla* (center, April, 1956, June, 1951), and *Emberiza calandra* (bottom, April 1956, May 1938).

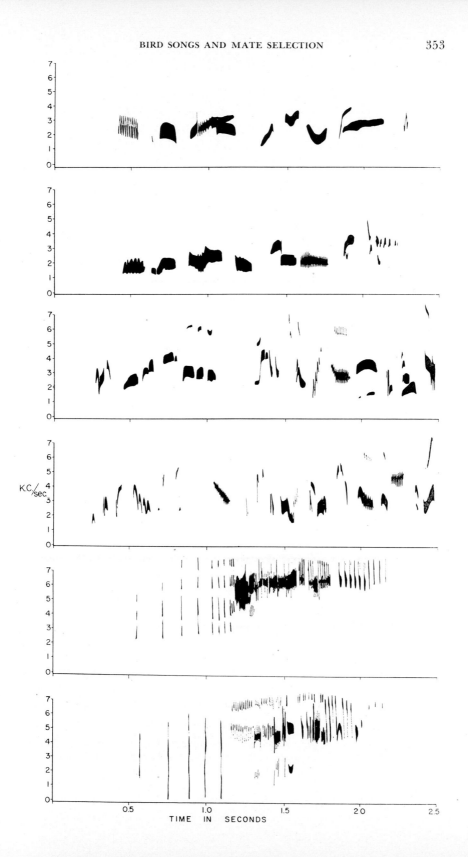

K.C./sec

TIME IN SECONDS

There are similar observations on other species such as the snow bunting, *Plectrophenax nivalis* (Tinbergen, 1939), blackbird, song sparrow, *Melospiza melodia* (Nice, 1943), the white-crowned sparrow, *Zonotrichia leucophrys*, (Blanchard, 1941) and the eastern and western meadowlarks *Sturnella magna* and *S. neglecta* (Lanyon, 1957). In the chaffinch we know that the *dialects* arise because young males learn their songs from older birds in their first year and then return to breed in the same area in subsequent seasons. This encourages the persistence in one area of a limited number of song types. The effect is aided by the habit of countersinging in which a male tends to reply to another with a similar song type, if he possesses one, so that songs uncommon in the area tend to fall into disuse.

It is difficult to see what function is served by this dialect variation, but we may note that learned traditions of this type may be as susceptible to natural selection as entirely inherited songs and may adjust more readily, especially if there is a certain *inertia* in the genetic mechanism underlying innate songs.

VARIATION WITHIN A POPULATION

One of the difficulties in describing song variation is that, even within a population, there are so many song types that large samples are necessary. This is all the more surprising when we reflect that if the facilitation of specific sexual recognition were the only function song had to perform, there should be an ideal for this purpose to which all members of the population should conform. The rarity of this condition—if it exists at all—only serves to emphasize our ignorance of song function.

It is not uncommon for songs of different individuals to differ with sufficient consistency that an observer can use them for individual identification. Mrs. Nice found this with the song sparrow (1943) and the same is true of meadowlarks (Lanyon, 1957), the chaffinch, yellow bunting, *Emberiza citrinella*, Mexican junco, *Junco phaeonotus*, and brown towhee, *Pipilo fuscus*. Leaving aside the excessive variation on small islands which has already been mentioned, the range of variation within mainland populations may be surprisingly wide.

In the chaffinch a considerable number of types can be discerned by ear alone (Marler, 1952). More extreme is the situation recently found in the Mexican junco in the Durango pine forests, in Mexico. Songs of some seventy individuals were recorded, and on analysis no two of them

---

FIG. 3. A sample from the great variety of songs heard from *Parus caeruleus* in Tenerife (April 1956). Some are similar to the corresponding European species (g,h) while others resemble *Parus cristatus* (d,i) and *Parus ater* (a,b,c,e).

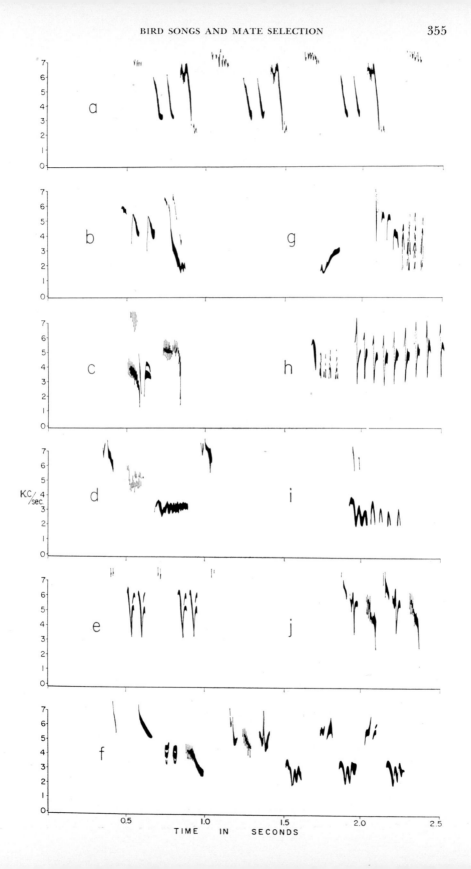

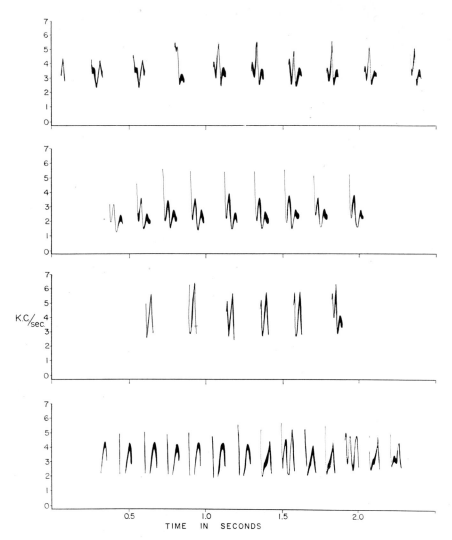

FIG. 4. Some song variations of the Tenerife chiffchaff, *Phylloscopus collybita* (April 1956). While the individual notes are often similar to those of the European bird, at times they are arranged into a short two-second song, particularly clear in the bottom record, reminiscent of the European willow warbler (cf. fig. 1).

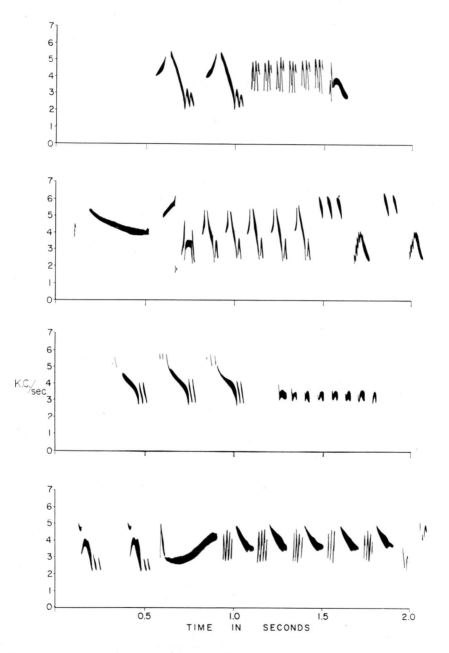

Fig. 5. Songs of four neighboring Mexican juncos (*Junco phaeonotus*) recorded in the pine woods near El Salto in Durango, Mexico. Although there are marked differences between each one, they all have one similar pattern of notes in common (Selection 1, July 1958).

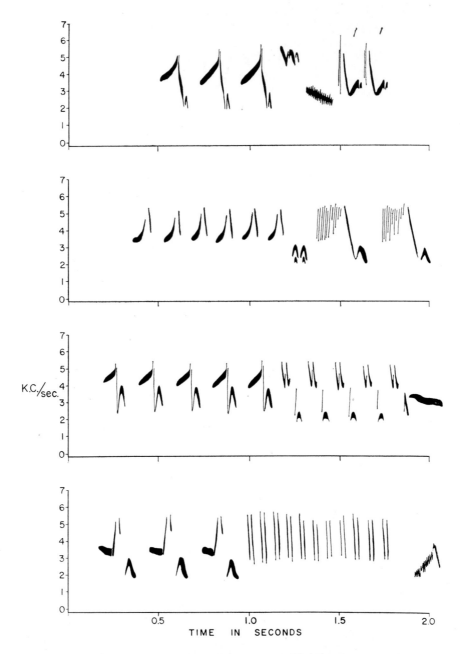

FIG. 6. Songs of four more adjacent Mexican juncos from another part of the same pine wood. Here the variations on the shared note pattern are more free, but share the same basic form (Selection 2, July 1958).

were identical (Selections 1 and 2 on the Demonstration Record). Adjacent birds sometimes shared certain characteristics (Figs. 5 and 6), which are reminiscent of the dialects discussed above (although in an ecological sense, the whole sample was drawn from one population). The songs which contrasted most strongly were so different that it was at first difficult to believe that they came from members of the same species. Another example of divergence within a population comes from brown towhees in Mexico (Fig. 7 and Selection 3), and even songs as homogeneous as those of the chipping sparrow, *Spizella passerina,* show considerable variation in detail.

What is the explanation for this variation in song which seems to hinder the usually accepted function of specific recognition? Again only experiment can give the answer, but a hint is provided by the help which the variation gives ornithologists in identifying individual birds. It is conceivable that it facilitates individual recognition for the birds themselves, both between rival males, and between mates. The evidence for this recognition is at present only circumstantial (Marler, 1956). But we can see how it might come to have survival value by enabling males to distinguish between new intruders and old rivals, and by helping females to locate males with whom they have previously bred.

Individual identification of chaffinches is made easier by the possession of more than one song type, some contrasting more strongly with the songs of neighbors than others. Occasionally a particular combination of song types may serve to identify a bird, even though each of them may be shared with other individuals.

REPERTOIRES OF INDIVIDUAL BIRDS

Perhaps even more surprising than variation within a population is this variation in the individual. Apart from the slight variations of repetition or omission, many birds have several distinct themes. If this were only an occasional phenomenon it would hardly be worth remarking on. But it is noticeable how few birds sing exactly the same theme all the time, even among those which one tends to regard as monotonous singers. The European willow and wood warblers usually have several themes, so does the yellow bunting. Among a group 71 chaffinches the mean number of song themes per birds was 2.8 (Marler, 1956). Mrs. Nice (1943) found from 6 to 24 themes in the repertoire of individual song sparrows. A Carolina wren, *Thryothorus ludovicianus,* gave 22 themes in 24 bursts of singing (Borror, 1956). Up to nine songs per bird are recorded for western meadowlarks, and many more for the eastern form (Lanyon, 1958). Among more versatile singers the repertoire may be still larger, the greatest recorded so far being 173 themes used by a song thrush, *Turdus ericetorum,* near Cambridge, England (Marler, 1959). The way in which these various themes are constructed is of great interest, but it would be out of place to discuss it here. The point which concerns us is the function of this variation. Is it simply a manifestation of aesthetic exercise without any special significance, or does it have survival value?

SPECIFIC CHARACTERS VERSUS INDIVIDUAL CHARACTERS

If song variation within a population is an aid to individual recognition of other members of the species, is it not possible that variation within the individual is another contribution to this function? Within

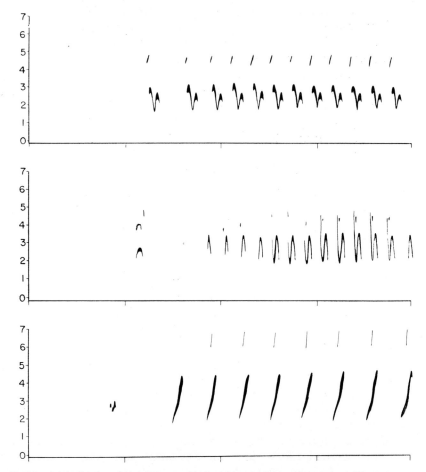

FIG. 7. Songs of six brown towhees (*Pipilo fuscus*) from the same population at La Labor, near Calvillo, in Aguascalientes, Mexico (Selection 3, July 1958).

the repertoire, each additional theme varies but little, and so adds to
the clues on which individual recognition can be based.

Again, we have the apparent conflict between the use of variations
for individual recognition and the need for stereotyped characteristics
for species recognition. However, we ourselves can usually identify the
species even of the most varied singers and we must impute to the birds
themselves at least an equal ability in this regard. This implies that
some constant characteristic survives through the variations. In fact it
seems as though the conflict is resolved in many cases by relegating

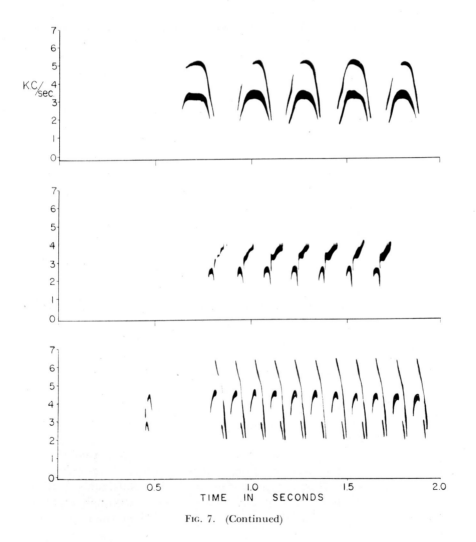

FIG. 7. (Continued)

specific and individual characteristics to different parameters of the song. Often it looks as though the specific properties lie in the overall time pattern of the song while individuality is portrayed by the detailed changes of frequency. The situation in the *Hylocichla* thrushes seems consistent wth this (Stein, 1956), though there are undoubtedly alternative methods as well.

THE SIGNIFICANCE OF SONG LEARNING

Dr. Lanyon has discussed elsewhere the roles of learning and inheritance in the development of song, but one aspect bears on the present discussion. We have no satisfactory explanation of why some birds elaborate their innate song by learning from others. It may be that this provides an alternative means of responding to selection pressure, without relying on the rather slower selection of genetic mutations. As pointed out by Huxley (1942), learned traditions are equally susceptible to selection effects. From the studies so far carried out, it appears that the copying of another's song is never quite precise, so that learning may also facilitate the development of individual characteristics. To achieve a similar effect with an innate song would require either some kind of polymorphism, or an element of indeterminacy in the ontogenetic process through variable expressivity of the genes concerned, both possibilities to be born in mind in studies on the development of song.

SOME EXAMPLES OF SPECIFIC "INDISTINCTIVENESS" IN SONGS

It was pointed out at the beginning of this paper that the assumption on which all of this discussion is based ,that loud and conspicuous songs, where used, play a dominant role in reproductive isolation, is unproven in the strictest sense; though Dilger (1956) has clearly demonstrated in *Catharus* and *Hylocichla* thrushes the role of song in territorial defense. There is little doubt that great differences will in fact be found in the functions of song, and it is already clear that the meadowlarks do not fit into this simplified picture (Lanyon, 1957). The strongest line of indirect evidence is the specific distinctiveness of sympatric species (Marler, 1957). During a study of the songs of some Mexican birds in the summer of 1958, two cases of a relative lack of specific distinctiveness were noted.

In the pine woods of Durango three species live within earshot, with rather similar songs: the chipping sparrow, *Spizella passerina,* the striped sparrow, *Oriturus superciliosa,* and the Hartlaub's warbler, *Vermivora superciliosa* (Fig. 8 and Selection 4). Although there are differences, I suggest that these songs are less distinct than we should

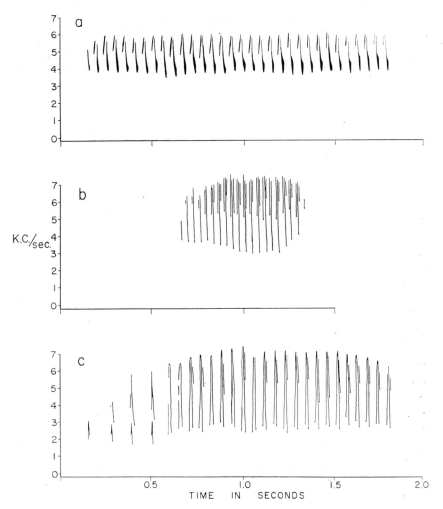

Fig. 8. A comparison of songs of three species, (a) the chipping sparrow (*Spizella passerina*), (b) Hartlaub's warbler (*Vermivora superciliosa*) and (c) the striped sparrow (*Oriturus superciliosa*) illustrating their relative lack of specific distinctiveness (Selection 4, July 1958). These were all recorded near El Salto in Durango, Mexico.

expect if they played a dominant role in reproductive isolation of these species. In fact those three species are rather different ecologically, which may help to keep them apart.

In a rocky wooded valley in Aguascalientes four species with rather similar songs were observed, three of them engaging in what seemed to be interspecific countersinging. These were the brown towhee, *Pipilo fuscus,* the cactus wren, *Campylorhynchus brunneicapillus,* and the

ladderback woodpecker, *Dendrocopus scalaris,* the fourth being the
yellow-breasted chat, *Icteria virens* (Fig. 9, and Selection 5). Again,
there are differences, and the chat has other themes which are quite
different. But the relatively limited specific distinctiveness is worthy
of note.

OTHER FUNCTIONS FOR SONG THAN MATE SELECTION

It is possible that the slight differences between the songs of these
species are adequate for quick and accurate specific recognition, though
we would still need to explain why a relatively slight specific distinctiveness suffices here, and not in other cases. On the other hand we must
not forget that song may serve other functions which are not necessarily
aided by specific distinctiveness.

The repulsion of intruders from the territory is often accomplished
by song. When such defense is restricted to members of the same species
a highly specifically-distinct song will be suitable, and can serve for
reproductive isolation as well. If song is freed from this latter function,
however, selection may favor a different situation. Specific distinctiveness becomes at less of a premium, for nothing is lost if a song repells
other species as well. If there is the slightest degree of competition with
other species selection may shift in favor of a degree of resemblance
between their songs. The similarities in voice between species of *Parus,*
described by Dixon, in areas where they overlap, may be such a case,
for the territories are mutually exclusive (Dixon, 1950), and voice
plays an important role in territorial defense (Dixon, 1949). The
resemblances between the threat displays of many species (Marler, 1957)
is no doubt related to these same considerations.

There may also be variation in the role which song plays in the
relationship between male and female. Specific distinctiveness will be
crucial if the song is concerned with establishment of the bond which
leads to copulation. In species where the pair bond lasts a long time,
song may also be concerned with its maintenance. In this case it may
be important to the female to recognize her mate's song individually,
thus encouraging the different types of variation discussed earlier in
this paper. As pointed out, this too may run counter to the trend
towards a stereotyped species specific song. In the same direction,
stimulation of the female as an aid to synchronization of the physiological
cycles of the pair may be achieved in part by song, again, likely to be
related to individual characteristics as well as to specific ones.

Extreme specific distinctiveness in bird song is therefore unlikely to
be a general rule, since in a given species the same song may serve several
of the functions discussed above. The hypothesis with which this paper

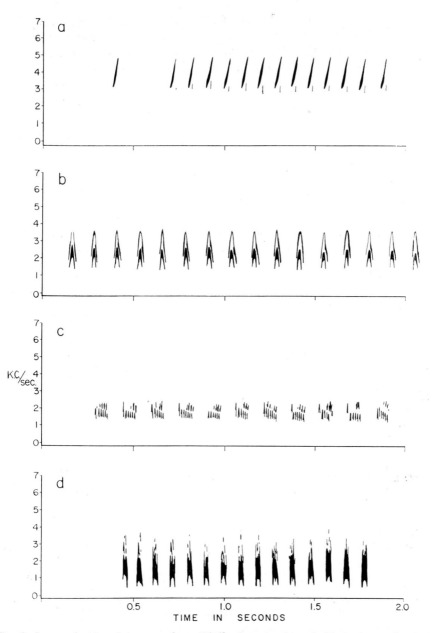

FIG. 9. Songs of (a) a brown towhee (*Pipilo fuscus*), (b) a ladderback woodpecker (*Dendrocopus scalaris*), (c) a cactus wren (*Campylorhynchus brunnei-capillus*), and (d) a sample from a yellow-breasted chat (*Icteria virens*), recorded within earshot of each other, at La Labor, near Calvillo in Aguascalientes, Mexico (Selection 5, July 1958).

opened, that the structural characteristics of loud and conspicuous song play a dominant role in reproductive isolation of the species, is clearly an oversimplification. The extent to which we are able to understand the evolution of bird song in the future depends on how far we can establish the precise functions which it serves, and this calls for a different approach than that used in this paper; that is, experimental rather than simple observational methods are necessary.

LITERATURE CITED

Benson, C. W. 1958. Geographical voice variation in African birds. Ibis *90:* 48–71.
Blanchard, B. D. 1941. The white-crowned sparrows (*Zonotrichia leucophrys*) of the Pacific seaboard: Environment and annual cycle. Univ. Calif., Publ. Zool. *46:* 1–178.
Borror, D. J. 1956. Variation in Carolina wren songs. Auk *73:* 211–229.
Dilger, W. C. 1956. Hostile behavior and reproductive isolating mechanisms in the avian genera *Catharus* and *Hylocichla.* Auk. *73:* 313–353.
Dixon, K. 1949. Behavior of the plain titmouse. Condor. *51:* 110–136. 1950. Notes on the ecological distribution of plain and bridled titmice in Arizona. Condor. *52:* 140–141.
Heinroth, O. 1924. Lautäusserungen der Vögel. Jour. Ornith. *72:* 223–244.
Huxley, J. 1942. Evolution, the modern synthesis. London, Harper and Bros. 645 pp.
Lack, D. and H. N. Southern. 1949. The birds of Tenerife. Ibis. *91:* 607–626.
Lanyon, W. 1957. The comparative biology of the meadowlarks (*Sturnella*) in Wisconsin. Pub. Nutall Ornith. Club, No. 1, Cambridge, Mass. 67 pp.
Lynes, H. 1914. Remarks on the distribution of the chiffchaff and willow warbler. Ibis *2:* 304–314.
Marler, P. 1952. Variation in the song of the chaffinch, *Fringilla coelebs.* Ibis. *94:* 458–47. 1956. The voice of the chaffinch and its function as a language. Ibis. *98:* 231–261. 1957. Specific distinctiveness in the communication signals of birds. Behaviour. *11:* 13–39. 1959. Developments in the study of animal communication. *In* Bell, P. (ed.), Darwin's Biological Work. Cambridge, England, 343 pp.
Marler, P. and D. J. Boatman. 1951. Observations on the birds of Pico, Azores. Ibis. *93:* 90–99.
Mayr, E. 1942. Systematics and the origin of species. Columbia Univ. Press. New York. 334 pp.
Messmer, E. 1956. Die Entwicklung der Lautäusserungen und einiger Verhaltensweisen der Amsel (*Turdus merula merula* L.) unter naturlichen bedingungen und nach Einzelaufsucht in schalldichten Räumen. Ztschr. f. Tierpsychol. *13:* 341–441.
Nice, M. M. 1943. Studies in the life history of the song sparrow II. Trans. N. Y. Linn. Soc *6:* 1–328.
Perdeck, A. C. 1958. The isolating value of specific song patterns in two sibling species of grasshoppers (*Chorthippus bruneus* Thunb. and *C. biguttulus* L.). Behavior. *12:* 1–75.
Promptov, A. N. and E. V. Lukina. 1945. Conditioned reflectory differentiation in Passeres and its biological value. C. R. (Dolklady). Ac. Sci. U.S.S.R. *46:* 382–384.

Saunders, A. A. 1951. A guide to bird songs. Rev. ed., Doubleday and Co. New York. 307 pp.

Stein, R. S. 1956. A comparative study of advertising song in the Hyocichla thrushes. Auk. *73:* 503–512.

Thorpe, W. H. 1954. The process of song learning in the chaffinch as studied by means of the sound spectrograph. Nature. *173:* 465. 1956. Learning and instinct in animals. Methuen and Co. London. 493 pp. 1958. The learning of song patterns by birds with especial reference to the song of the chaffinch, *Fringilla coelebs.* Ibis. *100:* 535–570.

Tinbergen, N. 1939. The behaviour of the snow bunting in spring. Proc. N. Y. Linn. Soc. *5:* 1–94.

Walker, T. J. 1957. Specificity in the response of female tree crickets (Orthoptera, Gryllidae, Oecanthinae) to calling songs of the males. Ann. Ent. Soc. Amer. *50:* 626–636.

White, G. 1879. The natural history of Selborne. Frederick Warne and Co., London.

CAPTIONS TO SELECTIONS ON DEMONSTRATION RECORD

Selection 1. Songs of four neighboring Mexican juncos (*Junco phaeonotus*) recorded in the same part of a pinewood near El Salto in Durango, Mexico. Although there are marked differences between each one, they all have one similar pattern of notes in common (see Fig. 5).

Selection 2. Songs of four more adjacent Mexican juncos from another part of the same pine wood. Here the variations on the shared note pattern are more free, but share the same basic form (see Fig. 6).

Selection 3. Songs of six brown towhees (*Pipilo fuscus*) from the same population, at La Labor, near Calvillo, in Aguascalientes, Mexico (see Fig. 7).

Selection 4. A comparison of similar songs of three species which may be heard at the same time and place: Bird 1—the striped sparrow (*Oriturus superciliosa*); Bird 2—Hartlaub's warbler (*Vermivora superciliosa*); Bird 3—the chipping sparrow (*Spizella passerina*). This illustrates their relative lack of specific distinctiveness. Recorded near El Salto in Durango, Mexico (see Fig. 8).

Selection 5. Similar songs of a brown towhee, *Pipilo fuscus* (Bird 1); a ladderback woodpecker, *Dendrocopus scalaris* (Bird 2); a cactus wren, *Campylorhynchus brunnei-capillus* (Bird 3); and a yellow breasted chat, *Icteria virens* (Bird 4). The latter is selected from a variable song, some parts of which are quite different from songs of the other three species. Recorded within earshot of each other, at La Labor, near Calvillo in Aguascalientes, Mexico (see Fig. 9).

An Ecological And Functional Classification Of Animal Sounds [1,2]

NICHOLAS E. COLLIAS

Department of Zoology, University of California, Los Angeles

THE MAIN PURPOSE of this synthesis is to describe the ecological background of animal sounds. If we understand the natural context of animal language, we should be able to understand more fully the nature of animal communication.

Animal sounds can readily be classified into ecological categories: food problems, avoidance of enemies, reproduction, and group movements. The possible function as signals of the various sounds made by animals has greatly interested me, and is a subject that I have studied at convenient times during the last ten years. During this time, I have had the benefit of helpful discussions with many specialists and assistance in the field from many colleagues, especially from Arthur A. Allen, James and Ruth Chapin, John T. Emlen, Jr., Fred and Frances Hamerstrom, P. Hershkovitz, H. Albert Hochbaum, Robert Inger, Martin Joos, P. Paul Kellogg, Robert Nero, Peter Ward, and Milton Weller. I am particularly indebted to my wife, Elsie, for frequent aid in field and study. For financial assistance I am grateful to the Wisconsin Alumni Research Foundation, the North American Wildlife Foundation, the Wildlife Management Institute, the National Institute of Mental Health, and the National Science Foundation. I wish to thank Drs. George A. Bartholomew, Jr., Raymond C. Cowles, and Thomas Howell for critical reading of the manuscript and for useful comments on it.

A brief version of this report was presented at the meetings of the American Institute of Biological Sciences in the summer of 1958, at which time the author was a Research Associate in the Department of Zoology at the University of Chicago. An abstract of some of the conclusions has been published (Collias, 1958).

Emphasis here will be on birds and mammals, the groups with which I am most familiar, but they will be compared with other groups of

---

[1] Manuscript received March 1959.
[2] Recordings illustrating this chapter are on Side II, Band 4 of the Demonstration Record. We are grateful to Folkways Records and Service Corp. for permission to reproduce these recordings.

animals to bring out the generality of this ecological classification of auditory signals.   In addition to the literature, various unpublished observations of my own will be included to help round out the picture, and for the sake of giving more of a first-hand account.

FOOD PROBLEMS

Sounds indicating *hunger* are well known.   The baah-ing of hungry sheep waiting to be fed is familiar to many people, as are the strident food begging vocalizations of young birds.

A young American robin, *Turdus migratorius,* that I raised in the summer of 1950 could express different *degrees* of hunger by its vocalizations (Collias, 1952).   After being fed a worm or two it would be silent for a time, then it would begin to utter light peeps, followed after some minutes by much louder notes of one syllable, and finally by a series of still louder two-syllabled notes.   The last type of vocalization appeared in what would normally have been the last part of nestling life, and might be an adaptation to facilitate finding of the young one by the parent, after the fledgling has left the nest.   Just before being fed the bird would utter a call of apparent *anticipation*: a high, strident, insistent and rapidly repeated series of brief notes.

Hunger notes also function to inform the parent of the *location* of the fledgling, and are greatly stimulated by sight of the parent.   My young robin would cease its insistent calling when I hid myself, but promptly resumed its outcries as soon as I reappeared.   It is evident that the tendency to silence in absence of a suitable stimulus object would add to the safety of fledgling robins from predators.   Muir (1954), during night-time observations in nature of fledged tawny owls *(Strix aluco)* in England, found that unfed chicks called more than fed ones, and presumably there was thus some appropriate apportionment of the food brought by the parent.

Parent birds often utter *food calls* that stimulate the feeding reactions of the young.   The aforementioned young robin would gape at once whenever I gave a light, low whistle in imitation of the normal feeding note of the parent to small nestlings.   The presence of food was not at all necessary to stimulate the gaping response.   We have observed that the food call that stimulates gaping by the nestling is a faint zeep in the yellow warbler, *Dendroica petechia,* and a light, musical trill in the least flycatcher, *Empidonax minimus.*   A brooding domestic hen has an excited series of brief notes (Fig. 1), that causes her chicks to come running to the food she has found (Selection 4).   As she calls, the hen may, for example, peck at and cut up a piece of lettuce into smaller bits of convenient size for her chicks before eating any of the lettuce herself. The mallard hen *(Anas platyrhynchus)* gives a rapid series of relatively soft, brief notes in the presence of food; this call is imitated the world over by hunters to lure mallards to the gun (Hochbaum, 1955.) These notes entirely lack the stridency of the alarm calls and of the aggressive vocalizations of this species.

According to Frings and his collaborators (1955), when a herring gull, *Larus argentatus,* sees food it gives a special *food-finding call,* with three main notes, the middle one higher pitched than the other two and accented. These authors make the interesting remark that small quantities of food discovered by one gull are usually consumed without vocal announcement while larger quantities elicit the food call. They recorded this call on tape (mixed in to some extent with squeaks of immature gulls) and when they played it in a suitable spot along the sea coast, gulls were attracted very soon after they began to play their recording.

The rhesus monkey, *Macaca mulatta,* has a somewhat plaintive call, which we often heard whenever the monkeys at the University of Wisconsin Zoology Department were given food. Many years ago, Garner (1892) noted that rhesus monkeys would answer either his imitation or a disc recording of their food call. Chimpanzees also emit a food grunt while eating or getting food.

Animals that seek prey may use special *hunting cries* in connection with their hunting. According to Seton (1929), the grey wolf, *Canis lupus,* makes three different hunting vocalizations, that serve as a rallying call, an indication of a fresh scent, and of a closing-in on the prey, respectively. The first call is a long, smooth howl, which Seton interprets as a signal by the calling wolf to the rest of the pack that he has found game. The second sound, or "hunting song," he describes as a higher-pitched howl, vibrating on two notes, and corresponding with the full cry of a pack of hounds on a hot scent. The third is a combination of a short bark and a howl, and seems to mean "closing in" for a finish. Thus, when wolves sight a deer, they may leave the trail and make straight for it. While their quarry is being pulled down and killed they howl and growl like many dogs. Seton quotes a hunter who claims to have decoyed wolves within revolver shot by imitating the "call-howl."

The upper range of hearing of cats (50 kc), rats (40 kc), (Jahn and Wulff, 1950) and certain mice is considerably higher than that of humans (20 kc), indicating that cats are probably able to hear even supersonic cries of their prey, and presumably use these cries as clues in their hunting.

Griffin (1958) has recently reviewed in detail much evidence that bats such as *Eptesicus fuscus,* find their insect prey by echo-location. The bat provides its own signals by emitting supersonic clicks that are reflected back to its huge and sensitive ears from the surface of small objects in the air, whether they be insects or merely small pebbles tossed up by the experimenter. There is also some evidence that porpoises, *Tursiops truncatus,* may be able to locate the fish on which they feed by the aid of echolocation (Griffin, 1958; Kellogg, 1958).

Many birds and mammals have a low-pitched harsh threat sound or *growl* frequently used during *competition for food.* A subordinate individual in chickens or goats will often leave the food at the threat-sound of a despot, without turning to face its aggressor. Odum (1942) frequently heard blackcapped chickadees *(Parus atricapillus)* give a dominance note at his feeding station, and noted that a dominant bird may put to flight a subordinate bird simply by using this note. We have often seen a male yellow-headed blackbird, *Xanthocephalus xanthocephalus,* drive other birds of its species as well as other species of passerine birds from feed put out for ducks at the Delta Waterfowl Research Station in Manitoba. Its threat sound was the lowest-pitched and one of the harshest of the various notes we heard this species give.

According to Crowcroft (1957) the territorial behavior of the common shrew, *Sorex araneus,* of Europe is primarily given in defense of its hunting grounds. When two shrews meet they may engage in a screaming contest, and many disputes appear to be decided solely by vocal duels. Vincent (1958) has described quite similar screaming contests between wild, unconfined red fox, *Vulpes fulva,* in Alaska, competing for food.

Interspecific cooperation in food-finding is a topic that has scarcely been investigated insofar as vocalizations are concerned. Many species of birds hunt for food in mixed groups, e.g., titmice in the north temperate zone and flocks of certain small birds in the tropics. It is not unlikely that these birds learn to know each other's food calls. The fact that the feeding responses of animals can be conditioned to specific sounds has of course been long known, as for example, the classic experiments of Pavlov with the dog.

The most spectacular case known of interspecific cooperation in food-finding appears to be the guiding of the honey badger or of man, in Africa, to a nest of wild bees by the honey guide, *Indicator indicator.* Details have been reviewed recently by Friedman (1955). When ready to guide, this bird may come to a person and start a repetitive series of churring notes, or it may stay where it is and it begins calling and waits for the human to approach it more closely. It then flies off to another tree, quite often out of sight, and churrs loudly, until the observer again approaches. This goes on until the vicinity of the bee's nest is reached, when the bird often suddenly ceases calling, and waits for the follower to open the hive. After the person leaves the spot with his loot of honey-comb, the bird comes down and feeds on the bits of comb left strewn about.

ENEMIES

One of the first solutions to the presence of an enemy is to *announce the enemy* and so expose the danger. Auditory signals are often of central importance in this regard in the case of birds and mammals.

Hubert and Mabel Frings (1957) tape-recorded the assembly call emitted by the American crow, *Corvus brachyrhynchos,* sighting a cat or owl. They reported that when this call was played over a loud speaker at very high intensities, in 71 out of 80 tests in Maine and Pennsylvania, crows came to the source of sound within 6 minutes, and then joined in a strident chorus of sharp caws. But tests with the cries of nestlings or with what was designated as ordinary cawing generally got no reaction from wild crows.

By playing recorded alarm calls at high intensities, the Frings and their collaborators also found that they were able to *repel* herring gulls from dumps and fish-processing plants (Frings, et al., 1955) , and star-lings, *Sturnus vulgaris,* from roosts (Frings and Jumber, 1954).

The *type of enemy* is indicated by the warning cries of some birds and mammals. Many birds typically use one sort of call for an aerial predator and another for one on the ground. The hawk call of the domestic fowl is a loud, harsh scream that instantly causes baby chicks to run a short distance and then freeze into silent immobility. Playbacks of this call as recorded on tape have the same effect (Collias and Joos, 1953) . But the segmented, cackling alarm that everyone has heard is given to a dog or man. In the red jungle fowl, *Gallus gallus,* this cackling cry is accom-panied by flying up into the safety of the trees, according to Beebe (1922) .

Various small passerine birds (Odum, 1942; Hinde, 1951; Marler, 1955, 1957) , when a hawk flies over, utter a thin, very high-pitched whistle or squeak which, as Marler has pointed out, is a type of sound that is very difficult for predators to locate. The normal response is to dash to cover and then to immobilize.

When a sharp-shinned hawk, *Accipiter striatus,* or sparrow hawk, *Falco sparverius,* approaches a flock of the bushtit, *Psaltriparus minimus,* these tiny birds unite in a shrill quavering trill for as long as 2 minutes, and Joseph Grinnell (1903) who described this shrill *confusion chorus* said that the remarkable thing about it is that it is absolutely impossible to locate any single one of the birds by it.

The notes of small birds when scolding a cat or owl often consist of short, repeated notes of wide frequency range (Marler, 1955, 1957). The reaction is contagious, and birds that cannot because of their position see the owl, will also begin calling and fluttering about (Altmann, 1958). Such calls are quite easily localized, and Marler has made the interesting generalization that the degree of segmentation of animal sounds may parallel the ease of localizing of these sounds.

The California ground squirrel, *Citellus beecheyi*, according to Fitch (1948), has three different kinds of warning chirps that are more or less specific for hawks, snakes, and mammalian predators, respectively. In fact, the snake chirp was found to be the most convenient clue to locating rattlesnakes on the area of study.

The *degree* of alarm may also be specified by warning sounds to some extent. Mrs. Nice (1943) mentions that she used to consider the fright call (a high *"tik-tik-tik"*) of the song sparrow, *Melospiza melodia*, as a hawk call until further experience showed that it was sometimes also given to various other enemies under stress of a strong stimulus, such as the sudden appearance of a cat or person. The usual alarm note to a cat or person is described as a *"tschunk"* note of lower pitch. There is probably no sharp line between a "hawk call" and a call denoting an extreme degree of alarm in many birds.

The *degree* of alarm may also parallel the *closeness* of the enemy. As one approaches the nest of a catbird, *Dumetella carolinensis*, the alarm calls change abruptly from relatively short notes to prolonged and cat-like meows. As another example, while observing red-winged blackbirds, *Agelaius phoeniceus*, in Wisconsin, I noticed that as soon as I had stepped out of the blind, the nearby territorial males would begin to give their various alarm notes—first uttering brief, deep, and repeated "scolding" notes, then louder, high disyllabic notes slurred downward as I approached closer, and when I came nearer to a given male, he would begin a prolonged, high, thin note. Similarly, a female marsh hawk, *Circus cyaneus*, would give a shrill, segmented alarm call whenever we first approached her nest; when we came close to her nestlings she would often change to high, drawn out screams while she kept diving down at us. Some birds call at an *increased rate* as the danger becomes greater, as I noticed in a pair of indigo buntings whenever I approached their recently fledged young.

Birds and mammals appear to heed the warning cries of *other species*. For example, gulls and cormorants are much more alert to the approach of danger than are associated seals and sea lions, and their cries and alarm behavior induce fleeing responses in the latter (Bartholomew,

1952). Birds (Brand & Kellogg, 1939), like mammals, readily learn that various specific sounds signify danger, in laboratory experiments.

The responses to various notes of disturbance or alarm are concerned largely with various techniques of *evading* the enemy. Hens cluck to their chicks and lead them away (Selection 3); the female canvasback duck calls her young with a soft, low-pitched, very rapidly uttered series of brief notes. In both of these cases, young in their first day after hatching can readily be attracted by imitations of the parental notes (Collias and Collias, 1956). The alarm chatter of the English sparrow, *Passer domesticus,* at once *inhibits* and quiets the noisy cheeping of its nestlings which often being enclosed in a nest box could scarcely respond to any but auditory stimuli from a distance. We have also observed that the alarm call of the goldfinch, *Spinus tristis,* causes its fledglings to cease their incessant cries for food and to hold still; instant quiescence even follows the play-back of a tape-recording of the parental voice. The freezing response to the alarm notes of the parent is marked in many birds, and I have picked up and replaced on the ground recently-hatched killdeer plover, *Charadrius vociferus,* without breaking their trance-like immobility, while their parents shrieked in the air nearby.

When the parent sandhill crane, *Grus canadensis,* sounds its loud, harsh, and grating alarm call, its young at once rush off the nest and hide in the surrounding marsh vegetation. They return on hearing the purring note of the parent and this note seems to function as an *all clear* note. By imitating these two calls Walkinshaw (1949) was able to produce the same results as did the parent birds.

Birds may seek safety from an enemy by *flight,* rather than by attempting to hide. The alarmed honking of a flock of Canada geese, *Branta canadensis,* helps signal a preparation for flight, and normally accompanies the take-off. Many ungulate mammals rely on running away to escape a predator, and the loud hissing alarm snort of white-tailed deer, *Odocoileus virginianus,* will set a whole group into sudden motion. We could alarm white-tailed deer from our hiding place by imitation of this call, when ordinary talking had no apparent effect.

If evasion fails, animals may resort to *threatening* sounds in an apparent attempt to frighten away predators, e.g., the hiss of hole-nesting titmouse and screech owls, the growling of coots, *Fulica americana,* defending their nest or young (Gullion, 1952), or the growling that accompanies a surprising lunge toward the enemy of baby snowshoe hares, *Lepus americanus* (Severaid, 1942) or of baby European hares, *Lepus europaeus,* (Hediger, 1948). Young *Platypus* when disturbed in the nest keep up a continuous growling noise which is usually compared to the growling of puppies (Burrell, 1927). The collared peccary, *Pecari angulatus,* when alarmed gives a loud, prolonged snort and gnashes its big canine teeth in a fearsome way (Elder, 1956), while the adult male howling monkey, *Alouatta palliata,* roars at intruders with a truly impressive sound (Carpenter, 1934).

If threats fail, there always remains defense by *active fighting.* The honking of the Canada goose defending its nest is often a prelude to an actual attack, which may be painful even to humans. The distress cries of young birds or mammals captured by a predator may help stimulate active attack by the parents on the enemy. For example, the shrill and piercing scream of a fawn under attack by a wildcat or dogs might thus bring the doe to its defense (Linsdale & Tomich, 1953). A few alarm calls by a young gibbon, *Hylobates lar,* will bring the male of a family swinging rapidly to its location. The male will even attack and bite humans who try to catch the young (Carpenter, 1940).

An *all clear* signal, following the departure of a predator is uttered by some highly social animals, e.g., by prairie dogs, *Cynomys ludovicianus,* after the passage of an eagle (King, 1955).

REPRODUCTIVE BEHAVIOR

Reproductive behavior may be divided into a sexual and a parental phase. In chickens, and no doubt in many other birds, each of these two phases is dominated by sexual hormones and by prolactin, respectively (Collias, 1952). Vocalizations, which are specifically stimulated by male hormone, for example, the crowing of the rooster and the song of the male canary, may serve as general indicators of sexual motivation and the whole syndrome of behavior concerned. Similarly, clucking which is known in fowl to be specifically stimulated by prolactin can serve as an indicator of parental motivation and the entire repertoire of behavioral responses that are involved.

SEXUAL PHASE OF BEHAVIOR

The problems of sexual behavior are to obtain and hold a mate, and to achieve effective copulation and fertilization of the eggs.

In many birds and mammals, the male must stake and defend a suitable area, or *territory,* which the female visits. He *advertises* his claim by distinctive vocalizations or sounds, especially when another male intrudes on his territory. When I placed a stuffed male red-winged blackbird in the territory of a male of this species, the owner, in 15 minutes sang 67 times directly to it and also attacked the stuffed bird. Vocalizations by intruders are also strong stimuli to the defensive reactions of territorial males. Allen (1932) long ago described how a male mocking-bird came to a loudspeaker which was playing back a recording of the bird's own voice in its territory. The native hunters in India can call a wild red jungle fowl cock to them by hiding in its territory and imitating its crowing, even without using decoys (Kirkpatrick, 1954). Gunn (1951) trapped woodcock, *Philohela minor,* in Canada successfully by playing a recording of the male's song near nets placed in the territory of the male. Dilger (1956) has demonstrated that recognition of its own species by a territorial male in thrushes of eastern North America is mainly by the song, rather than by visual stimuli. He also observed that by increasing the volume of the loudspeaker that was being threat-ened by a territorial male, the bird could be made to flee, and, con-versely, when the volume was turned down the bird would return. More subtle uses of song have been suggested by Robinson (1949). He has observed considerable intraspecific variation in the song of magpie larks *(Grallina cyanoleuca)* in Australia, and believes that such variations may aid recognition of different neighbors as individuals.

The adult male Alaskan fur seal, *Callorhinus ursinus,* has a variety of *threat sounds* concerned with the defense of his territory, as described in detail by Bartholomew (1953). "The rattling growl, the harsh rasping pants, and the explosive growls which accompany the threats of adjacent harem bulls evoke no perceptible response except from the two bulls directly involved. The hoarse and ferocious fighting sounds which ac-company a pitched battle excite and alert the adjacent harem bulls and sometimes stimulate them to round up their harems or patrol the bound-aries of their territories. The loud trumpeting threat with which bulls whose territories abut on the unclaimed area inland greet the arrival of transient males, however, evokes a much more general response. One of these trumpeting threats may cause an intruding male to withdraw even though he be 40 or 50 feet away. At the same time it alerts all the other males on the periphery of the rookery who then threaten the newcomer and make short charges in his direction. The harem bulls with territories inside the rookery, however, pay no attention to this vocalization." (We are indebted to the editor of the Transactions of the North American Wildlife Conference for permission to quote this passage.)

Similarly, Bartholomew (1952) observed that the vocal challenge of a dominant, adult male elephant seal *(Mirounga angustirostris)* often sufficed to cause precipitous withdrawal of subordinate males from the vicinity of the females.

The song of male birds apparently functions to *attract the female.* Once a male song sparrow, for instance, has secured a mate there may be a 90 per cent reduction in the frequency of his singing (Nice, 1943). Similarly Stoddard (1931) has shown that the familiar "Bob-White!" call of *Colinus virginianus* is given mainly by unmated cocks.

We have observed that some male birds that display and hold individual territories in a close community *announce the arrival of the females* with a special call, e.g., in the red-winged blackbird, the prairie chicken, *Tympanuchus cupido,* and the village weaverbird, *Textor cucullatus,* in Africa (Collias & Collias, 1959).

In birds in which the sexes have similar plumage, voice differences may aid *sex recognition.* A stuffed corn-crake or land-rail, *Crex crex,* elicited attack from a territorial male if the latter's "crake" call or challenge was answered by the hidden observer, but when the stuffed bird was "silent," male attempted coition instead (Mason, 1945).

In some species the female voice is distinctive. An imitation of the call of the female moose, *Alces americana,* is said to be used with some success by hunters in Canada to decoy the bulls (Seton, 1929).

The pairing bond in birds appears to be *reinforced* by mutual vocalizations and *greeting ceremonies,* or *contact-notes,* between the sexes. Canada geese seem to recognize the voice of individual mates and answer even when they cannot see each other. When male and female come together after a period of separation they invariably call in a rapid duet, and the male also adds a snoring vocalization that he gives only to his own mate (Collias & Jahn, 1959). In the ring dove, *Streptopelia risoria,* members of a pair call to each other with a distinctive sound known as the "perch-coo." Whenever we separated the birds of a pair by placing an opaque partition between them in the middle of their cage, we observed a marked rise in the frequency of perch-coos as the birds called back and forth. Similarly, both sexes of a pair of *Galago senegalensis,* a primitive primate, when separated utter a distinctive vocalization (Lowther, 1940). On the other hand, the female *Galago* uses a chattering note of *repulsion,* when apparently annoyed by the attentions of the male.

Pre-coitional notes precede and sometimes accompany copulation in many birds and mammals, and presumably serve to facilitate copulation. However, experimental proof seems to be scarce. The female house wren, *Troglodytes aedon,* gives a series of squeaking notes that apparently function as an invitation to copulate, and Kendeigh (1941) notes one occasion where imitation of these notes by the human observer induced the male house wren to try and copulate with an unmated female wren which had been scolding nearby.

In the female mink, *Mustela vison,* with approach of the breeding season both sexes begin to utter a chuckling sound. Ovulation in this species is induced normally by coition, and the male normally "chuckles" during the prolonged copulation (Enders, 1952). However, the precise function of this vocalization is apparently not yet understood.

Some birds have calls related specifically to the nest. In ring-doves, *Streptopelia risoria,* one bird has a special call that attracts its mate to a *prospective nest-site* (Craig, 1908). We have noted a call with similar function in the mourning dove, *Zenaidura macroura.* The male village weaverbird, *Textor cucullatus,* of Africa, has a special call that we heard only when the birds were in a good spot for gathering *nest-material* (Collias and Collias, 1959).

PARENT-YOUNG RELATIONS

This topic has already been covered in part in the description of vocalizations which have to do with food and enemies. In birds, the ecological problems concerned are those having to do with care of eggs as well as of the young. During incubation the male goldfinch, *Spinus tristis,* feeds the female, who does all the incubating. He *announces his arrival* by calling often before he is in sight, at least of the human observer, and the female at once answers with an excited call, very like some of the food begging notes of older young. We have also observed that in the mourning dove, *Zenaidura macroura,* where both sexes incubate, the incoming bird invariably announces its arrival in the vicinity by cooing, shortly before relieving its partner of incubation duties.

Leaving of the nest by the young in birds may sometimes be stimulated by calling of the parent, as in the wood duck, *Aix sponsa,* which nests in a hole in a tree high above the ground (Forbush, 1929). The female opossum, *Didelphis virginiana,* stimulates her young to leave the den with her by uttering a clicking sound; if she does not click when she leaves, the young remain in the den (Reynolds, 1952).

Contact notes between parents and young are of the highest importance in the life of birds and mammals. In general, the young of birds and mammals often seem to have two characteristic types of sounds, *distress calls* and softer, less conspicuous notes, which could be termed *pleasure or contentment notes.* Examples of distress calls of young mammals when separated from their mother are the bleat of lambs, kids and fawns, the mew of kittens, the whistle of young porpoises, *Tursiops truncatus* (Wood, 1953), and the wail of an infant howling monkey, *Alouatta palliata,* (Carpenter, 1934). The purr of apparently contented infants of mongoose, *Herpestes auropunctatus* (cf. Baldwin, 1952) and howling monkey (Carpenter, 1934) are less familiar examples of contentment notes than is the purring of kittens.

The *spectrogram* (Fig. 1 and Selections 1 and 2) illustrates the typical structure of distress calls and pleasure notes for chicks of the domestic fowl. The vertical axis on the spectrograms shows frequency in cycles per second; the horizontal axis shows time in seconds, or fractions thereof. The distress calls of baby chicks are given repeatedly under many conditions of distress that at the same time inhibit pleasure notes: isolation from companion, cold, hunger, thirst, pain, restraint, or approach of a large object. Conversely, relief from any of these presumably distressing conditions, inhibits distress calls and stimulates pleasure notes (Collias, 1952). Much the same sort of sounds and responses are to be seen with baby ducklings of various species (Collias and Collias, 1956).

The responses of a broody hen to the distress cries of a chick are clucking, ruffling of her feathers and going to the chick. Clucking, whether by a hen, a person, or a tape-recorder, quiets and *attracts* the chick. Again, quite similar responses are to be seen with ducks. For example, canvasback, *Aythya valisineria.* and redhead, *Aythya americana,* ducklings on the day of hatching readily go toward an imitation of parental attraction notes, but they move away from alarm notes (Collias and Collias, 1956). We also found that the faster the parental notes were repeated, the more they attracted the ducklings. In these experiments the sound source was hidden, but we also found that redhead ducklings followed a person walking away from them much better if he uttered the parental attraction notes. Fabricius (1951) had made somewhat similar observations in Finland with tufted ducks, *Aythya fuligula,* and eider ducks, *Somateria mollissima,* and Ramsay & Hess (1954) with mechanical models and domestic mallard ducklings.

Experiments with artificial sounds have demonstrated that the attractive elements for the young one in the voice of a broody hen (Collias & Joos, 1953) or duck (Collias & Collias, 1956) are the *shortness* and the *low-pitch* of the soft, repetitive notes in which she calls (Selection 3).

Fabricius (1951) observed that the contentment notes functioned to hold a brood of ducklings together in the tufted and eider duck, and we confirmed this for redhead and canvasback ducklings (Collias & Collias, 1956). We also found that these ducklings moved more readily toward contentment notes than toward distress calls of other ducklings of these species.

GROUP MOVEMENTS

In group movements the problems are to assemble, prepare to move, start, maintain contact while moving, and to stop together.

The bob-white quail, *Colinus virginianus*, has a "scatter" call, usually used to bring the scattered birds of coveys or pairs together. According to Stoddard (1931), this call develops by imperceptible degrees from the shrill, piping "lost call" of the baby chicks.

Odum (1942) observed that the *"chick-a-dee-dee-dee"* call of the black-capped chickadee, *Parus atricapillus,* is most often given when one bird becomes separated or the flock scattered, with the result that the flock tends to *consolidate* again. A thin, weak single note is the common contact note, and becomes higher-pitched and louder *just before extended flights* across open spaces. Robert Hinde (1952) has made a detailed study of the flock-movements of the great tit, *Parus major,* of Europe, and found that the birds gave characteristic *starting* and *stopping* notes. I have often observed, as no doubt have many others, that the American goldfinch, *Spinus tristis,* gives its characteristic *"per-chick-a-ree"* flight note as it launches itself into the air and also as it flies along, but utters a very different call when it lands again.

The loud honking of Canada geese, *Branta canadensis,* is a familiar sound that serves to keep the flock together in the air; it is customarily given also shortly before and during the take-off, which it signalizes. But when on the ground, the assembling note of the Canada goose is a low-pitched and quiet grunting, serving adequately for the shorter distances and slower rate of travel on the ground (Collias and Jahn, 1959).

The migrations of small land birds which often travel in flocks and at night would seem to place heavy reliance on *contact notes* between the migrating individuals. Thus, a certain note of low intensity is invariably heard from migrant meadowlarks *(Sturnella)* flying overhead, but is only rarely given, by the males at least, after their arrival on the breeding grounds. The females also use this note during the early phases of courtship as well as when approaching the nest with food (Lanyon, 1957).

Among mammals, the nature of vocalizations concerned with group movements may be exemplified in howling monkeys (Carpenter, 1934; Collias and Southwick, 1951). At the start and during the progression of the clan, a deep, hoarse clucking is given by the leading animal, usually a male, and apparently serves to direct the monkeys as they file through the dense forest.

Porpoises and bats emit supersonic clicks (Griffin, 1958), and it is possible that such cries are used to prevent collision of the individuals of a group in the ocean and in dark caves, respectively.

GENERAL PHYSICAL CHARACTERISTICS OF ACOUSTIC SIGNALS OF ANIMALS

Close study of any one species of bird or mammal soon makes it evident that much the same call may often have different uses in different situations. The variety of situations that evoke the distress cries and pleasure notes of baby chicks and ducklings has been mentioned. In any case, the distress call attracts the mother, who may then help its young to remove the particular distress, whatever this might be. The honking of Canada geese may serve in defense of territory, in defense of the mate, in food competition, as a call for and greeting to the mate, as an alarm call, and as a contact call just before and during flight (Collias and Jahn, 1959).

When we examine the physical properties of different functional classes of auditory signals in birds and mammals we find certain quite definite characteristics. The copy of the spectrograms of the basic sound-signals of the domestic fowl gives a visual example of these characteristics (Fig. 1). These are not peculiar to the domesticated bird; Beebe (1922) mentions that the calls in nature of the red jungle fowl *(Gallus gallus)*,

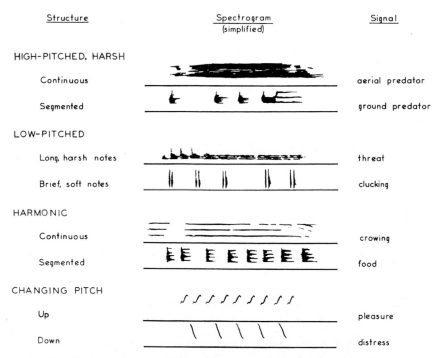

Fig. 1. Simplified spectrograms of the classes of auditory signals of the domestic fowl. Examples of these sounds are given on the Demonstration Record.

are essentially similar to those of the domestic fowl, of which it seems to be the ancestor. The alarm cries are often harsh and high-pitched. Harshness on a spectrogram is indicated by a wide spread of frequencies, combined with harmonic streaks. The hawk warning call has considerable continuity, but the ground predator call, given to a dog or man, is segmented. Threat sounds and clucking are both low-pitched. But the former, which is apparently designed to repel, is harsh and the individual notes relatively long, in contrast to clucking, which attracts baby chicks, and is segmented with very brief notes. Crowing by the rooster and the food call of a hen have considerable harmonic structure, especially the former. Both of these somewhat melodious calls may function to attract, particularly the food call. Notes of changing pitch are particularly characteristic of baby chicks, i.e., the pleasure note, with its upward lilt and the distress cry with its marked drop in pitch. (Refer to Selections 1-10 on Demonstration Record.)

Alarm cries of various birds and mammals are often harsh, loud, and high-pitched. Alarm cries may be of a segmented type, or may be prolonged and continuous, or where a species has both types, the continuous one generally indicates the greater intensity of alarm, for example, we have observed that the harsh scream of the black tern replaces the lower-pitched disyllabic call of relatively mild alarm as one comes closer to their nests or young. The fear-inducing effects of a loud, harsh, high-pitched and prolonged sound are extreme in some animals; at the ringing of an alarm clock some abnormally sensitive strains of mice race madly about, go into convulsions and die (Hall, 1947).

Threat sounds, like alarm cries, are harsh and are often made up of single, relatively long notes when compared with attraction notes. They differ in often being lower pitched than are alarm cries, at least where no element of alarm or excessive excitement appears to be involved, as when a dominant animal is threatening a subordinate. The growl of a dog scarcely needs mention; less familiar examples are the growl-like threat sound of a house sparrow, *Passer domesticus*, purple martin, *Progne subis*, ground squirrel or hare—examples could readily be multiplied by anyone who chooses to look into the volumes of Seton for mammals and of A. C. Bent for birds. Body size of course modifies the pitch and volume of the sound—I have observed that the threat sound of the tiny yellow warbler, *Dendroica petechia*, is a low buzz, of a demoiselle crane, *Anthropoides virgo*, a harsh, strong rattle.

Attraction notes to small young by the parent are often relatively soft, low-pitched, brief, and repetitive notes, as we have observed, for example, in the clucking of hen ring-necked pheasants, *Phasianus col-*

chicus, and blue peafowl, *Pavo cristatus,* and in the grunting of female Canada geese, *Branta canadensis;* in the *kuk-kuk* sounds of certain ducks (Collias & Collias, 1956), coots, *Fulica americana,* and the pied-billed grebe, *Podilymbus podiceps;* in the faint zeeps of a yellow warbler, *Dendroica petechia,* calling its fledglings; and in the grunting of domestic goats and the gurgling of domestic ewes with newborn young (Collias, 1956). Similar characteristics of the maternal voice have been reported for other species: the clucking of wild turkeys, *Meleagris gallopavo* (Mosby & Handley, 1943), and woodcock, *Philohela minor* (Pettingill, 1936), and the clicking of female opossum, *Didelphis virginiana* (Reynolds, 1952). The call of the mother *Galago senegalensis* to her babies is described by Lowther (1940) as a soft, caressing sound. Just after her young are born, the voice of a mother goat undergoes a definite drop in pitch (Collias, 1956); similarly, the clucking of the parent stone-curlew *(Burhinus oedicnemus),* according to Simms (1955) shows a very noticeable mellowing and drop in pitch as the young hatch. An exception to the use of segmented calls to attract the young is the mewing food call of the herring gull, as described by Tinbergen and Perdeck (1950).

In some species, the male, in courting or attracting the female, uses a call very similar to that used by the female to attract her young, for example, in opossums (Reynolds, 1952),goats (Collias, 1956), and Canada geese (Collias and Jahn, 1959).

It will be apparent that the characteristic physical properties of the main functional classes of auditory signals in birds and non-human mammals suggest a common emotional language with man, and indeed certain sounds of other species may stimulate an emotional response in man. Long ago, Charles Darwin (1890) made a detailed comparison of emotional expression, including vocalizations, in man and nonhuman animals. The different types of calls do sometimes intergrade, but rather infrequently, and distinct and specific types of calls very definitely exist.

One fact that underscores the significance of the many parallel resemblances of the auditory signals used by birds and mammals, is that the sounds of birds are made by a syrinx, those of mammals by vocal cords; in other words the resemblances are due to convergent evolution.

Areas of study that largely remain to be explored include especially possible functions of sounds beyond the range of human hearing, since such sounds are common in many mammals (Griffin, 1958). For example, the laboratory rat can produce and probably can hear a whole series of sounds above 20 kcps which are not correlated with sounds audible to us (Anderson, 1954).

COMPARISON OF THE AUDITORY SIGNALS OF BIRDS AND MAMMALS WITH THOSE OF OTHER ANIMALS

It remains to compare vocal communication in birds and in mammals with communication by means of sounds in other groups of animals. Some recent reviews of the sounds of insects (Alexander, 1957; Frings and Frings, 1958; Haskell, 1957), fishes (Fish, 1954, 1956), and anuran amphibians (Bogert, 1958) suggest that the auditory signals of these forms have ecological uses very similar to those that have been described above for birds and mammals, and can be classified in similar categories. The literature dealing with other groups of poikilothermal animals is still sparse and widely scattered.

The sounds produced by insects and fishes are mainly of the type caused by stridulation or drumming. In addition, insects may produce sound-signals by vibrating their wings, as well as by other means. Sounds made by insects as said by Pringle (1956) are "characterized by differences in the time distribution of pulses of sound rather than by differences in pitch or tone quality as with birds and mammals." The sounds of the lower vertebrates—fishes (Fish, et al., 1952) and anuran amphibians (Potter, 1950)—in general, are more restricted in range of frequencies, particularly the higher frequencies, than is the case with birds and mammals.

Salamanders are often thought to be silent, but Maslin (1950) has reviewed evidence that quite a few species are vocal. For example, the Pacific giant salamander, *Dicamptodon ensatus,* has vocal cords and utters a barking cry when disturbed.

Hissing occurs among amphibia (Maslin, 1950), and also occurs in virtually all of the orders of reptiles, birds, and mammals. Perhaps some of the various types of vocalizations made by land vertebrates evolved from the hiss, which appears to be one of the most primitive sounds made by them.

Phonoreception has been demonstrated to be of widespread occurrence in various arthropods and vertebrates (Jahn and Wulff, 1950). One of the main differences between the sound reception of birds and mammals in contrast to other groups of animals is in the ability of birds and mammals to discriminate a wide range of different frequencies or pitch of sound (Jahn and Wulff, ibid.; Pumphrey, 1940), and this difference is correlated with the generally much richer vocabulary of birds and mammals, compared with other animals. This sensory advantage has been ascribed by Adrian, et al. (1938) to the neural facilitation and stability conferred by a high, constant body temperature.

Sounds associated with feeding have been described for certain fishes,

(Fish, 1954, 1956). Among insects, the purring of the red milkweed beetle, *Tetraopes tetraopthalmus,* is often associated with feeding (Alexander, 1957). The pistol shrimp *(Crangon californiensis)* captures small fishes and other shrimps that pass in front of its burrow by stunning them with a loud snapping sound made by the large claw (MacGinitie and MacGinitie, 1949). According to Kahn and Offenhauser (1949), the playing of mosquito sounds at high intensity attracts not only mosquitoes but also frogs, chameleons, bats, dragonflies, and other forms of life that prey upon the mosquitoes.

Alarm calls are of very general occurrence, and most sound-producing species may utter some form of outcry when seized by a predator or disturbed, for example: spiny lobsters (Moulton, 1957), scorpions (Alexander, 1958), thomisoid spiders (Gertsch, 1949), cicadas (Alexander, 1957), sea robins (Fish, 1956), tiger salamanders (Maslin, 1950), frogs (Bogert, 1958), geckos (Fitzsimmons, 1943), the New Zealand tuatara (Oliver, 1953), etc.

These sounds have been but little investigated experimentally, and for the invertebrates in particular may sometimes function as interspecific warnings, serving to startle or frighten away a predator, rather than to warn a fellow-member of the same species. For example, Alexander (1958) reported that the stridulatory hiss of the scorpion, *Opisthopthalmus latimanus,* served to repulse mammalian predators. Similarly, among vertebrate animals, there is evidence that rattlesnakes are deaf and cannot hear their own rattle (Manning, 1923).

In the case of frogs, the splash given when one frog jumps into the water serves to alert other frogs in the vicinity (cf. Holmes, 1923). The smack of a beaver's tail on the water is a specialized example of the same sort of thing in mammals.

Sounds that signalize breeding condition or reproductive activities are widespread and appear to occur in all the main groups of sound-producing animals. A male toadfish guarding his nest may growl at intruders, and sea robins, *Prionotus,* give their staccato call in the breeding season, and will reply to recordings of this call played into the water (Moulton, 1956). The roar of a bull alligator at his den and the chirping of a male cricket near his burrow, are both associated with territorial defense, and stimulate other males to call, (McIlhenny, 1935; Alexander, 1957; Haskell, 1957). Male alligators will roar in response to artificial tones that approximate the normal frequency range of this sound, but not to other sounds and also show increased aggressiveness when so challenged (Beach, 1949; Evans and Quaranta, 1949).

When two starlings, *Sturnus vulgaris,* start to fight, their low, harsh preliminary growls may change to a shrill, excited rattle as the birds rise in the air beak to beak (personal observation). Similarly, when an intruding ghost crab *(Ocypode macrocerca)* forced into the burrow of another individual is prevented from escaping, the low and broken tones of the rightful owner gradually rise in loudness and shrillness and frequency, the burrow acting as a resonator (Schmitt, 1934). In the spiny lobster, *Palinurus interruptus,* of the Pacific, Lindberg (1955) observed that stridulation by one lobster might precede conflicts or cause other lobsters to become alert and back away, even when they could not see the stridulating individual. However, Moulton (1957), working with a related form in the Atlantic, was unable to influence the behavior of spiny lobsters by playing recordings of their stridulations to the animals.

Special sounds by males may *attract* the female in lower vertebrates and insects just as such sounds presumably do in birds. Bogert (1958), in an experimental study of the responses of southern toads, *Bufo t. terrestris,* to recordings of the male voice noted that females were attracted, but males tended to be repelled. In the chorus frog, *Pseudacris nigrita,* Martof and Thompson (1958) observed that play-backs of the breeding call of males stimulated similar calling by males in breeding condition and attracted gravid females. There have been a number of experimental demonstrations that in various crickets and grasshoppers, the unmated female is attracted to records of the song of the male (cf. Alexander, 1957; Frings and Frings, 1958). Play-backs of sounds made by female mosquitoes, *Aedes aegypti,* attract males of the same species (Roth, 1948; Kahn, 1947; Kahn and Offenhauser, 1949).

Sex recognition is aided in these lower forms, as in birds and mammals, by acoustic signals. The copulatory song of the male cricket is said to induce the female not to move while the male engages the genitalia (Haskell, 1958). Tavolga (1956, 1958) has described how play-backs of the courtship grunts of the male gobiid fish, *Bathygobius soporator,* induce approach behavior in gravid females. If a male leopard frog, *Rana pipiens,* is clasped by another, he utters a croaking sound that causes the other male to release him, whereas a gravid female so clasped, is silent (Noble and Aronson, 1942).

Parent-young communication by sounds appears to be of rare occurrence outside the birds and mammals. However, the female alligator responds to the shrill grunts of her newly hatched young by removing the upper layers of earth and debris from the nest, so aiding them to make their escape from their nursery. She then assembles them and calls them to her at the edge of the water by a series of low, pig-like grunts (McIlhenny, 1935).

Little has been written about the use of sounds in group movements of insects and lower vertebrates, although it has been suggested that eels and catfishes which live in muddy, murky waters and croakers which are active after sunset must find sound useful for aggregating (Fish, 1956).

Roeder and Treat (1957) have reported that the sensory nerve from the auditory organ of a noctuid moth responds not only to the pulses emitted by certain artificial ultrasonic sounds, but also to the clicking of the wingbeats of another moth of the same species.

SUMMARY

Present knowledge of animal language indicates considerable variety and specificity in the information that can be transmitted, although experimental verification of the functions of sounds made by many animals is still needed. However, the various acoustic signals fall readily into ecological and functional categories related to 1) food, 2) predators, 3) sexual behavior and related fighting, 4) parent-young interrelations, and 5) aggregation and group movements.

The same sound may have more than one specific use depending on ecological context, and sounds with similar function even when produced by different mechanisms, in different animals are frequently characterized by certain common properties in physical structure of these sounds.

All indications are that the study of animal language is a most promising field for investigation, particularly with the modern techniques now available. It is hoped that this article will provide an outline for continued research.

LITERATURE CITED

Adrian, E. D., K. J. W. Craik, and R. S. Sturdy. 1938. The electrical response of the ear: vertebrates. Proc. Royal Soc. London, Ser. B. *125:* 435–455.

Alexander, A. J. 1958. On the stridulation of scorpions. Behaviour. *12:* 339–352.

Alexander, R. D. 1957. Sound production and associated behaviour in insects. Ohio Jour. of Sci. *57:* 101–113.

Allen, A. A. 1932. Hunting with a microphone the voices of vanishing birds. Natl. Geo. Soc. Washington, D. C. The Book of Birds. Vol. I: 189–218.

Altmann, S. A. 1958. Avian mobbing behavior and predator recognition. Condor. *58:* 241–253.

Anderson, J. W. 1954. The production of ultrasonic sounds by laboratory rats and other mammals. Science. *119:* 808–809.

Baldwin, P. H. 1952. Life history and economic status of mongoose in Hawaii. Mammalogy. *33:* 335–356.

Bartholomew, G. A., Jr. 1952. Reproductive and social behavior of the northern elephant seal. Univ. Calif. Pub. Zool. *47:* 369–472.

————. 1953. Behavioral factors affecting social structure in Alaska fur seal. Trans. 18th N. Amer. Wildlife Confer., Wash., D.C., 1953. 481–502.

Beach, F. A. 1944. Responses of captive alligators to auditory stimulation. Amer. Naturalist. *78:* 481–515.

Beebe, W. 1922. A monograph of the pheasants. 4 vols. London. Witherby and Co.

Bogert, C. M. 1958. Sounds of North American frogs. Folkways records Album No. FX6166. New York. Folkways Records and Service Corporation.

Brand, A. R. and P. P. Kellogg. 1939. Auditory responses of starlings, English Sparrows and domestic pigeons. Wilson Bull. *51:* 38–41.

Burrell, H. 1927. The platypus. Australia. Angus and Robertson, Limited. 227 pp.

Carpenter, C. R. 1934. A field study of the behavior and social relations of howling monkeys *(Alouatta palliata).* Compar. Psychol. Monogr. *10:* 1–168.

––––. 1940. A field study in Siam of the behavior and social relations of the gibbon *(Hylobates lar).* Compar. Psychol. Monogr. *16:* 1–212.

Collias, N. E. 1952. The development of social behavior in birds. Auk. *69:* 127–159.

––––. 1956. The analysis of socialization in sheep and goats. Ecology. *37:* 228–239.

––––. 1958. Functions of animal sounds; an ecological classification of animal communication. Bull. Ecol. Soc. Amer. *39:* 107–108.

––––, and E. C. Collias. 1956. Some mechanisms of family integration in ducks. Auk. *73:* 378–400.

––––, and ––––. 1959. Breeding behaviour of the black-headed weaverbird, *Textor cucullatus graueri* (Hartert) in the Belgian Congo. Proc. First Pan-African Ornithol. Congr., Ostrich, Suppl. No. 3, pp. 233–241.

––––, and L. R. Jahn. 1959. Social behavior and breeding success in Canada geese *(Branta canadensis)* confined under semi-natural conditions. Auk. *76:* 478–509.

––––, and M. Joos. 1953. The spectrographic analysis of sound signals of the domestic fowl. Behavior. *5:* 176–188.

––––, and C. Southwick. 1952. A field study of population density and social organization in howling monkeys. Proc. Amer. Phil. Soc. *96:* 143–156.

Craig, W. 1908. Voices of pigeons regarded as a means of social control. Amer. Jour. Sociol. *14:* 86–100.

Crowcroft, P. 1957. The life of the shrew. London. Max Rheinhardt. 166 pp.

Darwin, C. 1890. The expression of the emotions in man and animals. 2nd edition. London. James Murray.

Dilger, W. C. 1956. Hostile behavior and reproductive isolating mechanisms in the genera *Catharus* and *Hylocichla.* Auk. *73:* 313–353.

Elder, J. B. 1956. Watering patterns of some desert game animals. Jour. Wildlife Mgmt. *20:* 368–378.

Enders, R. K. 1952. Reproduction in the mink. Proc. Amer. Phil. Soc. *96:* 691–755.

Evans, L. T. and J. J. Quaranta. 1949. Vocality as a factor in the ecology of the alligator. Anat. Rec. *105:* 581–582.

Fabricius, E. 1951. Zur Ethologie Junger Anatiden. Acta Zool. Fennica. *68:* 1–178.

Fish, M. P. 1954. The character and significance of sound production among fishes of the western North Atlantic. Bull. Bingham Oceanogr. Coll. *14:* 1–109.

––––. 1956. Animal sounds in the sea. Sci. Amer. *194:* 93–102.

––––, A. S. Kelsey, Jr. and W. H. Mowbray. 1952. Studies on the production of underwater sound by North Atlantic coastal fishes. Jour. Mar. Res. *11:* 180–193.

Fitch, H. S. 1948. Ecology of the California ground squirrel on grazing lands. Amer. Midland Naturalist. *39:* 513–596.

Fitzsimons, V. F. 1943. The lizards of South Africa. Pretoria. Pub. by Transvaal Mus. 528 pp.

Forbush, E. H. 1929. Birds of Massachusetts and other New England states. Vol. I. Mass. Dept. Agri. 481 pp.

Friedmann, H. 1955. The honey-guides. U.S. Nat. Mus. Smithsn. Inst. Bull. 208. Washington, D.C. 292 pp.

Frings, H. and M. Frings. 1957. Recorded calls of the eastern crow as attractants and repellents. Jour. Wildlife Mgmt. 21: 91.

————, and ————. 1958. Uses of sounds by insects. Ann. Rev. Ent. 3: 87–106.

————, ————, B. Cox and L. Peissner. 1955. Auditory and visual mechanisms in food-finding behavior of the herring gull. Wilson Bull. 67: 155–170.

————, and J. Jumber. 1954. Preliminary studies in the use of a specific sound to repel starlings (Sturnus vulgaris) from objectionable roosts. Science. 119: 318–319.

Garner, R. L. 1892. The speech of monkeys. New York. C. L. Webster and Co. 217 pp.

Gertsch, W. J. 1949. American spiders. New York. D. Van Nostrand Co., Inc. 285 pp.

Griffin, D. R. 1958. Listening in the dark. The acoustic orientation of bats and men. New Haven. Yale Univ. Press. 413 pp.

Grinnell, J. 1903. Call notes of the bush-tit. Condor. 5: 85–87.

Gullion, G. W. 1952. The displays and calls of the American coot. Wilson Bull. 64: 83–98.

Gunn, W. W. H. 1951. The woodcock program. Ontario Dept. of Lands and Forests, Div. of Res., Wildlife Sec. 30 pp. (mimeographed).

Hall, C. S. 1947. Genetic differences in fatal audiogenic seizures between two inbred strains of house mice. Jour. Hered. 38: 3–6.

Haskell, P. T. 1957. Sound in the insect world. New Bio. No. 23: 29–47.

Hediger, H. 1948. Die Zucht des Feldhasen (Lepus europaeus Pallas) in Gefangenschaft. Physiol Comp. et Oecol. 1: 46–62.

Hinde, R. A. 1952. The behavior of the great tit (Parus major) and some other related species. Behavior (Sup. 2): 1–201.

Hochbaum, H. A. 1955. Travels and traditions of waterfowl. Minneapolis. Univ. of Minn. Press. 301 pp.

Holmes, S. J. 1923. The biology of the frog. 3rd ed. London. Macmillan and Co. 370 pp.

Jahn, T. L. and V. J. Wulff. 1950. Phonoreception. Chap. 13 In Prosser, C. L. (ed.) Comparative animal physiology. Philadelphia. W. B. Saunders Co. 471–501.

Kahn, M. C. 1947. Female mosquito "calls" and their possible significance in control. Revista Kuba Med. Trop. Parisit. Havana. 3: 119–120.

————, and W. Offenhauser. 1949. The first field tests of recorded mosquito sounds used for mosquito destruction. Amer. Jour. Trop. Med. 29: 811–825.

Kellogg, W. N. 1958. Echo ranging in the porpoise. Science. 128: 982–988.

Kendeigh, S. C. 1941. Territorial and mating behavior of the house wren. Ill. Biol. Monog. 18: 1–120.

King, J. A. 1955. Social behavior, social organization, and population dynamics in a black-tailed prairie dog town in the Black Hills of South Dakota. Contrib. Lab. Vert. Biol. Univ. of Mich. No. 67.

Kirkpatrick, K. M. 1954. Aboriginal methods employed in killing and capturing game. Jour. Bombay Nat. Hist. Soc. 52: 285–300.

Lanyon, W. E. 1957. The comparative biology of the meadowlarks (Sturnella) in Wisconsin. Pub. Nuttall Ornith. Club. No. 1. Cambridge, Mass. 67 pp.

Lindberg, R. G. 1955. Growth, population dynamics, and field behavior in the spiny lobster, *Palinurus interruptus* (Randall). Univ. Calif. Pub. Zool. *59:* 157–247.

Linsdale, J. M. and P. Q. Tomich. 1953. A herd of mule deer. Berkeley and Los Angeles. Univ. Calif. Press. 567 pp.

Lowther, F. de L. 1940. A study of a pair of *Galago senegalensis moholi* in captivity, including the birth and postnatal development of twins. Zool. *25:* 433–462.

MacGinitie, G. E. and N. MacGinitie. 1949. Natural history of marine animals. N.Y. McGraw-Hill. 473 pp.

Manning, F. B. 1923. Hearing in rattlesnakes. Jour. Comp. Psychol. *3:* 241–247.

Marler, P. 1955. The characteristics of some animal calls. Nature. *176:* 6–8.

————. 1957. Specific distinctiveness in the communication signals of birds. Behaviour. *11:* 13–39.

Martof, B. S. and E. F. Thompson. 1958. Reproductive behavior of the chorus frog, *Pseudacris nigrita*. Behaviour *13:* 243–258.

Maslin, T. P. 1950. The production of sound in caudate amphibia. Univ. Colo. Stud. Ser. Biol. *1:* 29–48.

Mason, A. G. 1950. The behaviour of corn-crakes. Brit. Birds. *43:* 70–78.

McIlhenny, E. A. 1935. The alligator's life history. Boston. Christopher Pub. House. 117 pp.

Mosby, H. S. and C. O. Handley. 1943. The wild turkey in Virginia. Comm. of Game and Inland Fisheries. Richmond, Va. 281 pp.

Moulton, J. M. 1956. Influencing the calling of sea robins (*Prionotus* spp.) with sound. Biol. Bull. *111:* 393–398.

————. 1957. Sound production in the spiny lobster, *Palinurus argus* (Latreille). Biol. Bull. *113:* 286–295.

Muir, R. C. 1954. Calling and feeding rates of fledged tawny owls. Bird Study. *1:* 111–117.

Nice, M. M. 1943. Studies in the life history of the song sparrow II. Trans. N.Y. Linn. Soc. *6:* 1–328.

Noble, G. K. and L. R. Aronson. 1942. The sexual behavior of Anura I. The normal mating pattern of *Rana pipiens*. Bull. Amer. Mus. Nat. Hist. *80:* 127–142.

Odum, E. P. 1942. Annual cycle of the black-capped chickadee. Auk. *59:* 499–535.

Oliver, J. A. 1953. The timeless tuatara. Animal Kingdom. *56:* 2–8, 31.

Pettingill, O. S. 1936. The American woodcock. Mem. Boston Soc. Nat. Hist. No. 2. 391 pp.

Potter, R. K. 1950. Frog calls. Sci. Amer. *182* (May): 45–47.

Pringle, J. W. G. 1956. Insect song. Endeavour. *15:* 68–72.

Pumphrey, R. J. 1940. Hearing in insects. Biol. Rev. *15:* 107–132.

Ramsay, A. O. and Eckhard Hess. 1954. A laboratory approach to the study of imprinting. Wilson Bull. *66:* 196–206.

Reynolds, H. C. 1952. Studies on reproduction in the opossum (*Didelphis virginiana virginiana*). Univ. Calif. Pub. Zool. *52:* 223–275.

Robinson, A. 1949. The biological function of bird song in Australia. Emu. *49:* 291–315.

Roeder, K. and A. Treat. 1957. Ultrasonic reception by the tympanic organ of noctuid moths. Jour. Expt. Zool. *134:* 127–157.

Roth, L. M. 1948. An experimental laboratory study of the sexual behavior of *Aedes aegypti* (L.). Amer. Midland Naturalist. *40:* 265–352.

Schmitt, W. L. 1934. Crustaceans. Pt. II. *In* Abbott, C. G. (ed.), Shelled inverte-brates of the past and present. Vol. 10. Smithsn. Sci. Ser. Pub. Smithsn. Inst. Ser., Inc. N.Y.

Seton, E. T. 1929. Lives of the game animals. Garden City, N.Y. Doubleday, Doran and Co. 4 vols.

Severaid, J. H. 1942. The snowshoe hare. Its life history and artificial propagation. Maine Dept. Inland Fish and Game. 95 pp.

Simms, E. 1955. The conversational calls of birds as revealed by new methods of field recording. Proc. XI Internatl. Ornith. Cong. (1954): 623–626.

Stoddard, H. L. 1931. The bobwhite quail: its habits, preservation and increase. New York. Charles Scribner's Sons. 559 pp.

Tavolga, W. N. 1956. Visual, chemical and sound stimuli in the sex discriminatory behavior of the gobiid fish, *Bathygobius soporator*. Zoologica. *41:* 49–64.

————. 1958. The significance of underwater sounds produced by males of the gobiid fish, *Bathygobius soporator*. Physiol. Zool. *31:* 259–271.

Tinbergen, N. and A. C. Perdeck. 1950. On the stimulus situation releasing the begging response in the newly hatched herring gull chick (*Larus a. argentatus* Pontopp). Behaviour. *3:* 1–38.

Vincent, R. E. 1958. Observations of red fox behavior. Ecology. *39:* 755–757.

Walkinshaw, L. H. 1949. The sandhill cranes. Cranbrook Inst. Sci. Bull. *29:* 1–202.

Wood, F. G., Jr. 1953. Underwater sound production and concurrent behavior of captive porpoises, *Tursiops truncatus* and *Stenella plagiodon*. Bull. Mar. Sci. Gulf and Caribbean. *3:* 120–133.

CAPTIONS TO SELECTIONS ON DEMONSTRATION RECORD

Selection 1. Distress calls of a baby chick. Such sounds are produced when the chick is lost, cold or hungry.

Selection 2. When the baby chick is returned to its parent, to a warm place, or given food, it produces pleasure or contentment notes.

Selection 3. The clucking sounds of a mother hen induce a following response by the chicks.

Selection 4. When the mother hen finds food, she scratches and utters excited food calls and the chicks come running to her.

Selection 5. At night the mother hen settles down and brings her chicks to her by using a roosting call.

Selection 6. Warning notes by the adult chickens signify the approach of a ground predator, such as a dog or a man.

Selection 7. The approach of a hawk elicits loud screams from the adult chickens which cause the chicks to run and hide.

Selection 8. The distant approach by a predator, such as a man, elicits alerting calls, causing the chicks to freeze in position.

Selection 9. When caught by a predator, or held in the hand, the chicken utters loud fear squawks.

Selection 10. Two sparring roosters signify their readiness to attack with threat notes.

Logical Considerations In The Study Of Animal Communication [1]

CHARLES F. HOCKETT

Division of Modern Languages and Department of Sociology and Anthropology, Cornell University, Ithaca, New York

THE ANCIENT GREEK MAXIM, "man is the measure of all things," is poor advice for the zoologist, who learns as much by comparing snails and birds as by comparing either of those with *Homo sapiens.* Yet this does not preclude the occasional use of our own species as a point of departure. The comparative study of human and animal communication bears on the problem of Man's place in Nature. Also, this study may yield viewpoints of value to the zoologist who is investigating the communicative and social behavior of some other species in its own right.

Some three or four thousand human languages are spoken in the world today. Each is a communicative system the conventions of which are shared more or less precisely by a group of human beings. The small number of languages on which we have fairly adequate information show wide variation in many respects, and as reports on other languages become available the range of known variation increases. Yet, in the face of the variety, we are confident that all languages share certain basic design-features.

Our confidence stems partly from the reasonably random nature of the sample of languages about which more is known, and partly from definition. If a community were discovered, in some hidden corner of the world, in which there was no communicative system characterized by these basic features, we should conclude that the community had no language, and might even refuse to call the individuals in it human beings. (Needless to say, no such revolutionary discovery is anticipated.) Contrariwise, if some species of animal is discovered on the deep sea bottoms, or on Mars or 61-Cygni-C, that uses a communicative system with all the basic design-features of human language, we shall have to recognize that system as genuinely, rather than merely metaphorically, a language, even if not a human one. Pending such discovery, the

---

[1] Manuscript received October 1959.

epithet "human" before the word "language" is tautologous, and will be omitted in the rest of this paper.

Below we shall discuss in turn thirteen design-features of language that seem to be most crucial. They are not all of equal importance, and they vary a good deal as to the extent to which they can be characterized in purely abstract terms. There are probably other design-features waiting to be singled out and described—the list given here has grown from seven during a single year's part-time research (Hockett, 1959). In connection with the discussion of each feature, we list animal communicative systems (if any are known) that seem to have the feature and others that do not, drawing insofar as possible from the other articles in this volume.

1. THE VOCAL-AUDITORY CHANNEL

The signals used in any language consist, without residue, of patterns of sound, produced by motions of the respiratory and upper alimentary tracts. No concomitant activity of a speaker, even if it produces sound, is part of his language. The signals are received through the ears, though on occasion the sight of the speaker's articulatory motions helps a hearer to understand signals that might otherwise be distorted beyond recognition by ambient noise.

Not all the sounds and features of sound produced by articulatory motions are part of language. The activity of speaking produces also a variety of sound effects, "vocal gestures" and the like, that are not part of language and that are classed together under the term *paralinguistic phenomena*. The systematic analysis of these has recently begun; the most complete treatment so far is Trager (1958). The distinction between language and paralinguistic phenomena is not arbitrary. It turns, however, on some of the criteria that will be discussed below; therefore the reader is asked to accept the distinction for the present without further discussion.

As pointed out by Alexander in his summary (this volume), apparently only vertebrates and arthropods have developed systems of sound communication, but in those two phyla such systems are widespread. Our internal ear is an early vertebrate development. The external ear is part of our amphibian heritage, adapted to the exigencies of hearing in air rather than water. Breathing with thoracic muscles rather than by swallowing is necessary for the production of speech sounds as humans produce them; this is common to the reptiles and their descendants (Romer, 1959, for the last three points). Almost all mammals (the giraffe is an exception) produce vocal sounds. In a general way, then, the vocal-auditory channel used by language, as opposed to other varieties of channels involving sound, is a common mammalian trait. The mechanisms of sound production and detection among birds are so similar that one might wish to subsume bird song also under the term "vocal-auditory."

Anthropologists have always been somewhat hesitant about referring to the human organs of speech as "organs of speech." Sapir (1921) humorously pointed out that this is something like calling the hands organs of piano-playing or the knees organs of prayer, and others (Bloomfield, 1933; Hockett, 1958) have accepted this view. On the other hand, to reject the designation or to insist that it is purely metaphorical might be something like insisting, on evolutionary grounds, that a swimming bladder is "really" a lung or that external ears are "really" gills. There is a difference: swimming bladders and external ears perform no respiratory function, whereas the organs of speech all still perform the functions they had before the development of language—the lungs breathe, the tongue manipulates, the teeth tear and masticate, and so on. Yet the human speech apparatus is structurally different in a number of ways from the homologous organs even in other Primates, and language (or its immediate functional precursors) may be old enough to have conditioned the anatomical changes that have occurred. In other Primates (Spuhler, 1959; DuBrul, 1958) the larynx is very close to the soft palate, or even touches it; the human larynx is further down the throat, and the root of the tongue can be bulged backward into the space in the lower pharyngeal cavity thus supplied. The human soft palate is freely moved back and upwards to close off the nasal passages from the nasal pharynx; other Primates cannot do this with ease. To a considerable extent, these and other alterations are doubtless tied in with the development of upright posture and the migration of the face from the end to the ventral side of the head, placing the oral and nasal cavities approximately at right angles to the pharynx instead of in line therewith, but there is every reason to believe that these grosser modifications, also, have constantly conditioned and been conditioned by communicative and social behavior.

Vowel Color

In speech, air passing (usually but not always outwards) through the larynx sometimes sets the vocal cords into vibration and sometimes does not. The air stream is largely controlled by the lungs, operated by the diaphragm and the interior and exterior intercostal muscles; this sublaryngeal apparatus must not be dismissed as a "mere bellows," since it is involved in subtle variations of rhythm and volume that are relevant in most languages, probably in all (for instance, in English, compare the noun *PERmit,* with the first syllable louder, with the verb *perMIT,* with the second syllable louder). The sound produced by the vibration of the vocal cords, or by cavity friction when they are quiescent, is distinctively modulated by motions and positions of the movable parts of the throat and mouth. In addition to the brief silences, mufflings, and hissings produced by these motions, they yield a constantly changing acoustic effect called *vowel color,* which is known to do much of the work of carrying information from speaker to hearer (Hockett, 1955 and literature cited).

Borror (this volume) describes sound spectrography. Spectrograms of human speech look somewhat different from any reproduced in this volume; for examples, see Joos (1948). Voicing—the vibration of the vocal cords—appears as a dark trace near the bottom of the spectrogram, representing the fundamental, with a number of spaced-out lighter traces above and roughly parallel to it, representing the harmonics. The intensity of the harmonics varies, because of the changing shape of the supraglottal cavities, in such a way that one can discern darker bands sometimes coinciding with a bundle of adjacent harmonic traces and sometimes cutting across them. These darker bands represent *formants*: resonant reinforcements of the energy at certain absolute frequencies, regardless of the pitch of the fundamental. Combinations of formants at specified frequencies constitute vowel colors. Thus the formants for the English vowel *a* (as in *father*) are essentially the same for a male and a female voice, despite the differences in pitch of fundamental and in tone quality.

There is considerable doubt whether any animal vocal-auditory system makes distinctive use of vowel color. There is even doubt that such a domesticated animal as a dog, in responding to human vocal signals, pays any attention to differences of vowel color. The repertory of human commands to which a trained dog reacts is usually rather small, so that in general any two commands are differentiated not only in vowel color but in many other ways—rhythm, volume, voice quality, even accompanying body motions and, for all we know, subtle differences of odor that humans ignore but dogs do not. Experimental testing of this is a desideratum.

Cortical Control

It is abundantly clear that speaking is a cortically governed function. Spuhler (1959) writes as follows: "Consider the muscles used in speaking. Most of our coordinated muscular movement involves corrections and adjustments from proprioceptors. But the largyngeal muscles lack proprioceptors, and feedback control of speech comes by way of the ear and the 8th cranial nerve. When we talk, the voice box, tongue, and lips must work together smoothly and precisely. The 10th nerve controls the adjustment of the vocal cords and the 5th nerve the movement of the lips. Both of these involve branchial muscle while the 12th nerve moves the tongue with somato-motor muscle." We may add that the diaphragm and intercostal muscles, whose cooperation is crucial, are controlled by a whole series of spinal nerves. "The neurological basis of speech is not clear, but it is clear that the only place where the motor organs and steering apparatus of speech are wired together is in the cerebral cortex."

The importance of mouth and ear in human life is reflected in the large cortical representation of those two regions: both sensory and motor for the mouth, and sensory for the ear. This is shown by the two "homunculi" presented by Penfield and Rasmussen (1950), summarizing extensive studies of cortical representation via pinpoint electrode stimulation. Washburn (1959) reproduces Penfield and Rasmussen's motor homunculus alongside a similar homunculus for a monkey of unidentified species. The differences in proportional representation are enormous.

Hand, Eye, Mouth, and Ear

It is not particularly surprising—hindsight being of the keenest—that our pre-human ancestors should have "selected" the vocal-auditory channel for the development of a truly flexible and fluent system of communication. Primates have hands, which, under the feedback control of the excellent primate eye, perform a great deal of the manipulation of objects that many other animals perform with the mouth. The cooperation of hand and eye is most highly developed in the Hominid line, where bipedal locomotion frees the forelimbs completely from participation in walking. It has been guessed (Spuhler, 1959; Washburn, 1959) that the advantages of hand-eye cooperation set the stage for increased complexity of cortical control in general; it could also be guessed that the same advantages promote the development of upright posture and bipedal locomotion. These various functional shifts free the mouth from some of its classical burden, so that it can perform new duties. At the same time, flexibility in a vocal-auditory communicative system, as opposed, say, to a gestural system, leaves hand and eye free for other activities. Several individuals, using their hands and eyes at some joint task, can coordinate their actions with a vocal-auditory system without having to interrupt their task in order to communicate about it. This is a meaningful convenience as soon as cooperative environmental manipulations (as over against the interactions of sex, infant-care, and fighting) are undertaken; the beginnings of such cooperation, to judge from its absence among contemporary non-human primates (Sahlins, 1959), must have taken place somewhere in the Hominid line between *Proconsul* and modern man (Spuhler, 1959). True, a vocal-auditory system has also at least one major disadvantage, but this is better discussed in the next section.

Inter-Species Communication

Differences in the structure of sound-producing and sound-detecting mechanisms have an important bearing on intra-species communication, including the variety thereof involved when human zoologists study the sounds of other animals. As a point of departure for our discussion of this, let us consider first what happens when a speaker of one language is exposed to speech in another. Suppose an American who knows no German hears a German say *Buch* ("book"). It is probable that he will hear this word as though it began with a consonant like the English *b* of *book*, continued with a vowel like the English *oo* of *moon*, and ended with a consonant like the English *k* of *book*. If the American repeats the German word, he will probably use these English sounds in the sequence indicated. But if he does, he will be saying a different German word, *buk* ("baked"). The point is that although all human beings speak with the same anatomical apparatus, different languages make use of different articulatory motions. We hear speech in another language, at first, either as an impossible jumble or in terms of the articulatory-acoustic patterns of our own language, and only in time adapt to the different articulatory-acoustic patterns of the other language. That the adaptation is rarely complete is attested by the prevalence of people who speak one or more non-native languages with a "foreign accent."

In the case of the human naturalist attempting to imitate and to describe the sounds of another species, say bird songs, the situation is a good deal more complicated. Many ornithologists have attempted to describe bird calls in English orthographic form: *tsee-tsee-tsee, kuk-kuk-kuk-kuk,* and so on. It is not enough merely to say, as every naturalist knows, that such renderings are impressionistic. We must come to grips with the transductions actually involved. A bird does not have the same structures above the syrinx that a human has above the glottis— and a syrinx is not a glottis. Though birds do modulate their syrinx tone (or tones) with supra-syringeal, and in some cases with sub-syringeal, motions, the modulations cannot possibly be congruent with those produced in human speaking. What happens, then, is that as the bird call enters the naturalist's ears it is processed *as though* it had been produced by human speech organs. Certain effects of pitch and tone quality are interpreted as vowel colors, and certain percussive effects as consonants. The data are then further processed according to the complex correlations of English speech sounds and English spelling, to yield an orthographic representation. The first part of this process is probably a very old human habit, since many bird-names in many languages (*cuckoo, bob-white;* Potawatomi *kokkok'o* "owl") have been shaped in this way. But the transductions cannot be reversed. The experienced naturalist, who remembers what the bird call really sounds like, may ignore the orthographic form and imitate the call from memory—sometimes well enough to fool the birds. But if anyone else, not familiar with the particular call through direct experience, tries to produce it by following the orthographic representation, he fails miserably.

Such considerations as the foregoing have been partly responsible for the resort to devices like the oscillograph and spectrograph for the study of animal sounds. Clearly this is desirable, but there are important things that spectrographs and oscillographs cannot find out for us. The spectrograph does not hear sound as the human ear and brain do, nor as a bluebird ear and brain do. A spectrogram can show in fine physical detail what sounds have been produced, but cannot show which features of the sound are communicatively significant for the species or for the particular animal community. In working with a hitherto undescribed language, linguists know fairly well how to find out what articulations and sounds are relevant for that language and which are not. In essence, the method turns on the fact that the observer has the same basic equipment and capacities as the observed: the linguist learns the new language and observes his own articulatory motions. This technique is not in general feasible in the study of animal communication. The development of methods by which one can determine, for example, which features of bluebird song are communicatively functional *for bluebirds* is probably the knottiest problem in the whole field of animal communication.

2. BROADCAST TRANSMISSION AND DIRECTIONAL RECEPTION

Unless guided, as in a stethoscope tube, sound, like light, moves in all directions from its source through any uniform medium, its intensity diminishing according to the familiar inverse square law. Unlike light, sound waves pass through or around certain types of obstacles: we can hear someone speaking around a corner where we cannot see him.

In any communicative system that uses a sound channel (vocal-auditory or other), transmission is therefore basically of the broadcast type: any receiver within range will detect the signal. A message transmitted to friends can also be received by predators and by prey. The situation is like that in bidding at bridge, where any information sent to one's partner is also (barring resort to unannounced conventions, which is cheating) transmitted to opponents. There must be many ecological conditions in which this public nature of sound communication is potentially contra-survival. This is the disadvantage of the vocal-auditory channel mentioned, but not described, earlier.

The complement to broadcast transmission is that hearing is reasonably directional under many circumstances. The parallax of binaural hearing can always be supplemented by motions of the ears or of the whole body. Consequently, the sound signals transmitted by an animal do not usually need to include specification of where the animal is: this information is conveyed by the physical structure of the channel itself—and is, indeed, difficult to withhold. A gibbon, finding food, emits the food call (Carpenter, 1940), which is distinctively different from the danger call and certain others. But the acoustic properties of the food call do not tell where the food is; only the location of the source of the call tells that. In somewhat the same way (or for the same ultimate reason), all languages have words like *here* and *I,* the denotations of which have to be inferred from our observation of where and who the speaker is as the words are spoken.

Privacy in communication can be achieved in several ways:

1) Under some momentary conditions, by transmitting at a power level that will allow the signal to reach the intended destination but become unintelligible or inaudible at greater distances: for example, whispering. (In line with this is the fact that those animal cries indicative of the most imminent danger tend to be the loudest—there is little hope left for the yelping victim, so that a loud cry loses him nothing, while others of his band are more likely to be saved by a loud cry than by a quiet one. Human vocal signals do not always conform to this tendency.)

2) By using a channel for which undesired receivers have no sensory organs: for example, walkie-talkies in a man-hunt. The use of sounds of very high frequencies by some birds and insects (Collias, this volume) might well exemplify this, in that some of their natural enemies may have only lower ranges of hearing.

3) By so encoding the information that undesired receivers cannot decode it, so that, at most, they can observe that transmission is occurring

and the location of the transmitter. Speech during a hunt for animal prey would illustrate this. Birds that mock the calls of other birds perhaps imitate accurately enough to fool enemies, and yet retain characteristic features by virtue of which others of their own species can distinguish between the mocking call and the mocked one. If so, then this illustrates also a further measure for privacy: concealment of the very fact that certain information is being transmitted. Human spies or military agents sometimes attempt this: see Pratt (1939).

4) With a tight beam. Although familiar enough in recent human history, otherwise this technique is apparently very rare. But there is one sure non-human example: the interconnecting nerve net of a coelenterate colony, which, according to some, was the precursor of the nervous system of the individual chordate.

3. RAPID FADING

The physical nature of sound yields another design-feature in any communicative system that uses a sound channel: a signal has to be received just at the right time or it is irrecoverably gone. The sound waves keep travelling, and continue to attenuate until any communicatively distinctive contours are totally masked by thermal noise.

In time, of course, any message encoded in any way is subject to fading. This is a simple corollary of the second law of thermodynamics. A cuneiform inscription six thousand years old may still be legible today, but eventually it will be worn smooth or disintegrated. Yet, relative to the time scale of individual animal lives, we can usefully distinguish between *non-recording* and *recording* communicative systems. A signal transmitted in a system of the former kind has to be received just at the right moment or it is gone. A signal transmitted in a recording system can be received thereafter at the convenience of the receiver, in some cases repeatedly. Recording systems are required for what has come to be called *information storage*. Information originally encoded with a non-recording system can be stored by transducing it into storable form, as when a stenographer takes dictation or a microphone and stylus transduce sound into a wiggly groove on a wax disc.

There is a rather obvious axiom about information storage that will be important to us later in this paper: the storage of information requires the construction of an internally stable and enduring spatial array. Thus the sheet of paper that bears the printer's ink that forms the words that the reader is now perusing can be moved from one place to another as a whole; also, the molecules that compose it are jiggling around; but within these boundaries of size-level the array of paper and ink is stable.

Even circulating storage in some computing machines, where a train of signals traverses a column of mercury and then is fed electronically back to the starting end of the column, conforms to this axiom: the whole array is moving, but its internal organization is reasonably invariant. Similarly, we do not try to make yardsticks out of water or air. Whether stored information can be "read" or not depends on the availability of equipment to perform a transduction the inverse of that by which the information was stored. Subject to this limitation, the axiom can be turned hind end to: any internally stable array is stored information about past events. This is the assumption on which geology, paleontology, archeology, and all other historical sciences are founded.

A widespread characteristic of animal sounds is that a particular call is repeated as long as the condition for which it is appropriate continues. If a single signal could hang in the air, at least for a while, and be received repeatedly at leisure, there would be no need for more than the one transmission. This latter is what happens in the case of trails and spoors. As an animal moves about it leaves a spoor, which may vary somewhat in chemical structure depending on what the animal is doing and what is happening to it. A spoor is not permanent, nor are broken twigs and bent grass, but under most conditions these signs of passage fade much more slowly than does a sound signal. Thus there is an interval of time during which other animals, encountering the spoor, can react to it after their own fashion. Olfactory signals have the advantage (or at least the property) of slow fading, but also the disadvantage of slow diffusion, so that an urgent signal cannot be transmitted over any great distance rapidly enough to be of use. Sound signals have the advantage of rapid transit, but the disadvantage of virtually instantaneous fading, a disadvantage overcome by repetitive transmission.

Human sound communication also shows this characteristic of repetitive transmission. A man in difficulties may call repeatedly for help, even after he has seen his rescuers approaching. A mother croons to her infant until she gets tired or the infant goes to sleep. Lovers may talk about a huge variety of things, but they use appropriate tones of voice, that alter only when a quarrel develops or there is some sort of intrusion. However, these features of continuity or repetition are manifested more in the aura of paralinguistic signals accompanying speech than in linguistic material proper.

The non-recording nature of language has been compensated for in recent human history by the development of various derivative recording systems, of which writing, only a few thousand years old, was clearly the first. The information stored by a writing system is first coded into linguistic form, and then transduced into marks on a flat surface. Writing seems to have no analog anywhere else in the animal kingdom.

4. INTERCHANGEABILITY

Alexander (this volume) mentions certain insects (Gryllidae and Tettigoniidae) for which there is a sharp sex difference in communicative use of sound: the males emit certain calls to which females and other males react, but which females do not produce. In some species, at least, the females do produce sounds, but of a different type from those produced by males.

Again, in the courtship behavior of sticklebacks (*Gasterosteus aculeatus;* Tinbergen, 1953) each participant assumes an appearance and moves in contours that, together, serve as adequate stimulus for the partner. But neither participant could transmit the signals characteristic of the other—the roles are not interchangeable.

Bee dancing (von Frisch, 1950) shows interchangeability among the workers, in that any worker may dance and any may heed the instructions danced by another. From this interchangeability queens and drones are excluded.

Any speaker of a human language is capable, in theory, of saying anything he can understand when someone else says it. For language, humans are what engineers call "transceivers": units freely usable for either transmission or reception.

To be sure, there are certain apparent, or real but marginal, exceptions to this interchangeability among humans. A pathological exception is the mute who understands what others say but does not speak himself, whether this be due to injury to the speech organs, brain lesion, or socially induced neurosis; or, conversely, the totally deaf person who can still talk intelligibly. An interesting apparent exception is found in certain communities where men and women use markedly different vocabulary, even to different sets of inflectional endings (Bloomfield, 1933). In such a community, no male would ordinarily use women's speech forms, or vice versa—at first sight, there seems to be a sort of sexual dimorphism in speech behavior. But if a member of either sex happens to be telling a story in which some of the characters are of the other sex, the narrator does not hesitate to use the appropriate vocabulary in direct quotations from the characters. The seeming lack of interchangeability thus does not cut very deep. A third kind of exception, obviously marginal, is the virtuoso speech performance of certain people who have worked hard to acquire the special skills involved: few of us could even recite a Gilbert and Sullivan patter song as rapidly as the D'Oyly Carte specialist sings it. Finally, it is obviously true that interchangeability does not extend to young humans who have not yet acquired the language habits of their community.

With similar apparent or marginal exceptions, interchangeability seems to be the rule for a great many mammalian and avian systems of vocal-auditory communication.

5. TOTAL FEEDBACK

In the courtship behavior of sticklebacks, mentioned above in 4, one of the necessary visual stimuli to the male is the appearance of the female's abdomen, distended with roe; among the necessary cues to the female are the seasonal colors of the male's eyes and belly. Neither can see its own belly, nor can the male see his own eyes. Each participant transmits crucial signals that he cannot receive. The only feedback to, say, the male, is of an indirect and transformed sort: if the courted female responds properly, the male has transmitted the proper signals.

In normal circumstances (that is, barring deafness and perhaps sleep-talking), a speaker of a human language hears everything he says as he says it. Auditory feedback is supplemented by kinesthetic and proprioceptive feedback from the speech organs, except that there is no proprioceptive feedback from the laryngeal muscles (1 above, quoting Spuhler, 1959). Informal experiment and observation show that both sorts of feedback are important for intelligible speech. The clarity of articulation tends to deteriorate with deafness, though this leaves kinesthetic and proprioceptive feedback unimpaired; it also deteriorates under the influence of ethyl alcohol, which apparently affects the latter before it disturbs hearing.

It is true that one's voice does not sound the same to oneself as it does to others. This can be shown by recording one's voice and listening to it. The difference lies in the bone conduction of sound, operative between a speaker's vocal organs and his own ears but obviously not between the former and the ears of others (or a microphone). However, this auditory difference has to do with the basic voice quality, not with the superimposed modulations that constitute the signalling units of a language. The latter are transmitted equally well with or without bone conduction.

It seems likely that every vocal-auditory communicative system—perhaps, indeed, every sound system, vocal-auditory or other—shares this property of total feedback. There may be exceptions of a trivial sort in cross-species communication: one species might react to frequencies in the sound signals of another species to which the hearing organs of the latter cannot respond. A bat might be flushed by a dog making no sound audible to canine (or human) ears.

The significance of total feedback is twofold.

In the first place, for any animal that typically emits whole trains of sound signals, whether relatively repetitious (as for many insects) or varying (as for some birds and mammals), one must consider the possibility that the feedback reception of each emitted signal forms part of the stimulus conditioning the emission and nature of the next. Wherever this is discovered to be so, there is the further possibility that the feedback serves as the basis for adjustments in the train of signals, towards some norm the image of which is stored within the central nervous system of the animal. From information currently available, we should expect these mechanisms to be most important for communicative systems that are not fully participated in by the newly born or hatched young, and the acquisition of which seems in the ordinary course of events to involve, if not to require, appropriate stimuli at appropriate times from surrounding adults (see 13, below). Thus Lanyon (this volume) cites instances in which passerine birds, deafened at an early age, have failed to develop the full panoply of song normal for their respective species. Apparently it is not the facts but their interpretation that is still in doubt here. In seeking the correct interpretation, we should remember (as Lanyon points out) that a deafened animal suffers a major loss of feedback, as well as of stimuli from other animals. On the other hand, a bird raised in acoustic isolation in a soundproof chamber is cut off from stimuli from adults but loses no feedback. A comparison of the results of experiments of these two types should thus shed much light on the mechanisms described above.

The second implication of total feedback rests not alone thereon, but on the joint presence of total feedback and of interchangeability. This is the possibility of "short-circuiting." A sequence of signals normally, or originally, passed around among several members of a group of animals, each signal serving at once as part of the response to the preceding signal and as part of the stimulus for the following, may come to be acted out entirely by a single animal playing all the "roles" involved. It may be that this does not happen anywhere in the animal kingdom save among humans. But it is clear that it cannot happen in a communicative system not characterized by interchangeability and total feedback, and it is also clear that much of the power of language lies in such short-circuiting. A group of humans, facing a practical problem, typically talk the situation over before arriving at a program for action. Any single human, once he has participated in such consultations, can hold a conference with himself about a problem he encounters when alone, thus indirectly bringing to bear on the problem some of the experience and tradition of the whole group. A further short-circuiting also seems to take place, at least for our own species: the single human being holding his lone conference comes to transmit signals at such a low power level—perhaps confining them entirely to his own central nervous system—that others cannot receive them, so that the only immediate consequences of the signals are the internal ones via feedback. This is one version of the behaviorist theory of "thinking." It may be quite erroneous, but as a hypothesis it has the advantage of underscoring realistically the lines of connection and the direction of causality between the social and the "mental."

6. SPECIALIZATION

A husband may be cued to wash his hands and come to dinner by the sight and sound of his wife setting the table. Or he may be brought to the table when his wife announces that dinner is ready. There is a clear difference between these two situations. The difference is easily described if we are willing to speak teleologically: when the wife announces that dinner is ready the obvious purpose of her act of speech is to bring the husband to the table; whereas when she sets the table the obvious purpose is to get the table set, and any influence on her husband's behavior is, so to speak, a side-effect. For reasons too numerous and well-known to require itemization here, this simple explanation, even if in some sense true, cannot serve us. But a non-teleological paraphrase requires some preliminary discussion of seemingly unrelated matters.

Joe Snakebite hurls a spear at an elk; Peter Jones uses a shotgun. Joe must supply from within himself all the energy necessary for both aim and propulsion. Peter supplies personally only the energy for aiming and for pulling the trigger; the powder in the shell supplies the rest. If we take a line of sight through Joe and the spear trajectory, or through the powder in the shell and the shot trajectory, we see only direct (energetic) action. This is the orientation constantly sought by the physicist, who consequently discovers such generalizations as the conservation of energy. If, instead, we sight through each hunter's behavior and its consequences, we see direct action in the first case, but trigger action in the second. Both hunters succeed, we shall say, in bagging their quarry, but by significantly different operations. In trigger sequences there is no principle of conservation, of energy or of any other definable commodity.

It is tempting to draw a comparison between the simple paradigm of triggering just given and certain phenomena that have not customarily been discussed in quite these terms. Thus a virus or a gene, in the proper medium, might be said to trigger the synthesis of replicas of itself. The genetic pattern of a fertilized ovum supplies neither the material substance nor the energy for maturation, but guides the development of the new individual in a way that might well be called triggering. When a catalyst speeds up the rate of a chemical reaction by lowering the free energy of activation, something similar to triggering seems to be taking place. A neutron striking an atomic nucleus may trigger the release of much more energy than it carries. Lotka (1925) reflects the classical dichotomy of physical science when he uses the terms *stoichiometry* and *energetics* for the analysis of the migrations and transformations respectively of matter and of energy. But these are only two of a triad of angles of approach to a wide variety of phenomena; the third, whatever term we might choose for it (perhaps "cybernetics," following Wiener, 1948), has to do with triggering sequences. At the smallest size-levels of concern in physics, the distinctions among these three angles of approach may break down, as witness the replacement in recent decades of the two traditional laws of conservation by a single law of conservation of matter-and-energy. But in such fields as ecology, animal or human sociology, or human behavioral science, the distinctions work quite well and all three approaches are fruitful.

Whether or not the notion of triggering has the far-reaching ramifications just suggested, and without attempting to foist a formal definition of "communication" on anyone who prefers some other approach, it seems fair to assert that when we study communicative behavior we are focussing our attention on the ways in which organisms (or, sometimes, machines or parts of organisms) trigger one another. This is very broad, but does not subsume everything. For example, suppose a man sees the sun going down, and prepares for bed: this is not communicative, because the sun is not an organism. Or suppose a bartender's bouncer throws a drunk out bodily: this is not essentially communicative, because the action is direct (it doubtless has communicative side-effects—the drunk's attitude towards the bouncer may be very different upon their next encounter). But if a man prepares for bed when someone tells him the sun is going down, or the bartender gets rid of the drunk with a threatening gesture, we have triggering between organisms, and hence communication.

Now we are ready to return to our original examples, of the husband being brought to the dinner table in either of two ways. Both ways are communicative—direct action would require that the wife deposit the husband at the table just as she puts the plates and silver there, and this is not often done. The difference can be gotten at if we remember that any act of an organism, including an act that transmits what some other organism takes as a signal, involves the expenditure of energy and therefore has direct energetic consequences. When the wife sets the table, the direct consequences of her actions are that the silver, plates, and food are in place; in the lifeways of our own society, these direct consequences are intimately tied up with the biological function of alimentation. When the wife calls out "Dinner's ready," it is only the trigger consequences that have any biological relevance. The direct consequences are a flurry of sound waves in the air, damping out with a slight rise in temperature of air and walls, all of which would seem to be quite trivial in terms of biological functions.

We shall say that a communicative act, or a whole communicative system, is *specialized* to the extent that its direct energetic consequences are biologically irrelevant. Obviously language is a specialized communicative system; so, also, are most varieties of animal communication to which our attention is normally apt to be drawn, since we are perhaps not inclined to think of communication as *systematic* and worthy of careful study unless it has this property. Some investigators, indeed, may prefer so to constrain the term "communication" that unspecialized triggering side-effects of functional behavior are excluded. Terminology is of no great importance, but it is important to recognize that what we would call unspecialized communication is extremely widespread and that, phylogenetically, it was probably the matrix within which and from which specialized communicative systems developed.

Thus the panting of a dog with tongue hanging out provides for cooling through evaporation, and constitutes part of the animal's machinery for thermostatic control. The panting produces characteristic sound, that can inform other dogs (and people) about the location and state of the panting animal and perhaps even identify him to them. The communication is unspecialized.

Again, the roe in a female stickleback during the breeding season is ultimately deposited in the nest in which the male then deposits his milt. Meanwhile, however, the roe distends the female's belly, and this altered bodily appearance is crucial in courtship, since a male will not court a female whose belly is not properly distended. This feature, at least, of stickleback courtship signalling is unspecialized.

The seasonal coloration of the male stickleback, like that of a great many animals of both sexes, is doubtless biochemically tied up in a very intimate way with the gonadal changes that prepare for reproduction. The basic metabolizing substances in both plants and animals, such as the chorophylls and hemoglobins, are pigments: tetrapyrrole ring compounds closely akin to others that supply coloration without functioning intimately in metabolism (Blum, 1955). A particular seasonal coloration can thus be a phylogenetically "accidental" by-product of a mutated pattern of metabolism, surviving only because it functions triggerwise to identify the animal and the animal's state to others. In this sense, the male stickleback's characteristically red belly and blue eyes during the breeding season can be regarded as communicatively specialized. However, this inference may stem from ignorance. Conceivably—though improbably—the color differential between belly and eyes plays a part in some internal energy-flow of key importance in sperm production. Similarly, the conversion of chemical into acoustic energy by the crepitation of a male cricket, or the bathing of the cricket's body in the sound waves thus produced, might possibly play some direct role in adjusting its body chemistry for reproduction, in addition to triggering females into approaching. The point of these rather dubious examples is that it is not necessarily easy to be sure whether communicative behavior is specialized or not. This is perhaps a good reason why we should not tip the scales in advance by choosing an overly narrow definition of the term "communication."

7. SEMANTICITY

The following example is from Hockett (1958). Let us picture two men seated side by side at a lunch counter. John has a cup of coffee for which he wants some sugar, but the sugar bowl is out of reach beyond Bill. John says, "Please pass the sugar." Bill passes it. This reveals, in bare outline form, the behavioral antecedents and consequences in which the act of speech is embedded. These antecedents and consequences are different for John and for Bill: John wants the sugar and gets it; Bill merely passes it. The same utterance could occur under other conditions: for example, Bill might have the coffee and ask John for the sugar. In the original situation, some of the behavioral consequences are not due to anything about the structure of the speech signal, but to concomitant circumstances. Bill passes the sugar to John rather than to Carl because it is John, not Carl, who produces the speech signal. But the way in which the act of speech serves to bridge between the antecedents and the consequences also depends on the fact that John and Bill share certain *semantic conventions* about constituent signals of English. Thus there is an associative tie between the word *sugar* and a certain familiar substance: Bill does not pass the salt. There is a tie between *pass* and a familiar action: Bill does not throw the sugar bowl to the floor. There is a shared understanding that *please,* with certain word order and intonation, is a polite request: Bill is not insulted or annoyed. Without these shared conventions, John would have had to get up and fetch the sugar himself, or else go without.

When the elements of a communicative system have such associative ties with things and situations, or types of things and situations, in the environment of its users, and when the functioning of the system rests on such ties, we say that the system is *semantic* or is characterized by *semanticity.* Human languages are semantic, despite the fact that every language includes a minority of forms that lack any obvious semantic tie— e.g., English *unicorn* or *and.* The possibility of such peculiar forms seems to rest on certain design features yet to be discussed (10 and 11, below).

Some anthropological theorists have tended to imply, perhaps unintentionally, that only human communicative systems are semantic (e.g., White, 1959, and earlier works cited). Under our definition this is clearly not so. A hungry gibbon reacts to the sight or smell of food by approaching the food, by emitting the food call, and, presumably, by salivation and other familiar anticipatory behavior. A hungry gibbon reacts to the sound of the food call by this same concatenation of behavior: motion in the direction of the source of the call, repetition of the call, and doubtless the other food-anticipating reactions. This does not mean that the gibbon "identifies" food and the food call, any more than John would try to sweeten his coffee with the word *sugar.* But it certainly implies that there is some sort of associative tie beween food and the food call, whereby either food or the food call elicits a pattern of reactions different from that elicited by, say, danger or the danger call. This is all the evidence we need to class gibbon calls as a semantic system.

Again, bee dancing is semantic, since the dance denotes a location in terms of direction and distance from the hive or swarm. The reaction of the observing workers is to proceed to the location denoted.

On the other hand, if we consider once again the courtship signalling of sticklebacks, there seems to be no semantics. The reaction of the male to the appearance of the female is not like his reaction to anything else, but merely a contour of behavior that in turn triggers the female into her next step in the courtship dance. A word is, as we say, a symbol for something. A gibbon call is a symbol for something. A rate or direction of a bee dance is a symbol for something. The darting dance of the male stickleback is an effective triggering, but is not a symbol for anything outside itself.

In judging semanticity it is important to distinguish between the

communicative behavior proper and the attendant circumstances. The
fact that Bill passes the sugar to John rather than to someone else is not
due to anything in the semantics of the English phrase "Please pass
the sugar," but to the attendant circumstance that it is John who utters
the phrase. The fact that a gibbon, hearing the food call, moves to the
northwest rather than in some other direction is not due to anything
in the semantics of the food call, but to the attendant circumstance
that the call he hears comes from that direction (compare point 2 above).
The location denoted by a bee dance is sometimes the location of a
source of nectar, sometimes that of a possible hive site. But the dance
itself does not make this distinction. If the bees are swarming, the
location is that of a possible hive site. If they are in or at a hive, the
location is that of a source of nectar.

8. ARBITRARINESS

In a semantic communicative system, the associative ties between meaningful elements and their meanings can be of either of two types, or can
have features of both. A symbol means what it does *iconically* to the
extent that it resembles its meaning in physical contours, or to the extent that the whole repertory of symbols in the system shows a geometrical
similarity to the whole repertory of meanings. To the extent that a symbol or system is not iconic, it is *arbitrary*. The signals of a non-semantic
system, be it noted, cannot be classed as either iconic or arbitrary, since
they have no meanings.

A road map involves a blend of these two types of semantic relation.
The iconic element is obvious: the dots and lines that represent towns,
hills, rivers, and roads are arranged on the map roughly the same way
the actual towns, hills, rivers, and roads are arranged on the surface of
the earth, with a specified reduction of scale. But the width of a line
representing a road or a river is not indicative of the width of the actual
road or river. The color of the line representing a road is not iconic:
we do not find in our peregrinations that main paved roads are red,
minor ones black, and unpaved roads checkered. Arbitrary features are
sometimes mistakenly taken as iconic. In *Tom Sawyer Abroad*, Huck
Finn looked out of the balloon in which he and Tom were travelling
and insisted that they must not yet have left Illinois, since the ground
was still green: in his geography book, Illinois was printed in green,
Indiana in some other color.

The iconic-arbitrary classification of symbols and signals is by no
means simple. It is tied up with many complex problems of the psy-
chology of perception and cognition, as well as with physics and geometry

(Gibson, 1954). It is doubtless safe to say that no semantic relationship is completely iconic, since for a symbol of anything to be completely iconic it would have to be indistinguishable from the original, and would thus *be* the original. But degrees, and perhaps kinds, of arbitrariness vary. A stereoscopic and stereophonic moving picture of a President of the United States is less arbitrary than a fine-grained still photograph, but the latter is less arbitrary than a cartoon caricature, and the latter less so than the phrase "President of the United States."

The basic semantic relations in a language are extremely arbitrary. There is no similarity between the sound of the word *dog* (or French *chien,* or German *Hund,* and so on) and the sight, sound, or smell of a dog. Nor is the difference between the sounds of the words *dog* and *cat* in any way parallel to the difference between the sight, sound, or smell of a dog and that of a cat. Big words can name small things and small words big things: *microorganism, whale.* There are probably faint traces of iconicity in so-called "onomatopoetic" forms, such as English *ding-dong, bow-wow, bob-white,* but any cross-language study shows that words like these also involve a large arbitrary element (Hockett, 1958, chapter 35; Brown, 1959, chapter 4; and literature cited). A clearer element of iconicity appears when we use the sound of a form as a name for the form, as in speaking of "the word *dog*" or "the suffix *-ing.*" A narration may be iconic in that events are described in the sequence in which they actually happened, but this is not an invariable rule.

In the paralinguistic accompaniments of language there may be instances of a kind of iconicity. In our culture, a speaker often increases his volume with anger, and there is perhaps some rough correlation between the degree of anger and the degree of increased volume. Degrees of anger are meanings and degrees of volume are the signals that carry the meanings, so that the continuous mapping of the former into the latter is iconic. Beyond this the situation is not clear. It is possible that the mapping of anger into increased volume rather than, say, into diminished volume or lowered pitch or something else, is arbitrary. More probably, however, increase in volume is one part of the whole behavioral gestalt known to us as anger. In this case, increase of volume is what Langer (1942) calls a *symptom,* and the semantic relation can hardly be regarded as arbitrary.

Insofar as mammalian and avian vocal-auditory systems are semantic, they seem also to be basically arbitrary. So, certainly, for gibbon calls, though the call system seems to be embedded in a framework of continuous variables just as language is embedded in a paralinguistic matrix, and in this framework there may be iconic features. The general intensity with which a gibbon emits the danger call may be a direct function of the imminence or seriousness of the danger. The association between danger and the characteristic danger call is then arbitrary, but the correlation of imminence and intensity is iconic.

Bee dancing is largely iconic. The rate of the dance is inversely proportional to the distance to the target location; the angle of the dance from the vertical is equal to the angle between the line of sight to the sun and the direction towards the target location. Presumably one could invent an organism (or a machine) that would transmit the same information with other underlying associations, say mapping distance into an angle and direction into a rate. That the bee dance gives the polar coordinates of the target location with rate and angle is therefore arbitrary, but within this arbitrary framework the further details of the system are iconic.

A degree of arbitrariness has a certain advantage, in that there are all sorts of things and situations about which communication may be important but which can be represented iconically only with great awkwardness. The Laputans, encountered by Gulliver in one of his later travels, carried a veritable hardware-store about with them in order to communicate with iconic examples rather than arbitrary words. It is interesting to note the difference in utility between analog (iconic) and digital (arbitrary) computers. An analog computer can often be extremely well adapted to a narrow operation defined clearly in advance. A digital computer is much more flexible, since it can be reprogrammed for an endless variety of operations. On the other hand, the very term "arbitrary" implies that the original development of an arbitrary system, by evolution or construction, is problematic, since the necessary circuitry seems so senseless.

9. DISCRETENESS

When asked where something is, we often respond by *pointing*. The orientation of the pointing finger can be to any of a non-denumerable infinity of directions, restricted only by degree of accuracy. But the relative positioning of hand and finger that constitutes pointing, as a signal, is an all-or-none matter. The gesture either occurs or it does not occur. Physically, of course, hand and finger can be placed in any of an infinity of contours, just as the finger can be turned to any of an infinity of directions. But we do not make communicative use of this whole infinity. One continuous subrange within the total range of possible hand and finger positions is classed together as "pointing," and the remaining continuous subrange as "non-pointing." The pointer directs his behavior roughly into one subrange or the other, and the observer pays attention only to the difference between the two subranges. This sort of segregation of regions out of a physical continuum of possibilities is *quantizing*: it yields a repertory of all-or-none *discrete* signals. If a continuum of possibilities is not thus quantized, then the repertory of signals is, of course, *continuous*. Pointing, as we have seen, involves both: the discrete contrast between non-pointing and pointing, and, within the latter, the continuous array of possible directions.

In semantic communicative systems there is one restriction between the matters discussed in the preceding section and those under discussion here: a continuous repertory implies iconicity. Rigorous proof of this is perhaps not possible, but the following considerations render it highly plausible. Given a continuous repertory, and iconicity, a slight error in a signal tends to yield only an equally slight error of interpretation, which under most conditions can be compensated for. If the dance of a bee is somewhat inaccurate, or if the bee that reads the dance does not fly in precisely the indicated direction, when the target comes into sight the course can be corrected. If, on the other hand, the signals of a continuous repertory were assigned arbitrary meanings, then any one signal would be surrounded by others indefinitely similar to it in physical contours but with totally dissimilar meanings. The slightest error of transmission or reception could then yield indefinitely large or serious misinterpretation. But errors—"noise" in the communication engineer's sense—are at bottom ineradicable (Shannon, 1947). One way to combat noise is to assign a continuous array of possible signals to a continuous array of meanings—yielding iconicity. Another way is to quantize the continuous array; meanings can then be either iconic or arbitrary. Quantization of a continuum leaves fuzzy boundaries between the adjacent communicatively distinct subregions, so that ambiguous signals can still occur. However, the size of each quantized region, within which differences are communicatively irrelevant, reduces the frequency of occurrence of ambiguous signals, and when one does occur it is ambiguous only among two or a few alternatives, whereas without quantization it would be ambiguous for a non-denumerable infinity of alternatives.[2]

We can now briefly pass in review the sample systems discussed in the preceding section. An analog computer is iconic and continuous. The iconic features of bee dancing are continuous. Gibbon calls are discretely different from one another; the range of variation in intensity

---

[2] Mathematical note: The term "continuous" is used loosely here. The argument actually turns only on denseness, and, if it proves anything, proves only that a dense repertory of signals is incompatible with arbitrariness.

(i.e., in volume, register, duration, or amount of repetition) for each call is perhaps continuous and, if so, also iconic. For many mammalian and avian systems we do not know the answers, partly because the relevant questions have not yet been put experimentally. An ornithologist's classification of the observed and recorded songs of a particular species or variety of birds may reflect a functional discreteness for the birds, but it may also—though this seems unlikely—be an artifact of the sampling and of our human tendency to pigeonhole rather than to scale.

This human tendency is a real one. In the nineteenth century it rendered a whole generation of European mathematicians unhappy about scales and continuities, until they worked out a way of "generating" the continuum from the discrete integers as raw-material (Dedekind, Cantor, and others; see, for example, Huntington, 1917). Possibly the source of this tendency inheres in the fact that our most typically human communicative system, language, is wholly founded on discreteness.

Any utterance in any language consists of an arrangement of certain basic signalling units called *phonemes,* of which a given language has a definite and finite stock. Phonemes are not sounds, but *ranges* of sound quarried by quantization out of the whole multidimensional continuum of physiologically possible vocal sound. In different languages this quarrying yields different sets of phonemes—a difference of sound that is functional in one language may or may not be in another. We can illustrate both the quantizing and the ways in which languages differ by considering just one physiologically given dimension: voicing, the vibration of the vocal cords. In English the scale of degrees of strength of voicing is quantized into two subregions. Thus the initial consonants of the words *pat* and *bat* differ only as to voicing: the *p* is most typically voiceless, the *b* most typically voiced. Yet some occurrences of *p* are slightly voiced, and in some occurrences of *b* the voicing is very weak. But if a hearer hears something that is not clearly marked as a *p* or as a *b,* it is only this two-way ambiguity that he has to try to resolve. There is no further alternative, except to leave the ambiguity unresolved—and this is not an alternative within the system, but a breakdown of the system. In some other languages, such as Menomini, the scale of degrees of strength of voicing is not quantized into smaller contrasting regions at all: a speaker of Menomini does not at first hear any difference between English *pat* and *bat.* In still other languages, such as Hindi, degree of strength of voicing is quantized into two regions, and exact timing of onset of voicing is likewise quantized into two, to yield four contrasting units where English has two and Menomini only one.

We do not yet know whether the paralinguistic accompaniments of language are continuous or discrete. At least some of them are certainly continuous (compare the discussion in 8 above). If any are discrete, then there would seem to be something of a problem in demonstrating that they are properly classed as paralinguistic rather than as part of the language; but it may be that other criteria (such as that discussed in 12 below) resolve the dilemma.

10. DISPLACEMENT

A few semantic communicative systems, including language and its derivatives, have the property that what is being communicated about can be removed, in time or space or both, from the setting in which the communication takes place. This property, *displacement* (Bloomfield, 1933), is apparently quite rare; outside of human behavior, the only really well-attested instance is in bee dancing, where the context is quite different. Even as to displacement itself, there is the difference that bee dancing is always and necessarily displaced, whereas language sometimes is and sometimes is not.

The survival value of displacement has never been described better than by V. Gordon Childe; but it should be noted that what he says, quoted just below, turns also on certain other design-features of language, especially that dealt with in 13 below. Once children have acquired the language of their community, says Childe (1936), "parents can, with the aid of language, instruct their offspring how to deal with situations which cannot conveniently be illustrated by actual concrete examples. The child need not wait till a bear attacks the family to learn how to avoid it. Instruction by example alone in such a case is liable to be fatal to some of the pupils. Language, however, enables the elders to forewarn the young of the danger while it is absent, and then demonstrate the appropriate course of action."

Gibbon calls are normally not displaced. A gibbon, finding food, does not return to the rest of the band to report it, but shouts his "Eureka!" as he proceeds to eat. This accords with the general rule for most mammals: out of sight, out of mind. However, if a gibbon encounters danger he does not stay still as he announces it, but flees—if he can. The direction of flight no doubt sometimes brings him closer to other members of the band, as though he were coming to warn them. Such an incident bears the outward guise of displacement. Similar incidents among our speechless proto-Hominoid ancestors may have been crucial forerunners of the displacement that subsequently developed in language. We can imagine a proto-Hominoid wandering away from his band and catching sight of a predator, without being detected thereby. If for any reason, say through fright, he did not immediately burst out with his danger call, but first sneaked silently away towards the remainder of his band, this would afford the whole band a head start in escaping the predator. The delaying of the call would thus have survival value, and would promote the selection of those factors, whatever they may be, that allow delay and point towards more extensive displacement.

Displacement implies, or consists of, the ability to discuss today what happened yesterday or what may come to pass tomorrow. A commoner way to talk about such abilities is to say that they rest on "retention" and "foresight." Upon closer scrutiny, this common phrasing develops the flavor of tautology or even of inverted definition, rather than of explanation. What could we possibly mean by "foresight," for example, except the ability to discuss now (in a group or with oneself; cf. 5 above) what may happen later?

Well, "foresight" might also refer to certain other typically and exclusively human phenomena, outstandingly the carrying and making of tools (Spuhler, 1959). A tool is a piece of the physico-geographical environment used by an animal in manipulating other parts of the physico-geographical environment, including other animals, but otherwise of no direct biological relevance. This definition is somehow supposed to exclude birds' nests and beavers' dams and houses, as well as the separate raw materials from which these structures are assembled. The difference between a tool and such behavioral products as those just named is perhaps reminiscent of the difference between specialized and unspecialized communicative behavior (above, 6). The mere *use* of an unshaped stick or stone as a tool is not unknown among non-human hominoids, at least in captivity; but only human beings seem to be willing to lug an awkward implement around because an occasion may arise in which it will be convenient to have it at hand, and only human beings spend time and energy manufacturing tools.

Since tool-carrying and displaced communication are both almost exclusively human (we can forget about the bees here, since they are phylogenetically so remote), it is difficult or impossible to tell which came first. The best guess is probably that neither really came first; each developed in small increments furthered by the already-achieved increments of itself and of the other, as a man can shinny up inside a chimney by moving his shoulders up one wall and his feet up the opposite one. Yet perhaps some slight edge of priority goes to tool-carrying: our Hominid ancestors achieved an essentially modern conformation of limbs long before the brain, skull, and teeth became as they are now (Le Gros Clark, 1959).

It is at this point that we evoke the axiom about information storage presented above in 3. If an animal participates in any sort of communicative system, then the conventions of that system must somehow be stored within the animal. This is a very general kind of storage. In a sense, it implies and is implied by the meta-stability of structure of any living matter, in which, over sizable periods of time, tiny constituent parts are replaced without disturbing the pattern of the whole. This is to assert that, by our axiom, an organism *is* a record, just as is a book, a spoor, or a fossil. But displacement implies the superimposition of the capacity for a further sort of information storage. Any delay between the reception of a stimulus and the appearance of the response means that the former has been coded into a stable spatial array, which endures at least until it is read off in the response. Action at a distance is imposible. The fact that our thoughts can turn in a twinkling from Andromeda to Arcturus does not mean that "thought travels faster than light"; the only "travelling" is the replacement of one symbol by another in ourselves or our immediate neighborhood.

During her return flight from target to hive or swarm, a worker bee somehow records within herself the relative location of target and homebase; the "reading-off" of this record is her dance. In one important sense, we have not the faintest idea how this is accomplished. That is, we do not know what internal circuitry is involved, nor just where nor how the record is laid down. In another sense we know rather more. It would not be too difficult ot build a mechanical bee (it might be rather large) which, having been moved from home base to a target and back, would display the polar coordinates of the target. This implies a kind of black-box knowledge about real bees that should not be underestimated. The "wiring diagrams" of the real bee and the mechanical one would doubtless be enormously different; but the "control-flow chart" of the mechanical bee would have some validity for the real one (Wiener, 1948).

The information storage required for displacement need not always be entirely within the organism. Our imagined proto-Hominoid, fleeing a predator silently until the latter is out of range and only then emitting the danger call, has to retain the fact that danger, not something else, is to be reported. But perhaps he does not outrun the odor of his own fear, which clings about him and serves as a mnemonic device. In the case of tool-carrying, the tool is itself stored information. In the case of tool-making, frequently an earlier exemplar of the same kind of tool is at hand to serve as a model.

Nevertheless, an increasing capacity for internal storage clearly has to accompany any radical increase in displacement, and it is not surprising that the development of language, from the proto-Hominoids to ourselves, has been paced by increase in size and complexity of the brain. For, whatever other functions the human brain may perform, it unquestionably supplies tremendous room for information storage. Recent experimentation has even begun to suggest what portions of the cortex may be primarily involved (Penfield and Roberts, 1959, especially pp. 45f).

11. PRODUCTIVITY

It is a commonplace that a human being may say something that he has never before said nor heard, and be perfectly understood, without either speaker or audience being in the slightest aware of the novelty (Wells, 1949, referring to Bertrand Russell).

A communicative system in which new messages can be coined and understood is *open* or *productive*. Bee dancing is open, since a worker may report a location which has never been reported before by either her or her coworkers. Some bird-song systems may be open, at least in that each individual bird works out elaborations on the basic repertory of his community, rendering his song characteristic of himself as well as of his community or species (Lanyon, this volume; Marler, this volume). In contrast, gibbon calls are effectively closed. The bands observed by Carpenter (1940) had a total repertory of some ten or a dozen distinct calls. No matter how novel may be the circumstances encountered by a gibbon, he is constrained to respond vocally with one or another of this small finite number of calls, or to remain silent. There is seemingly no mechanism for the coinage—and understanding—of a new call.

A continuous semantic (and therefore iconic) communicative system is necessarily also productive. A discrete system is not; and the mechanisms which render language productive are very different from those responsible for openness in bee dancing. Any language provides a large number of elementary signalling units that have meanings. Roughly, though not exactly, these are the units traditionally called "words"; the current technical term for them is *morphemes*. The language also provides certain patterns by which these elementary significant units can be combined into larger sequences, and conventions governing what sorts of meanings emerge from the arrangements. These patterns and conventions are the *grammar* of the language. A new message is built with familiar elements, put together by familiar patterns, but yielding a composite total that has not occurred before. The hearer understands the new message—usually, though of course not always—

because the parts and patterns are familiar to him as they are to the speaker. Confronting a novel situation, a human being is not constrained to react to it exactly as he has reacted to one or another earlier experience, but can, and often does, coin a new utterance, drawing on the partial similarities between the new situation and many diverse earlier experiences. Indeed, even when a speaker produces a complex utterance exactly like one he has heard or said before, he is often coining it anew anyway.

There is a distinction in principle between an open and a closed discrete semantic system, even if the latter has an enormous number of messages. For if a discrete system is closed, then although it may provide a very large number of messages, that number is necessarily finite. Openness, on the other hand, involves only a finite number of elementary signalling units (morphemes) and of patterns, but allows the generation of a transfinite, though countable, number of distinct whole messages. There is also a clear difference in efficiency. For the control of a single message of a closed system, let us posit that it requires on the average k "storage units"—whatever those may be: genes, weakened synapses, "punched molecules," reverberating neural circuits, relays, flip-flop tubes, or what have you. Then if an organism is to participate in a closed system with, say, 10,000 distinct messages, 10,000k storage units must be assigned to this task. Perhaps the control of a single elementary signalling unit or a single pattern of an open system requires ten or one hundred times as many storage units. Then, with just 10,000k such units, only 1000 or only 100 different signalling units and patterns could be provided for, but this would still generate an uncountable number of distinct whole messages, to yield an uncountably large net gain in efficiency.

The great advantage of openness of the sort language has, coupled with displacement, is that one can say things that are not necessarily so. This underlies lying, fictions (*unicorn*), and errors and superstition; but it also underlies the making of hypotheses. With displacement but without productivity, a child can be taught in relative safety how to deal with bears and other dangers; but openness is necessary if a community is to work out *better* ways to deal with such dangers. We cannot, of course, be sure, but it is at least reasonable to guess that the development of openness in language was the first step towards the ultimate growth of Man's fantastic powers of imagination, which now greatly exceed the bounds of what can comfortably be dealt with purely in terms of verbal symbols. If so, then the development of openness was also the Fall of Man, the Eating of the Fruit of the Tree of Knowledge, the Origin of

Sin: it is Man's imagination that exposes him to delusions of persecution or power, to feelings of guilt or anxiety—the whole sad panoply of neuroses and psychoses to which seemingly only our own species is significantly susceptible.

12. DUALITY

Suppose that Paul Revere and his confederate had needed a total repertory of several hundred messages, instead of just two. It would have been inconvenient to have had several hundred lanterns on hand in the Church tower. But it could have been agreed that each message would take the form of a row of five lights, each one either red, or yellow, or green. Then only fifteen lanterns would have been needed—one of each color for each position—but the system would have provided for a total of $3^5 = 243$ different messages. We assume that meanings would have been assigned only to the whole messages, so that, for example, "red light in first position" would not have had any separate meaning of its own, but would merely have served to distinguish certain messages from certain others. This expanded Paul Revere system would then show what we mean by *duality of patterning*: a set of conventions in terms of *smallest meaningful elements* (here the whole messages), and also a set of conventions in terms of *minimum meaningless but differentiating ingredients* (the three colors and five positions).

Another example of duality is found in commercial cable codes. Important words and phrases, apt to be needed repeatedly in transmitting information of commercial importance, are assigned as the meanings of arbitrary sequences of five letters. The smallest meaningful elements are then these five-letter sequences. The minimum meaningless but differentiating ingredients are the individual letters. Thus ADBQR might mean "credit rating" and ADBQS "yours received": the partial shared by these two, ADBQ, obviously does not correlate with any shared feature of the meanings of the two whole sequences, nor can any meaning be described for "R" or for "S" in fifth position.

Still another example appears in the Morse code as used for old-fashioned telegraphy and pre-voice radio (or, with differences of detail, in the Baudot code now used for cabling). Here the *cenemes*—the "minimum meaningless but differentiating ingredients"—are short voltage pulses (dots), longer voltage pulses (dashes), and pauses of several lengths. The *pleremes*—the "smallest meaningful elements"—are the arrangements of those cenemes to which meanings have been assigned: a single dot means the letter "E", two dots the letter "I", and so on.

For the users of most semantic communicative systems, the problem of transmission has two phases, *encoding* and *emission,* and the problem of reception has a converse two, *detection* and *decoding*. Longfellow's Paul Revere had to look sharp to tell whether one or two lights were on display across the river (detection), and he had to remember which signal had been assigned which meaning (decoding). His n less confederate had to remember the assignment (encoding) in c er to know how many lights to hang out (emission). Failure either i emission and detection or in encoding and decoding would have destroyed the functioning of the whole system. Channel noise (mist rising from the river) could have interfered with emission and detection; code noise (discrepant memory between Paul and his confederate) could have interfered with encoding and decoding.

In a system with duality of patterning, the problems of emission and detection are to some extent separated from those of encoding and decoding. Emission and detection have to do with cenemes; encoding and decoding have to do with pleremes. The principle of duality is, in one way, a source of efficiency and economy for any communicative system for which a large number of different meaningful signals is desired. A small handful of cenemes, chosen so as to be easily emitted and so as to be easily distinguished by the sensory receptors or hardware receivers involved, can be ordered into a large number of brief groupings, and the meanings can be assigned to the latter. In this way emission and detection can be kept relatively simple despite complexities of encoding and decoding. As if by way of compensation for this gain in simplicity, the total amount of machinery required at transmitter and at receiver is increased, since, in addition to the rules of encoding and decoding, that machinery must provide for the transduction from pleremes to cenemes at the transmitting end and from cenemes to pleremes at the receiving end. Duality for telegraphy is economical because the end-point complexities can be handled by stationary machinery or by trained humans, at a cost less than the amount saved by using a very simple channel. The failure of chimpanzees or gibbons to talk—that is, to use a vocal-auditory system like human language—is not to be ascribed to their mouths or ears, but to their cortexes (Spuhler, 1959; Gerard, 1959; despite Kelemen, 1948).

It is implied by the above discussion that some communicative systems are not marked by duality. The original Paul Revere system was not. True, one could analyze the system and discover its cenemes: one light and two lights; and one could analyze from a different angle and discover its pleremes: one light and two lights. But if the cenemes and the pleremes are the same, then there is no point in speaking of duality. Again, one could undertake to determine the smaller graphic elements out of which the letters of the English alphabet are built, on the tentative assumption that the whole letters are the pleremes of the English writing system. In some type-faces,

$$p \qquad q$$
$$b \qquad d$$

constitute a small subset of letters built out of a vertical line and a flattened circle, in differing arrangements. But if one carries this through for the whole writing system, it turns out that there is a much larger stock of ostensible "meaningless but differentiating ingredients" than of different letters—even allowing for capital versus lower case and the like.

Significant duality, we can say, is found when a system not only has both cenemes and pleremes but also uses a relatively small stock of the former to build a relatively larger stock of the latter. Morse and Baudot codes build about thirty-two pleremes out of about five cenemes. A commercial cable code uses twenty-six cenemes to yield thousands of pleremes.

Languages have duality of patterning. The cenemes of a language are its phonemes (section 9 above) ; the pleremes are its morphemes (section 11). The number of phonemes in a language ranges from a dozen or so up to about one hundred. The number of morphemes runs to the thousands or tens of thousands. Phonemes do nothing but keep morphemes (and sequences of morphemes) apart. Thus, in English, the phoneme /b/ at the beginning of a word has no meaning of its own, but merely serves to distinguish *beat* from *meat, bat* from *pat, bet* from *debt, bill* from *ill,* and so on. The parallel with the other dual systems discussed in this section is complete.

Paralinguistic phenomena, on the other hand, do not have duality. This is probably true by definition, in that any portion of human vocal-auditory communication characterized by duality and by discreteness cannot be operationally distinguished from the portion we traditionally call language, and hence must be part thereof (compare the discussion in 9 above).

More generally, it can probably be proved (the reasoning is not entirely clear) that continuity and duality are incompatible, just as are continuity and arbitrariness (9 above).

There are no clearly attested instances of significant duality in animal communicative systems. Alexander (this volume) adopts the linguistic terms "phoneme" and "morpheme" for the description of certain types of insect communication, but since the system he describes has but one "phoneme" and two "morphemes" there is at least an enormous difference of degree between the duality of such a system and that of the human systems we have described in this section. Yet it would be premature to conclude that significant duality is an exclusively human prerogative. The complex song systems of some passerine birds—Western Meadowlark, Song Sparrow (Lanyon, this volume)—need further study with special attention to openness and duality. The songs of some of these species consist of different arrangements of a basic stock of motifs. New whole songs sometimes occur (or are sometimes observed for the first time), but built out of the same old motifs. If these systems are semantic, then there are several possibilities. Perhaps the motifs are cenemes and the whole songs pleremes: this would be duality without openness. Perhaps the motifs are pleremes and the whole songs are like the composite grammatically-structured sentences of a language: this would be openness, though doubtless with a much lower rate of incidence of newly coined "sentences" than holds for language. In the second case, it could still be that the motifs were functionally indivisible, so that the openness would be unaccompanied by duality, or it might be that the motifs are built out of a limited stock of even smaller figures, functionally comparable to the phonemes of a language.

13. CULTURAL OR TRADITIONAL TRANSMISSION

In a period of time the length of which depends on the species—from five to ten decades for human beings—the membership of any metazoan community is totally replaced. Yet the new members go about their affairs in pretty much the same way as did their predecessors. Ways of life change for all animals, but for the most part at a much more leisurely rate than that of births and deaths. This basic continuity of behavior patterns is due to a number of biological *mechanisms of continuity*. One of these is the generally non-catastrophic development of the physico-chemical environment: the sun continues to supply the earth with energy; the earth's gravity field hardly varies; available chemical raw-materials in any single ecological niche usually change but slowly. Another is the genetic mechanism, seemingly as widespread as life itself. A third, perhaps not so widespread but nonetheless important, is the mechanism that some anthropologists call *cultural transmission* and some ornithologists *tradition* (Hochbaum, 1955). As Dobzhansky has so beautifully pointed out (1956), it is not fruitful to approach the lifeways of any one species of animal with the notion of sorting out those that are genetically transmitted and those that are transmitted by some other mechanism. One does not hope to say "this is cultural," "that is genetic." The habits manifested by any single animal represent the blended result of the various contributing mechanisms of continuity.

The analytical problem is to sort out and describe the specific nature of the blend in any one case.

A human being speaks no language at birth. The language that he later comes to speak is the one used by those about him, whether or not that is the language of his biological forebears—and, if it is not, this makes not the slightest difference in the degree of skill he achieves in his language nor in the time it takes him to achieve it. If, as occasionally happens, an infant is raised in extreme isolation or by animals, he learns no language at all (Brown, 1958). If, on the other hand, an infant is raised in society and is biologically normal save for such a peripheral deficiency as deafness or blindness, it is noteworthy that such handicaps are frequently overcome. The sensory details of a deaf person's participation in language are necessarily different from those of normal people: where the normal person relies on stored motor-acoustic images, the deaf person must rely instead on stored images of finger or lip motions or the like. But some kind of special "switching code" is worked out, whereby the bulk of the deaf person's language habits are effectively isomorphic with the language habits of those with whom he lives. Finally, various efforts have been made to teach a language to a member of some other species (reviewed in Brown, 1958) ; they fail.

The inferences to be drawn from the above are clear. Human genes are not specific to the idiosyncrasies of any one language, but permissive for any and all. Human genes are a necessary but not a sufficient condition for acquiring a language. The role of genetics is not, however, purely and passively permissive. The human phenotype includes a strong positive drive towards participation in the communicative interchange of society, a drive that can be frustrated only by the most radical isolation (Lenneberg, unpublished MS).

So much for the role of genetics in language. The rest of the continuity of language habits from generation to generation is provided by the mechanism that we shall here call "tradition"—respecting the preference of some anthropologists for reserving the term "culture" for something a little more specific (see below).

All traditional behavior is learned, but not all learned behavior is traditional. Let us take maze-running as a paradigm for all learning. If members of one species (say human beings) place a member of another species (say a rat) in a maze, the latter may acquire the learned skill of running the maze; but that learned skill is not traditional, because the rat's teachers—those who build the maze and put him in it—are members of a different species. If the members of a species place another member of the same species in a maze and the pupil learns to run the maze, the acquired skill may still not be traditional. Whether it is or not depends on the nature of the teaching behavior. If the teaching behavior is itself purely or largely genetically determined, then the phenomenon is a sort of maternal effect. But if the teaching behavior is itself learned from still other teachers, then the acquired skill is traditional.

So defined, tradition is clearly not a human prerogative. Some short-lived traditions have been observed among chimpanzees in captivity (*fide* Spuhler). The kinds of observations that have led Hochbaum (1955) to posit the existence of traditional behavior among waterfowl might well, if carried out on a sufficient scale, lead us to conclude that tradition is widespread among birds and mammals; though it must be conceded that expert opinion is not unanimously in agreement with Hochbaum even for the several species that he has studied. The extent to which tradition supplements genetics in the transmission of bird songs from one generation to the next, or gibbon calls, or the vocal patterns of various other species—including the waterfowl that Hochbaum discusses—is still an open question; several articles in this volume report experiments and observations that bear on its ultimate solution.

In this connection something must be said of *imprinting* (Hess, 1959). The facts seem to be that the young of many species, in the course of maturation, pass through a stage, often very brief, during which certain experiences with the environment will "take": if exposure is too early or too late, the habit is not acquired, and in some instances this can lead to fatal results. We do not in general know whether or not the habits acquired during imprinting stages are traditional. But the existence of special imprinting stages could well have been of vital importance in evolution, in that it set a stage for the development of tradition. The very long period of pliability in the fetalized human life cycle (see the comparative developmental charts in Spuhler, 1959), during which each child acquires his language and his culture, could be thought of as a remarkably extended imprinting stage. It will be fascinating to find out, if we ever can, whether there is any similarity between the neurological and biochemical bases of imprinting stages in other species and of childhood plasticity in our own.

Tradition becomes transformed into cultural transmission (in the sense favored by many anthropologists, especially White, 1959) when the passing down of traditional habits is mediated in large part by the use of symbols, in the manner of Childe's fable about bear-handling. First the young begin to acquire the communicative system of their community. As soon as a little of it has been learned, further learning, both of the communicative system and of all manner of other lifeways, is carried on in terms of the communicative system as well as via direct demonstration and experience. For a communicative system to function efficiently in this way it must certainly have the properties of semanticity, arbitrariness (and hence discreteness), displacement, and productivity, and probably that of transmission via tradition. This combination of design features apparently yields symbols in the sense described by White and by Langer (1942).

Cultural transmission has an obvious survival value in that it allows a species to learn through experience, and to adapt to new living conditions, at a rate much greater than is possible purely with the genetic mechanism. This is a truism if we compare human history during the past few millenia with, say, what we know of Hymenopteran history since the Tertiary. But we must posit an early stage in Hominid, Hominoid, or Primate history when the capacity for tradition was but feebly developed, so that adaptation via genetic selection and via changing tradition were about equally powerful. Possibly some animal species living today have this same delicate balance. In our own ancestry, the balance was tipped in favor of a strengthening and deepening of the capacity for tradition. We do not know the attendant circumstances. We can guess, however, that at first the survival value of increased capacity for tradition was conservative rather than innovating: it made for greater efficiency in the acquisition by the young of the time-tested lifeways of their predecessors—just as the original importance of strong limbs among the Crossopterygians who evolved into amphibians was not that they could live on land, but that they could get back to the water when the occasion arose (Romer, 1959).

It should be noticed that our definition of cultural transmission, and of the design features of a communicative system that can make cultural transmission possible, is tantamount to an assertion that, so far as we know, only *Homo sapiens* has culture. We must not let this conclusion prejudice us against future empirical discoveries to the contrary (cf. Vercors, 1953). Yet one can argue that it would be highly improbable for two disparate species to develop the language-and-culture lifeway characteristic of ourselves unless they were, for a very long time, out of touch with each other. The ecological niche of a species that develops language and culture sooner or later expands into the whole world. If two different species started in this direction, they would eventually come into contact and one—perhaps both—would probably be eliminated. At least, the history of inter-species relations, and of relations between separate cultural strains of the only animal known to us that has culture, renders such an inference plausible. Furthermore, one such instance may be a matter of record. *Homo neanderthalensis,* with as big and as convoluted a brain as our own (Le Gros Clark, 1955), disappeared from Europe and the world in the late Pleistocene. Some believe that he was caught by the last glaciation, while *Homo sapiens* was carrying on in more favorable climes; but it is also possible (Le Gros Clark, 1959) that he was wiped out by invading groups of our ancestors. Perhaps we can discern, not in language and culture themselves, but in our modern struggle to analyze and understand those phenomena, the seeds of a kind of "maturity" that may in time put an end to our intra-species quarreling and may better equip us for eventual contact—however improbable this may be—with intelligent extra-terrestrial life.

SUMMARY

The essence of our summary is presented in Table 1. The eighth column has been added for purposes of comparison: the reference is to our own Western tradition, say from Bach to the present. A question mark means that the answer is doubtful, or not known, or not known to the writer. A dash means that the particular design feature cannot be determined because some other is lacking or indeterminate: e.g., arbitrariness and iconicity can be judged only for a system characterized by semanticity.

The reader's attention is called to the last part of Hockett (1959), in which there is a survey of the possible course of phylogenetic development of language from the proto-Hominoids to the present. Some of the more obvious errors and gaps in that survey are corrected by the phylogenetic asides in the present paper.

TABLE 1

	1 Some Gryllidae and Tettigoniidae	2 Bee dancing	3 Stickleback courtship	4 Western Meadowlark song	5 Gibbon calls	6 Paralinguistic phenomena	7 Language	8 Instrumental music
1. Vocal-auditory	auditory, not vocal	no	no	yes	yes	yes	yes	auditory, not vocal
2. Broadcast	yes	yes	yes	yes	yes	yes	yes	yes
3. Rapid fading	yes (repeated)?	?	?	yes	yes (rep.)	yes	yes	yes
4. Interchangeability	limited	limited	no	?	yes	yes (largely)	yes	?
5. Total feedback	yes	?	no	yes	yes	yes	yes	yes
6. Specialization	yes?	?	in part	yes?	yes	yes?	yes	yes
7. Semanticity	no?	yes	no	? partly?	yes	yes?	yes	no (in general)
8. Arbitrariness	?	no	—	if semantic, yes	yes	in part	yes	—
9. Discreteness	yes?	no	?	?	yes	largely no	yes	partly
10. Displacement	—	yes, always	—	?	no	in part	yes, often	—
11. Productivity	no	yes	no	one or both,	no	yes	yes	yes
12. Duality	? (trivial)	no	—	} yes	no	no	yes	—
13. Tradition	no?	probably not	no?	?	?	yes	yes	yes

LITERATURE CITED

Bloomfield, L. 1933. Language. Henry Holt: New York. 564 pp.

Blum, H. F. 1955. Time's arrow and evolution. Second edition. Princeton University Press: Princeton, New Jersey. 224 pp.

Brown, Roger. 1958. Words and things. The Free Press: Glencoe, Illinois. 398 pp.

Carpenter, C. R. 1940. A field study of the behavior and social relations of the gibbon. Compar. Psychol. Monog. 16: 5.

Childe, V. G. 1936. Man makes himself. C. A. Watts and Co.: London. 242 pp.

Dobzhansky, T. 1956. The biological basis of human freedom. Columbia University Press: New York. 139 pp.

DuBrul, E. L. 1958. Evolution of the speech apparatus. Thomas: Springfield, Illinois. 103 pp.

Frisch, K. von. 1950. Bees, their vision, chemical senses, and language. Cornell Univ. Press: Ithaca, N. Y. 118 pp.

Gerard, R. W. 1959. Brains and behavior. In Spuhler, J. N. (ed.), The evolution of man's capacity for culture. Wayne State University Press: Detroit. pp. 14-20.

Gibson, J. J. 1954. A theory of pictorial perception. Audio-Visual Communication Review 1: 3–23.

Hess, E. H. 1959. Imprinting. Science 130: 133–141.

Hochbaum, H. A. 1955. Travels and traditions of waterfowl. University of Minnesota Press: Minneapolis. 301 pp.

Hockett, C. F. 1955. A manual of phonology. Indiana Univ. Pub. in Anthropology and Linguistics 11.

————. 1958. A course in modern linguistics. Macmillan: New York. 621 pp.

————. 1959. Animal "languages" and human language. In Spuhler, J. N. (ed.), The evolution of man's capacity for culture. Wayne State University Press: Detroit. pp. 32–39.

Huntington, E. V. 1917. The continuum and other types of serial order. Harvard Univ. Press: Cambridge, Mass. 82 pp.

Joos, M. A. 1948. Acoustic phonetics. Linguistic Society of America, Baltimore. 136 pp.

Kelemen, G. 1948. The anatomical basis of phonation in the chimpanzee. Jour. of Morph. 82: 229–246.

Langer, S. K. 1942. Philosophy in a new key. Harvard Univ. Press: Cambridge, Mass. 313 pp.

Le Gros Clark, W. E. 1955. The fossil evidence for human evolution. The Univ of Chicago Press: Chicago. 181 pp.

————. 1959. The crucial evidence for human evolution. Amer. Scientist 47: 299–313.

Lotka, A. J. 1925. Elements of physical biology. Williams and Wilkins: Baltimore. 460 pp.

Penfield, W., and T. Rasmussen. 1950. The cerebral cortex of man. Macmillan: New York. 248 pp.

————, and L. Roberts. 1959. Speech and brain-mechanisms. The Princeton Univ Press: Princeton, New Jersey. 286 pp.

Pratt, F. 1939. Secret and urgent. Bobbs-Merrill: Indianapolis. 282 pp.

Romer, A. S. 1959. The vertebrate story. The Univ. of Chicago Press: Chicago. 437 pp.

Sahlins, M. D.   1959.   The social life of monkeys, apes, and primitive man.   *In* Spuhler, J. N. (ed.), The evolution of man's capacity for culture.   Wayne State University Press: Detroit.   pp. 54–73.

Sapir, E.   1921.   Language.   Harcourt, Brace and Company: New York.   258 pp.

Shannon, C. E.   1947.   The mathematical theory of communication.   Bell System Tech. Jour. July, October.   Reprinted *in* Shannon and Weaver [same title], The Univ. of Illinois Press: Urbana, 1949.   117 pp.

Spuhler, J. N.   1959.   Somatic paths to culture.   *In* Spuhler, J. N., (ed.), The evolution of man's capacity for culture.   Wayne State Univ. Press: Detroit.   pp. 1–13.

————.   (ed.).   1959.   The evolution of man's capacity for culture.   Wayne State Univ. Press: Detroit.   79 pp.

Tinbergen, N.   1953.   Social behaviour in animals.   Methuen: London; and Wiley: New York.   150 pp.

Trager, G. L.   1958.   Paralanguage: a first approximation.   Studies in Linguistics *13:* 1–12.

Vercors [pseudonym for Jean Bruller].   1953.   You shall know them.   Translated from the French by Rita Barisse.   Little, Brown and Company: Boston.   249 pp.

Washburn, S. L.   1959.   Speculations on the interrelations of the history of tools and biological evolution.   *In* Spuhler, J. N. (ed.), The evolution of man's capacity for culture.   Wayne State Univ. Press: Detroit.   pp. 21–31.

Wells, R. S.   1949   [Book review].   Language *25:* 322–325.

White, L. A.   1959.   Summary review.   *In* Spuhler, J. N. (ed.), The evolution of man's capacity for culture.   Wayne State Univ. Press: Detroit.   pp. 74–79.

Wiener, N.   1948.   Cybernetics.   The Technology Press: New York.   194 pp.

Index

Gryllotalpinae, 66.
Gryllus bimaculatus, 52.
Gull, 373; herring, see *Larus argentatus*.
Gullion, G. W., 374.
Gunn, D. L., 168.
Gunn, W. W. H., 376.

Habitat, correlation with sounds of: anurans, 160, 162, 173, 231, fishes, 109, 128, insects, 80-82.
Haddon, A. C., 106.
Hall, C. S., 382.
Handley, C. O., 383.
Hansen, K. L., 237.
Hardhead, see *Galeichthys felis*.
Hardy, D. F., 191, 211, 214.
Hare, 382; European, see *Lepus europaeus*; snowshoe, see *Lepus americanus*.
Harmonic frequency, defined, 26.
Harris, J. O., 332.
Harris, J. P., Jr., 144.
Hartshorne, J., 322, 333.
Haskell, P. T., 46, 50-52, 58, 60, 86, 384-386.
Hawk, marsh, see *Circus cyaneus*; sharp-shinned, see *Accipiter striatus*; sparrow, see *Falco sparverius*.
Haynes, N. M., 19.
Hearing, see Phonoreception.
Hediger, H., 374.
Heinroth, O., 323, 325, 326, 340, 352.
Hendrickson, J. R., 227.
Heron, black-crowned night, see *Nycticorax nycticorax*.
Herpestes auropunctatus, 378.
Herrick, E. H., 332.
Herter, K., 150, 221, 223.
Hess, E. H., 379, 425.
Heusser, H., 220, 221, 223, 224, 226, 241.
Hinckley, M. H., 201, 229.
Hinde, R. A., 322, 372, 380.
Hinsche, G., 179, 180.
Hochbaum, H. A., 370, 423, 425.
Hockett, C. F., 62, 393-395, 408, 411, 427.
Hoffman, R. L., 201.
Holmes, S. J., 173, 177, 215, 385.
Homo neanderthalensis, 426.
Honey-guide, see *Indicator indicator*.
Hoopes, I., 166, 234.
Hörmann-Heck, S. von, 52, 58.
Hormones, effects in: anurans, 183, 234, 235, birds, 327, 329, 332, 344, 375.
Houssay B. A., 240.
Howard, H. E., 186.
Hubbellia marginifera, spectrogram, 70.
Huber, F., 52, 58.

Humidity, effect on: anuran sounds, 198 ff., insect sounds, 44.
Huntington, E. V., 414.
Huxley, J., 194, 293, 362.
Hybrids, sounds in: anurans, 151, 162, 175, 229, 230, 283 ff., insects, 56, 74, 88.
Hydrophones, 4, 95-97.
Hyla, 175, 177, 218, 222, 223, 230, 238, 261, 291-293; *H. andersoni*, 177, 182, 199, 212, 217; *H. arborea*, 160, 282, 283; *H. a. savignyi*, 282; *H. arenicolor*, 203, 295, 302-305, spectrogram, 295, 304; *H. caerulea*, 204; *H. cinerea*, 167, 174, 175, 183, 193, 198, 227, 230, 241, 292, 293, 320, spectrogram, 175, 292, 294; *H. crucifer*, 197, 201, 209, 210, 222, 251; *H. eximia*, 32, 199, 201, 283, 296-300, 303, 304, 319, spectrogram, 296-298, 300; *H. femoralis*, 174, 304, 305, spectrogram, 304; *H. gratiosa*, 160, 174, 230, 291, 292, 320, spectrogram, 292, 294; *H. meridionalis*, 282, 283; *H. microeximia*, 199; *H. raddiana*, 184, 237; *H. regilla*, 150, 295, 302, 304, spectrogram, 302; *H. rosenbergi*, 227, 257; *H. smithi*, 173, 193, spectrogram, 175; *H. squirella*, 174, 178, 185, 198, 199, 201, 256, 303; *H. versicolor*, 199-201, 225, 227, 282, 286, 304, 305, spectrogram, 304; *H. v. chrysoscelis*, 199.
Hylobates lar, 375, 399, 409-411, 413, 415, 416, 428.
Hylocichla, 362; *H. guttata*, 31, 32, 35, 37, spectrogram, 33, 34; *H. mustelina*, 31, 37, 336, spectrogram, 32.
Hypleurocheilus geminatus, 129.
Hypopachus oxyrrhinus, 178.
Hypsoblennius hentz, 129.

Icteria virens, 364, 366, spectrogram, 365.
Ihering, R. von, 111.
Imitation in: anurans, 207, 208, birds, 325, 333 ff., 400.
Imprinting, 425.
Inborn, discussion of usage of the term, 323.
Indicator indicator, 371.
Information, in communicative systems, 400 ff., coding, 420 ff.
Inger, R. F., 158, 159, 160, 162, 193.
Inheritance, behavior, 423, communicative systems, 424, insect sounds, 61, 85 ff.
Innate, discussion of usage of the term, 323, 324.
Inter-modulation distortion, 9.
Isley, F. B., 48, 80.

Isolation experiments with birds, classification of, 322.
Isolation mechanisms in: anurans, 151, 152, 159, 251 ff., birds, 348-350.

Jacobs, W., 51.
Jahn, L. R., 377, 380, 381, 383.
Jahn, T. L., 142, 164, 370, 384.
Jameson, D. L., 151, 178, 188, 189, 193, 196-198, 202, 203, 211, 213, 214, 276.
Jenkins, see Warden, Jenkins, and Warner.
Johnson, C., 282.
Joos, M., 29, 153, 172, 372, 395.
Jordan, H. D., 226.
Jumber, J., 372.
Junco, Mexican, see *Junco phaeonotus*.
Junco phaeonotus, 354, 358, 366, spectrogram, 357.
Juszczyk, W., 223, 225.

Kahn, M. C., 385, 386.
Kaspar Hauser, defined, 322.
Katydids, see Decticinae, *Microcentrum*, Phaneropterinae.
Kelemen, G., 421.
Kellogg, P. P., 374.
Kellogg, W. N., 93, 94, 105, 154, 371.
Kendeigh, S. C., 377.
Kennedy, J. S., 83.
Khalifa, A., 50, 53.
Kikuchi, T., 191.
Killdeer, see *Charadrius vociferus*.
King, J. A., 375.
Kirkpatrick, K. M., 376.
Klauber, L. M., 140, 147.
Kleerekoper, H., 164-166, 170.
Klemmer, K., 153.
Kramer, G., 327.
Kremer, S., 86.

Lack, D., 350.
Lampyridae, 39, 43.
Land-rail, see *Crex crex*.
Langer, S. K., 411, 426.
Language, design—features of, 392 ff.
Lanius collurio, 326, 330, 335.
Lankes, K., 204.
Lanyon, W. E., 324, 326, 327, 329, 330, 332, 333, 336, 338, 340, 342-344, 354, 359, 362, 390, 404, 418, 423.
Lark, magpie, see *Grallina cyanoleuca*.
Larus argentatus, 325, 370, 372, 383.
Larynx, see Mechanisms of sound production.
Lawrence, B., 94.
Lee, A. K., 153.

Le Gros Clark, W. E., 416, 426, 427.
Leimadophis, 204.
Leiopelma, 157.
Lenneberg, H., 424.
Leonard, S. L., 332.
Leptodactylus, 203; *L. melanonotus*, 161; *L. ocellatus*, 225; *L. poecilochilus*, 227.
Lepus: L. americanus, 374; *L. europaeus*, 374.
Light intensity, effect on insect sounds, 43, 44, 45.
Lindberg, R. G., 386.
Lindsay, H. L., Jr., 281.
Linnet, see *Carduelis cannabina*.
Linsdale, J. M., 375.
Liopelma archeyi, 203, 205.
Liparoscelis nigrispina, 60.
Lister, M. D., 330.
Littlejohn, M. J., 153, 227, 228, 255, 258-260, 267, 268, 277-279, 284.
Liu, C. C., 144, 155, 157, 158, 160, 177, 179, 222.
Lobster, spiny, see *Palinurus interruptus*.
Localization of sounds, in anurans, 168; in birds, 372, 373.
Locust, Carolina, see *Dissosteira carolina*.
Loehrl, H., 329, 342.
Loher, W., 29, 51.
Lorenz, K., 327.
Lotka, A. J., 406.
Loudness, defined, 27; of vibralyzer, 29.
Loveridge, A., 145, 167.
Lowe, C. H., Jr., 151, 185.
Lowther, F. de L., 377, 383.
Lukina, E. V., 352.
Luscinia megarhynchos, 340.
Lutz, F. E., 43, 153, 182.
Lynes, H., 352.

Macaca mulatta, 370.
McAlister, W. H., 161, 162, 218, 280, 293.
McFarlane, J. E., 52.
MacGinitie, G. E., 385.
MacGinitie, N., 385.
McIlhenny, E. A., 145, 385.
Magicicada, 48, 61; *M. cassinii*, 59, 70, 78-80, 83, 92; *M. septendecim*, 44, 92.
Magnetic tape, see Tape.
Magnus, D. B. E., 39.
Main, A. R., 153, 167.
Mallard, see *Anas platyrhynchus*.
Manakin, 334.
Manion, J. J., 217, 229-231, 293.
Manning, F. B., 385.
Marler, P., 325, 327, 329, 336, 343, 350-352, 354, 359, 360, 362, 364, 372, 373, 418.

Martin, purple, see *Progne subis.*

Martof, B. S., 149, 152, 166, 176, 186, 187, 191-194, 197, 198, 207, 209, 213, 242, 249-251, 256, 277, 279, 386.

Maslin, T. P., 143, 144, 199, 384, 385.

Mason, A. G., 377.

Mate selection, in birds, 348 ff.; see also Sex discrimination.

Maynard, E. A., 150, 218, 225.

Mayr, E., 198, 255, 259, 283, 349.

Meadowlark, see *Sturnella;* eastern, see *S. magna;* western, see *S. neglecta.*

Mecham, J. S., 270, 281, 301.

Mechanisms of sound production, evolutionary aspects of, 393, 394; in: anurans, 149, 154 ff., 160 ff., 178, 205, birds, 324, 383, 397, 398, fishes, 94, 97, 99-101, 105 ff., 115 ff., 130, 131, insects, 39, 40, 384, mammals, 383, primates, 394 ff., reptiles, 145-147, salamanders, 143, 144, 384.

Megalobatrachus, 144.

Meleagris gallopavo, 383.

Melospiza melodia, 31, 37, 336, 354, 359, 373, 376; spectrogram, 32.

Mephitis macroura, 203.

Merriman, D., 107, 110.

Merzbacher, L., 164, 214.

Messmer, E., 323, 324, 326, 327, 329, 330, 332, 334, 335, 343, 352.

Messmer, I., 323, 324, 326, 327, 329, 330, 332, 334, 335, 343, 352.

Metfessel, M., 322, 326, 332, 334, 335.

Michaud, T. C., 277-279.

Microcentrum, 81; *M. retinerve,* spectrogram, 71; *M. rhombifolium,* 51, 52, 79, 85, 92, spectrogram, 71.

Microhyla, 178, 185, 209, 213, 219, 237, 239, 240, 266; *M. carolinensis,* 174, 178, 185, 195, 203, 211, 227, 236, 238, 239, 256, 265, 266; *M. olivacea,* 225, 265, 266.

Microphone preamplifiers, 16, 17.

Microphones, 3, 4; cables and connectors, 15, 16; manufacturers' specifications, 12; windscreens, 15.

Micruroides, 146; *M. euryxanthus,* spectrogram, 147.

Miller, N., 150, 177, 215, 216, 224.

Mimicry, see Imitation.

Mink, see *Mustela vison.*

Mirounga angustirostris, 376.

Misdorf, H., 164.

Miskimen, M., 324.

Mockingbird, 376.

Mogoplistinae, 66.

Mongoose, see *Herpestes auropunctatus.*

Monkey, howling, see *louatta palliata;* rhesus, see *Macaca mulatta.*

Moore, H. J., 225.

Moore, J. A., 229, 236, 255, 256, 264-266, 303, 305.

Moore, T. E., 29, 40, 43, 44, 46, 48, 58, 60, 70, 78, 79, 83.

Moose, see *Alces americana.*

Moriya, K., 258-260.

Morpheme, 63; defined, 418.

Mosby, H. S., 383.

Mosquito, 385; see also *Aedes aegypti.*

Moth, noctuid, 387; silkworm, see *Philosamia walkeri.*

Moulton, J. M., 29, 93, 94, 97, 99, 385.

Mouse, 370, 382.

Muir, R. C., 369.

Mustela vison, 377.

Mycteroperca, 99; *M. bonaci,* 97, 136, spectrogram, 98.

Myers, G. S., 144, 157.

Myers, J. G., 39.

Mylar, magnetic tape, 13, 14.

Neanderthal man, 426.

Necturus, 144.

Negus, V. E., 160.

Neill, W. T., 144.

Nemobius, 71, 77; *N. allardi,* 73; *N. carolinus,* 73; *N. fasciatus,* 74; *N. melodius,* 73; *N. tinnulus,* 73.

Neoconocephalus, 77, 81; *N. caudellianus,* 78; *N. ensiger,* 60, 78, 85; *N. exiliscanorus,* 60, 78, 85; *N. nebrascensis,* 78, 80.

Neoxabea bipunctata, spectrogram, 65.

Newt, red-bellied, see *Taricha rivularis.*

Nice, M. M., 187, 321, 326, 332, 336, 354, 359, 373, 377.

Nichols, J. T., 225.

Nicolai, J., 329, 340.

Nifterik, C. H. van, 164.

Night heron, black-crowned, see *Nycticorax nycticorax.*

Nightingale, see *Luscinia megarhynchos.*

Noble, G. K., 143, 144, 146, 150, 155, 157, 159, 162, 164, 173, 177, 180-182, 184, 188, 194, 198, 201, 203, 206, 207, 212, 217, 222, 227, 228, 231, 238, 241, 255, 329.

Noble, R. C., 150, 201, 212, 217.

Noise, defined, 26; in recorders, 22; in recordings, 8, 9; see also Distortion.

Non-passerine birds, development of sounds in, 324, 325.

Nycticorax nycticorax, 329.

Roeder, K., 387.
Romer, A. S., 148, 393, 426.
Rose, W., 158.
Roth, L. M., 386.
Ruibal, R., 229.
Ryan, R. A., 225.

Sahlins, M. D., 397.
Salamander, Pacific giant, see *Dicamptodon ensatus;* tiger, 385.
Salamandra salamandra, 143.
Saltatoria (Orthoptera), 39, 40.
Sanborn, H. C., 321, 326.
Sapir, E., 394.
Sauer, F., 322-324, 326, 327, 329, 330, 332, 334, 335, 342.
Saunders, A. A., 30, 350.
Savage, R. M., 150, 159, 169, 177-180, 182, 194, 195, 200, 218-225, 234, 236, 240, 242.
Scale, decibel, 27.
Scale, musical, defined, 26.
Scaphiopus, 151, 161, 162, 175, 178, 179, 193, 195, 218, 230, 239, 285-287, 293, 296; *S. bombifrons,* 195, 209, 218, 230, 231, 237, 285, 286, 320, spectrogram, 210, 287, 288; *S. couchi,* 203, 218, 231, 237, 254; *S. hammondi,* 194, 195, 218, 227, 230, 231, 237, 285, 286, 320, spectrogram, 287; *S. h. multiplicata,* 286; *S. holbrooki,* 148, 165, 195, 203, 219, 237; *S. hurteri,* 287; *S. intermontanus,* 195.
Schevill, W. E., 94.
Schjelderup-Ebbe, T., 325.
Schmalhausen, J. J., 143, 144, 159, 169.
Schmidt, K. P., 186.
Schmitt, W. L., 386.
Schneirla, T., 94, 293, 294.
Schwab, E., 227.
Schwink, I., 38.
Sciaenidae, 94.
Scorpion, 385, see also *Opisthopthalmus latimanus.*
Scott, W. E. D., 326, 342.
Scudderia, 81; *S. cuneata,* 76; *S. curvicauda,* spectrogram, 70; *S. fasciata,* 76; *S. furcata,* 76, spectrogram, 70; *S. pistillata,* spectrogram, 70; *S. texensis,* spectrogram, 70.
Seal, 373; Alaskan fur, see *Callorhinus ursinus;* elephant, see *Mirounga angustirostris.*
Sea-lion, 373.
Sebasticus marmoratus, 118.
Semantics, 408 ff.

Serinus: S. canarius, 326, 327, 329, 334-336, 338, 340, 342; S. mozambicus, 336.
Serranidae, 97.
Seton, E. T., 370, 377, 382.
Severaid, J. H., 374.
Sex discrimination in: anurans, 139, 149, 170, 176 ff., 185, 215 ff., 256, birds, 377, fishes, 128, 131, 132, 386, 402; see also Mate selection.
Sex recognition, see Sex discrimination and Mate selection.
Sexton, O., 238.
Shannon, C. E., 413.
Sheep, 383.
Sherrington, C. S., 83.
Shielding, microphone cables, 16.
Shrew, see *Sorex araneus.*
Shrike, red-backed, see *Lanius collurio.*
Shrimp, pistol, see *Crangon californiensis.*
Sialia sialis, 322, 326, 333.
Sibabin, K., 164-166, 170.
Simms, E., 326, 383.
Simpson, G. G., 140, 141, 192.
Siren, 143.
Sistrurus, 147.
Skunk, hooded, see *Mephitis macroura.*
Smith, H. M., 94, 271, 274.
Smith, M. A., 213, 220-222, 240.
Snake, egg-eating, see *Dasypeltis;* green, see *Leimadophis;* hooknosed, see *Ficimia cana;* ribbon, see *Thamnophis sauritus;* Sonoran coral, see *Micruoides.*
Somateria molissima, 379.
Sonar, 93, 96, 133.
Sörensen, W., 101, 106, 107.
Sorex araneus, 371.
Sound-proof room, defined, 322.
Sound reception, see Phonoreception.
Southern, H. N., 350.
Southwick, C., 380.
Sparrow, chipping, see *Spizella passerina;* English and house, see *Passer domesticus;* song, see *Melospiza melodia;* striped, see *Oriturus superciliosa;* white-crowned, see *Zonotrichia leucophrys.*
Species discrimination in: anurans, 151, 169, 170, 185, 242, 257 ff., 275 ff., birds, 342, 354 ff., fishes, 95, insects, 48, 64.
Species recognition, see Species discrimination.
Spectrograph, sound, 28 ff., 97, 398.
Speech, neurological basis of, 396.
Sphenodon, 145, 385.
Spider, thomisoid, 385.
Spinus tristis, 374, 378, 380.